TEACHER'S GUIDE

CONNECTED MATHEMATICS® 3

Symmetry and Transformations

Glenda Lappan, Elizabeth Difanis Phillips,
James T. Fey, Susan N. Friel

PEARSON

Boston, Massachusetts • Chandler, Arizona • Glenview, Illinois • Upper Saddle River, New Jersey

Connected Mathematics™ was developed at Michigan State University with financial support from the Michigan State University Office of the Provost, Computing and Technology, and the College of Natural Science.

This material is based upon work supported by the National Science Foundation under Grant No. MDR 9150217 and Grant No. ESI 9986372. Opinions expressed are those of the authors and not necessarily those of the Foundation.

As with prior editions of this work, the authors and administration of Michigan State University preserve a tradition of devoting royalties from this publication to support activities sponsored by the MSU Mathematics Education Enrichment Fund.

Acknowledgments appear on page 263, which constitutes an extension of this copyright page.

13-digit ISBN 978-0-13-327666-4
10-digit ISBN 0-13-327666-X
1 2 3 4 5 6 7 8 9 10 V001 17 16 15 14 13

PEARSON

Authors

A Team of Experts

Glenda Lappan is a University Distinguished Professor in the Program in Mathematics Education (PRIME) and the Department of Mathematics at Michigan State University. Her research and development interests are in the connected areas of students' learning of mathematics and mathematics teachers' professional growth and change related to the development and enactment of K–12 curriculum materials.

Elizabeth Difanis Phillips is a Senior Academic Specialist in the Program in Mathematics Education (PRIME) and the Department of Mathematics at Michigan State University. She is interested in teaching and learning mathematics for both teachers and students. These interests have led to curriculum and professional development projects at the middle school and high school levels, as well as projects related to the teaching and learning of algebra across the grades.

James T. Fey is a Professor Emeritus at the University of Maryland. His consistent professional interest has been development and research focused on curriculum materials that engage middle and high school students in problem-based collaborative investigations of mathematical ideas and their applications.

Susan N. Friel is a Professor of Mathematics Education in the School of Education at the University of North Carolina at Chapel Hill. Her research interests focus on statistics education for middle-grade students and, more broadly, on teachers' professional development and growth in teaching mathematics K–8.

With... Yvonne Grant and Jacqueline Stewart
Yvonne Grant teaches mathematics at Portland Middle School in Portland, Michigan. Jacqueline Stewart is a recently retired high school teacher of mathematics at Okemos High School in Okemos, Michigan. Both Yvonne and Jacqueline have worked on all aspects of the development, implementation, and professional development of the CMP curriculum from its beginnings in 1991.

Development Team

CMP3 Authors

Glenda Lappan, University Distinguished Professor, Michigan State University
Elizabeth Difanis Phillips, Senior Academic Specialist, Michigan State University
James T. Fey, Professor Emeritus, University of Maryland
Susan N. Friel, Professor, University of North Carolina – Chapel Hill

With...

Yvonne Grant, Portland Middle School, Michigan
Jacqueline Stewart, Mathematics Consultant, Mason, Michigan

In Memory of... William M. Fitzgerald, Professor (Deceased), Michigan State University, who made substantial contributions to conceptualizing and creating CMP1.

Administrative Assistant

Michigan State University
Judith Martus Miller

Support Staff

Michigan State University
Undergraduate Assistants:
Bradley Robert Corlett, Carly Fleming, Erin Lucian, Scooter Nowak

Development Assistants

Michigan State University
Graduate Research Assistants:
Richard "Abe" Edwards, Nic Gilbertson, Funda Gonulates, Aladar Horvath, Eun Mi Kim, Kevin Lawrence, Jennifer Nimtz, Joanne Philhower, Sasha Wang

Assessment Team

Maine

Falmouth Public Schools
Falmouth Middle School: Shawn Towle

Michigan

Ann Arbor Public Schools
Tappan Middle School:
Anne Marie Nicoll-Turner

Portland Public Schools
Portland Middle School:
Holly DeRosia, Yvonne Grant

Traverse City Area Public Schools
Traverse City East Middle School:
Jane Porath, Mary Beth Schmitt

Traverse City West Middle School:
Jennifer Rundio, Karrie Tufts

Ohio

Clark-Shawnee Local Schools
Rockway Middle School: Jim Mamer

Content Consultants

Michigan State University
Peter Lappan, Professor Emeritus, Department of Mathematics

Normandale Community College
Christopher Danielson, Instructor, Department of Mathematics & Statistics

University of North Carolina – Wilmington
Dargan Frierson, Jr., Professor, Department of Mathematics & Statistics

Student Activities

Michigan State University
Brin Keller, Associate Professor, Department of Mathematics

Consultants

Indiana
Purdue University
Mary Bouck, Mathematics Consultant

Michigan
Oakland Schools
Valerie Mills, Mathematics Education Supervisor

Mathematics Education Consultants:
Geraldine Devine, Dana Gosen

Ellen Bacon, Independent Mathematics Consultant

New York
University of Rochester
Jeffrey Choppin, Associate Professor

Ohio
University of Toledo
Debra Johanning, Associate Professor

Pennsylvania
University of Pittsburgh
Margaret Smith, Professor

Texas
University of Texas at Austin
Emma Trevino, Supervisor of Mathematics Programs, The Dana Center

Mathematics for All Consulting
Carmen Whitman, Mathematics Consultant

Reviewers

Michigan
Ionia Public Schools
Kathy Dole, Director of Curriculum and Instruction

Grand Valley State University
Lisa Kasmer, Assistant Professor

Portland Public Schools
Teri Keusch, Classroom Teacher

Minnesota
Hopkins School District 270
Michele Luke, Mathematics Coordinator

Field Test Sites for CMP3

Michigan
Ann Arbor Public Schools
Tappan Middle School: Anne Marie Nicoll-Turner*

Portland Public Schools
Portland Middle School: Mark Braun, Angela Buckland, Holly DeRosia, Holly Feldpausch, Angela Foote, Yvonne Grant*, Kristin Roberts, Angie Stump, Tammi Wardwell

Traverse City Area Public Schools
Traverse City East Middle School: Ivanka Baic Berkshire, Brenda Dunscombe, Tracie Herzberg, Deb Larimer, Jan Palkowski, Rebecca Perreault, Jane Porath*, Robert Sagan, Mary Beth Schmitt*

Traverse City West Middle School: Pamela Alfieri, Jennifer Rundio, Maria Taplin, Karrie Tufts*

Maine
Falmouth Public Schools
Falmouth Middle School: Sally Bennett, Chris Driscoll, Sara Jones, Shawn Towle*

Minnesota
Minneapolis Public Schools
Jefferson Community School: Leif Carlson*, Katrina Hayek Munsisoumang*

Ohio
Clark-Shawnee Local Schools
Reid School: Joanne Gilley
Rockway Middle School: Jim Mamer*
Possum School: Tami Thomas

*Indicates a Field Test Site Coordinator

Contents

Butterflies, Pinwheels, and Wallpaper

Symmetry and Transformations

Unit Planning

Unit Overview

Unit Description

The overarching goal of *Butterflies, Pinwheels, and Wallpaper* is to develop student understanding of congruence and similarity of geometric figures and the mathematical techniques for finding and applying those relationships of shapes. The basic idea of congruence is that two figures have the same shape and size if it is possible to perform one or more transformations that "move" one figure onto the other. The basic idea of similarity is that two figures have the same shape if it is possible to perform a dilation, and perhaps one or more rigid motions, to transform one figure onto the other.

The two main topics of this Unit that highlight congruence and similarity are rigid motions and dilation. Investigations 1–3 develop and apply properties of line reflections, rotations, and translations. These rigid motions are used to transform figures for creating symmetric designs and to compare the size and shape of congruent figures. Investigation 4 extends the transformation concept to include dilations of similar figures.

Butterflies, Pinwheels, and Wallpaper builds on important prior work in the Grade 7 Units *Shapes and Designs* and *Stretching and Shrinking*. It also makes significant connections to two prior Units on measurement, Grade 6 *Covering and Surrounding* and Grade 7 *Filling and Wrapping*.

Summary of Investigations

Investigation 1: **Symmetry and Transformations**

This Investigation has four Problems. The first Problem reviews the students' understanding of mirror or line symmetry and develops the definition of line reflection transformations. They will then test for and create such symmetries. The second Problem reviews the students' understanding of rotational symmetry and develops the definition of rotation transformations. The third Problem develops the idea of translations and translational symmetry. The fourth Problem summarizes basic properties of shapes that are preserved by the rigid motion transformations.

Investigation 2: **Transformations and Congruence**

This Investigation has three Problems. The first Problem introduces the concept that figures with the same size and shape can be matched in a way that shows corresponding sides, angles, and vertices. The second Problem develops the students' understanding of the ways in which the congruence of two triangles can be confirmed by transforming one onto the other. The third Problem develops the idea that the congruence of triangles can be determined without any transformation, but by matching the measures of three strategically chosen parts of each triangle.

Investigation 3: **Transforming Coordinates**

This investigation has five Problems. The first three Problems develop coordinate rules for line reflections, translations, and rotations. The fourth Problem develops the important special property of translations and half-turns that every line is mapped onto a parallel line. The fifth Problem applies that special result to review and prove important results about angles formed when parallel lines are cut by a transversal and about the angle sum of the interior or exterior angles of any triangle.

Investigation 4: **Dilations and Similar Figures**

This Investigation has four Problems. The first Problem reviews student understanding of dilations and their properties, which have been developed earlier in *Stretching and Shrinking* from Grade 7. The second Problem parallels the earlier work showing how constructing combinations of dilations and flips/turns/slides can be used to prove the similarity of figures. The third Problem develops the key similarity result for triangles—that any two triangles with two pairs of congruent corresponding angles must be similar. The fourth Problem applies notions of similarity to problems about finding lengths of inaccessible objects.

Unit Vocabulary

- angle of rotation
- basic design element
- center of rotation
- congruent figures
- dilation
- line of symmetry
- line reflection
- reflectional symmetry
- rotation
- rotational symmetry
- similarity transformation
- symmetry
- transformation
- translation
- translational symmetry

Planning Charts

Investigations & Assessments	Pacing	Materials	Resources
Unit Readiness	Optional		• Unit Readiness*
1 Symmetry and Transformations	5 days	**Labsheet 1.1** Questions A–C Diagrams **Labsheet 1.2** Question B **Labsheet 1.3** Questions A and B Diagrams **Labsheet 1.4** Transformation Properties **Labsheet 1ACE:** Exercises 14–17 (accessibility) rulers, angle rulers or protractors, miras or mirrors, tracing paper	**Teaching Aid 1.1A** Getting Ready **Teaching Aid 1.1B** A Basic Design Element **Teaching Aid 1.2A** Finding the Center **Teaching Aid 1.2B** Where is the Center? • Transformations • Tessellations
Mathematical Reflections	½ day		
Assessment: Check Up 1	½ day		• Check Up 1 • Spanish Check Up 1

continued on next page

Planning Charts *continued*

Investigations & Assessments	Pacing	Materials	Resources
2 Transformations and Congruence	3½ days	**Labsheet 2.1** Question D **Labsheet 2.2** Questions A–F **Labsheet 2.3** Questions C–E **Labsheet 2ACE:** Exercises 1–4 (accessibility) **Labsheet 2ACE:** Exercise 39 (accessibility) tracing paper, rulers, angle rulers or protractors	**Teaching Aid 2.1** Kaleidoscope Designs **Teaching Aid 2.3** Congruence Criteria • Transformations
Mathematical Reflections	½ day		
Assessment: Partner Quiz	1 day		• Partner Quiz • Spanish Partner Quiz

continued on next page

Planning Charts *continued*

Investigations & Assessments	Pacing	Materials	Resources
3 Transforming Coordinates	5 days	**Labsheet 3.1** Reflection **Labsheet 3.2** Translation Rules **Labsheet 3.3** Rotations of 90° and 180° **Labsheet 3.4** Special Property of Translations and 180° Rotations **Labsheet 3.5** 180° Rotation Around Midpoints **Labsheet 3ACE:** Exercises 1–3 (accessibility) **Labsheet 3ACE:** Exercises 4 and 5 (accessibility) **Labsheet 3ACE:** Exercises 6 and 7 (accessibility) **Labsheet 3ACE:** Exercise 8 (accessibility) **Labsheet 3ACE** Exercise 9 **Labsheet 3ACE:** Exercise 16 (accessibility) **Labsheet 3ACE:** Exercise 17 (accessibility) **Labsheet 3ACE:** Exercises 18 and 19 (accessibility) **Labsheet 3ACE** Exercise 20 **Labsheet 3ACE** Exercise 26 **Labsheet 3ACE** Exercise 27 **Labsheet 3ACE** Exercise 28 • Quarter-Inch Grid Paper graph paper, tracing paper, rulers, angle rulers or protractors (optional)	**Teaching Aid 3.1** Reflection Over the *y*- and *x*-axis **Teaching Aid 3.3** Rotations of 90° and 180° **Teaching Aid 3.4** Special Property of Translations and 180° Rotations • Transformations
Mathematical Reflections	½ day		
Assessment: Check Up 2	½ day		• Check Up 2 • Spanish Check Up 2

continued on next page

Planning Charts *continued*

Investigations & Assessments	Pacing	Materials	Resources
4 Dilations and Similar Figures	4½ days	**Labsheet 4.1** Dilation **Labsheet 4.2** Similarity **Labsheet 4.3** Similar Triangles and Slope of a Line **Labsheet 4ACE** Exercises 1–6 **Labsheet 4ACE** Exercises 7–10 **Labsheet 4ACE** Exercises 11–15 **Labsheet 4ACE** Exercise 25 **Labsheet 4ACE** Exercise 28 rulers, angle rulers or protractors (optional), mirrors, meter sticks	• Transformations
Mathematical Reflections	½ day		
Looking Back	1 day		
Assessment: Unit Project	Optional		
Assessment: Self-Assessment	Take Home		• Self-Assessment • Notebook Checklist • Spanish Self-Assessment • Spanish Notebook Checklist
Assessment: Unit Test	1 day		• Unit Test • Spanish Unit Test
Total	24 days	**Materials for All Investigations:** calculators; student notebooks; colored pens, pencils, or markers	

*Also available as an assignment in MathXL.

Block Pacing (Scheduling for 90-minute class periods)

Investigation	Block Pacing
1 Symmetry and Transformations	**5½ days**
Problem 1.1	1 day
Problem 1.2	1½ days
Problem 1.3	1 day
Problem 1.4	1½ days
Mathematical Reflections	½ day
2 Transformations and Congruence	**4 days**
Problem 2.1	1 day
Problem 2.2	1 day
Problem 2.3	1½ days
Mathematical Reflections	½ day

Investigation	Block Pacing
3 Transforming Coordinates	**5½ days**
Problem 3.1	1 day
Problem 3.2	1 day
Problem 3.3	1 day
Problem 3.4	1 day
Problem 3.5	1 day
Mathematical Reflections	½ day
4 Dilations and Similar Figures	**5 days**
Problem 4.1	1½ days
Problem 4.2	1 day
Problem 4.3	1 day
Problem 4.4	1 day
Mathematical Reflections	½ day

Parent Letter

- Parent Letter (English)
- Parent Letter (Spanish)

Goals and Standards

Goals

Transformations Describe types of transformations that relate points by the motions of reflections, rotations, and translations, and describe methods for identifying and creating symmetric plane figures

- Recognize properties of reflection, rotation, and translation transformations
- Explore techniques for using rigid motion transformations to create symmetric designs
- Use coordinate rules for basic rigid motion transformations

Congruence and Similarity Understand congruence and similarity and explore necessary and sufficient conditions for establishing congruent and similar shapes

- Recognize that two figures are congruent if one is derived from the other by a sequence of reflection, rotation, and/or translation transformations
- Recognize that two figures are similar if one can be obtained from the other by a sequence of reflections, rotations, translations, and/or dilations
- Use transformations to describe a sequence that exhibits the congruence between figures
- Use transformations to explore minimum measurement conditions for establishing congruence of triangles
- Use transformations to explore minimum measurement conditions for establishing similarity of triangles
- Relate properties of angles formed by parallel lines and transversals, and the angle sum in any triangle, to properties of transformations
- Use properties of congruent and similar triangles to solve problems about shapes and measurements

Standards

Common Core Content Standards

8.EE.B.6 Use similar triangles to explain why the slope m is the same between any two distinct points on a non-vertical line in the coordinate plane; derive the equation $y = mx$ for a line through the origin and the equation $y = mx + b$ for a line intercepting the vertical axis at b. *Investigation 4*

8.G.A.1 Verify experimentally the properties of rotations, reflections, and translations. *Investigations 1, 2, and 3*

8.G.A.1a Lines are taken to lines, and line segments to line segments of the same length. *Investigations 1 and 2*

8.G.A.1b Angles are taken to angles of the same measure. *Investigations 1, 2, and 3*

8.G.A.1c Parallel lines are taken to parallel lines. *Investigations 1, 2, and 3*

8.G.A.2 Understand that a two-dimensional figure is congruent to another if the second can be obtained from the first by a sequence of rotations, reflections, and translations; given two congruent figures, describe a sequence that exhibits the congruence between them. *Investigations 2 and 3*

8.G.A.3 Describe the effect of dilations, translations, rotations, and reflections on two-dimensional figures using coordinates. *Investigations 3 and 4*

8.G.A.4 Understand that a two-dimensional figure is similar to another if the second can be obtained from the first by a sequence of rotations, reflections, translations, and dilations; given two similar two-dimensional figures, describe a sequence that exhibits the similarity between them. *Investigation 4*

8.G.A.5 Use informal arguments to establish facts about the angle sum and exterior angle of triangles, about the angles created when parallel lines are cut by a transversal, and the angle-angle criterion for similarity of triangles. *Investigations 3 and 4*

Facilitating the Mathematical Practices

Students in *Connected Mathematics* classrooms display evidence of multiple Standards for Mathematical Practice every day. Here are just a few examples of when you might observe students demonstrating the Standards for Mathematical Practice during this Unit.

Practice 1: **Make sense of problems and persevere in solving them.**

Students are engaged every day in solving problems and, over time, learn to persevere in solving them. To be effective, the problems embody critical concepts and skills and have the potential to engage students in making sense of mathematics. Students build understanding by reflecting, connecting, and communicating. These student-centered problem situations engage students in articulating the "knowns" in a problem situation and determining a logical solution pathway. The student-student and student-teacher dialogues help students not only to make sense of the problems, but also to persevere in finding appropriate strategies to solve them. The suggested questions in the Teacher Guides provide the metacognitive scaffolding to help students monitor and refine their problem-solving strategies.

Practice 2: **Reason abstractly and quantitatively.**

In the Problems of Investigation 4, students use rigid and nonrigid transformations to discover that, for triangles, they only need to know that two corresponding angles are congruent to determine similarity. This minimum requirement is practical for determining vertical heights and distances that are unreachable assuming that the angle the vertical object makes with the ground is 90°.

Practice 3: Construct viable arguments and critique the reasoning of others.

In Problem 1.3, the students write a definition for the translation of given points. They know that a slide or translation transformation matches each point to its image. Some students will use the information to argue that if the image of two points is under translation, the distance between the points is equal to the distance between the two original points. Other students may argue that if a line connects each set of points, the two lines should have the same slope, because a translation does not change the orientation of points on any figure. Working as a group, the students will discuss their assumptions and develop an accurate definition.

Practice 4: Model with mathematics.

In Problem 4.4, students use the scale factor between two similar triangles to determine vertical heights that they are unable to measure. They use a mirror with the fact that angles of reflection are congruent and relate the corresponding parts of similar triangles in their diagram of the situation. With the angle of reflection and the assumption that the object they cannot measure forms a 90° angle with the ground, they know that two triangles are similar. The smaller triangle is used in this exploration as a model of the larger triangle. For example, they use height from the ground to their eyes when they are able to see the reflection of the top of the object that they want to measure in the mirror. They also use the distances from the mirror to the object and to their position given a pair of corresponding sides to calculate the scale factor. With the scale factor, they can use multiplication to estimate the height that they are unable to measure.

Practice 5: Use appropriate tools strategically.

In Investigation 4, Problems 1–3, students use their rulers and angle rulers or protractors to verify measurements of corresponding parts of triangles. They learn that they only need to measure two corresponding angles and verify congruence to determine similarity. If they decide to use measurements of sides, they learn that they need to verify that the scale factor is constant for all pairs of corresponding sides. In Problem 4, students use a mirror and meter stick to find the appropriate position to take measurements to estimate the height of an object they cannot reach using properties of similarity.

Practice 6: Attend to precision.

In Problem 2.2, the students describe a transformation that "moves" one triangle onto another. They learn to write very detailed instructions to describe an accurate sequence of transformations. First, they use tracing paper to determine the steps that transform one triangle to the location of the other. Next, they describe how each "move" was made. For flips, they provide the line of reflection. For turns, they provide the center and angle of rotation. For slides, they provide the direction and distance.

Practice 7: Look for and make use of structure.

In Investigation 3, Problems 1–3, students look for patterns in key coordinate points after applying a transformation or a sequence of transformations. After detecting the pattern, they write coordinate rules to describe the change of all coordinates under that transformation.

Practice 8: Look for and express regularity in repeated reasoning.

After experimenting with the transformations in Investigation 1, the students notice clues in the differences between the original figure and its image. They start to develop basic rules that determine the transformation they should test for first. For example, when they see the orientation of the figure is the same, they will automatically reason that the image is under translation. If the base of the original figure transformed to the side of the image, they will test for rotation first. Similarly, if they can picture a mirror in between the original figure and its image, they will reason that the design must have reflection symmetry. The repeated characteristics of the designs in Investigation 1 helped them to develop their own reasoning for noticing symmetry, which also helps them test for congruence in Investigation 2.

Students identify and record their personal experiences with the Standards for Mathematical Practice during the Mathematical Reflections at the end of each Investigation.

Mathematics Background

Types of Symmetry

In this Unit, students study symmetry and transformations. They connect these concepts to congruence and similarity. Symmetry and transformations have actually been studied in the Grade 7 Unit *Stretching and Shrinking*. In this Unit, students learn to recognize and make designs with symmetry, and to describe mathematically the transformations that lead to symmetric designs. They explore the concept and consequences of congruence of two figures by looking for symmetry transformations that will map one figure exactly onto the other.

In the first Investigation, students learn to recognize designs with symmetry and to identify lines of symmetry, centers and angles of rotation, and directions and lengths of translations.

Reflections

A design has reflection symmetry, also called mirror symmetry, if a reflection in a line maps the figure exactly onto itself. For example, the letter A has reflection symmetry because a reflection in a vertical line will match each point on the left half with a point on the right half. The vertical line is the line of symmetry for this design.

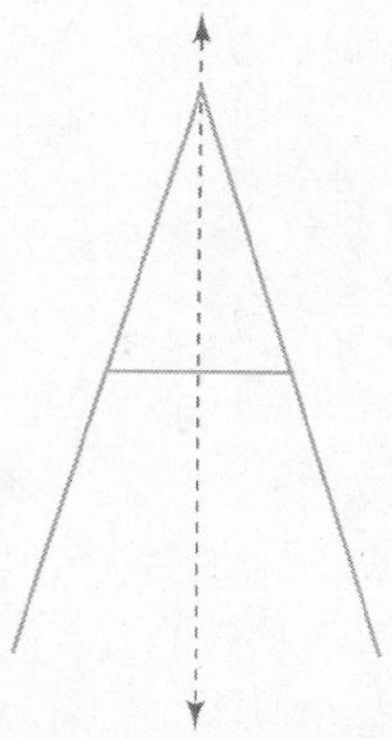

Rotations

A design has rotation symmetry if a rotation, other than a full turn, about a point maps the figure onto itself. The design below has rotation symmetry because a rotation of 120° or 240° about point *P* will match each flag to another flag. Point *P* is called the center of rotation. The angle of rotation for this design is 120°, which is the smallest angle through which the design can be rotated to match with its original position.

continued on next page

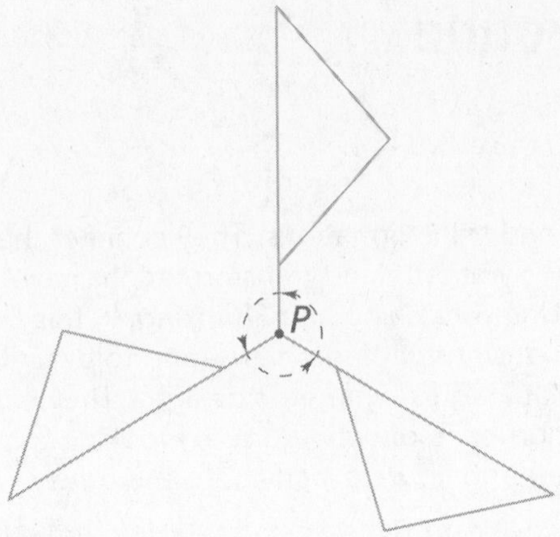

Translations

A design has translation symmetry if a translation, or a slide, maps the figure onto itself. The figure below is part of a translation-symmetric design. If this design continued in both directions, a slide of 1 inch to the right or left would match each element in the design with an identical copy of that design element.

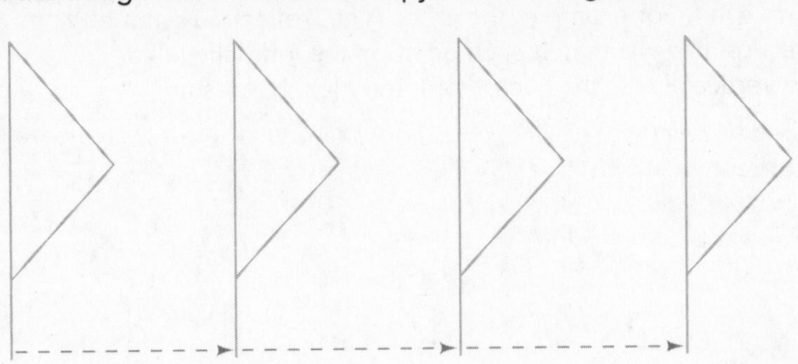

Making Symmetric Designs

Once students learn to recognize symmetry in given designs, they can make their own symmetric designs. Students may use reflecting devices, tracing paper, angle rulers or protractors, and geometry software to help them construct designs.

- A design with reflection symmetry can be made by starting with a basic figure and then drawing the reflection of the figure in a line. The original and its reflection image make a design with reflection symmetry.
- A design with rotation symmetry can be made by starting with a basic figure and making $n - 1$ copies of the figure, where each copy is rotated $\frac{360°}{n}$ about a center point starting from the previous copy. The original and its $n - 1$ rotation images make a design that has rotation symmetry.
- A figure with translation symmetry can be made by copying the basic figure, so that each copy is the same distance and same direction from the previous copy. The figure and its translation images make a design with translation symmetry.

Students are asked to develop two separate but related skills. The first is to recognize symmetries within a given design. The second is to make designs with one or more specified symmetries starting with an original figure (which may not, in itself, have any symmetries). Thus, it is important to give students experience both in analyzing existing designs to identify their symmetries and also in using transformations to make designs that have symmetry.

Symmetry Transformations

The concepts of symmetry are used as the starting point for the study of symmetry transformations, also called distance-preserving transformations, rigid motions, or isometries. The most familiar distance-preserving transformations—reflections, rotations, and translations—"move" points to image points so that the distance between any two original points is equal to the distance between their images. The informal language used to specify these transformations is *slides*, *flips*, and *turns*. Some children will have used this language and will have had informal experiences with these transformations in the elementary grades.

Reflections

In this Unit, students examine figures and their images under reflections, rotations, and translations by measuring key distances and angles. They use their findings to determine how they can specify a particular transformation so that another person could perform it exactly. Students learn that a reflection can be specified by its line of reflection. They learn that, under a reflection in a line k, the point A and its image point A' lie at opposite ends of a line segment that is bisected at right angles by the line of reflection.

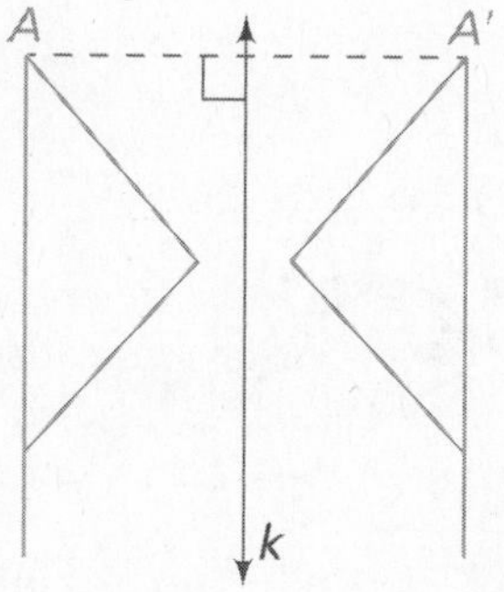

Rotations

A rotation can be specified by giving the center of rotation and the angle of the turn. In this Unit, the direction of the rotation is assumed to be counterclockwise unless a clockwise turn is specified. For example, a 57° rotation about a point C is a counterclockwise turn of 57° with C as the center of the rotation. Students learn that a point R and its image point R' are equidistant from the center of the rotation C.

continued on next page

They see that a point under a rotation travels on the arc of a circle and that the set of circles on which the points of the figure travel are concentric circles with center *C*. They also find that the angles formed by the vertex points of the figure and their rotation images, such as $\angle RCR'$, all have a measure equal to the angle of turn.

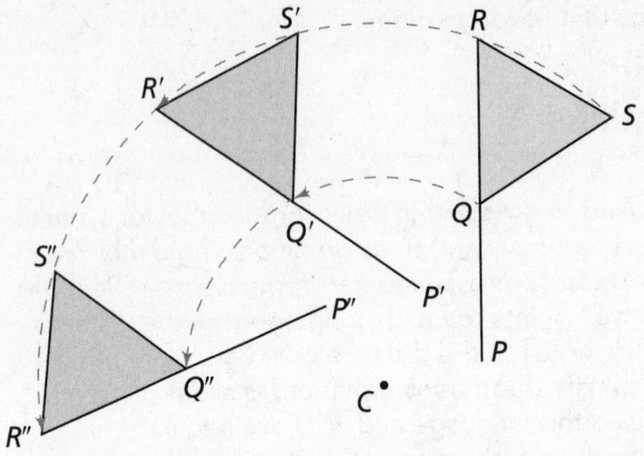

Translations

A translation can be specified by giving the length and direction of the slide. This can be done by drawing an arrow with the appropriate length and direction. Students find that if you draw the segments connecting points to their images, such as $\overline{CC'}$, the segments will be parallel and all the same length. The length is equal to the magnitude of the translation.

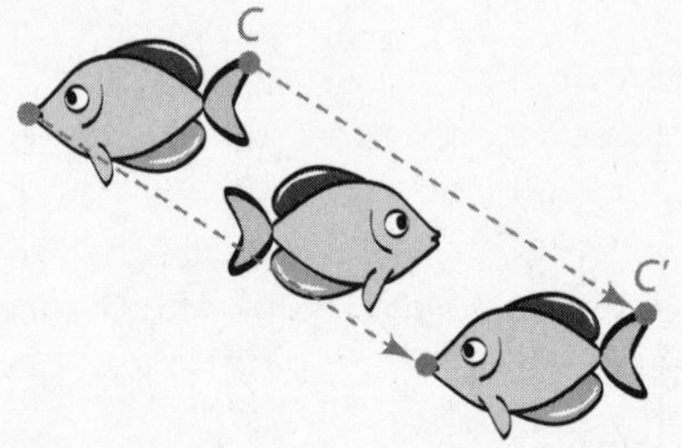

This work helps students to realize that any transformation of a figure is essentially a transformation of the entire plane. For every point in a plane, a transformation locates an image point. It is not uncommon to focus on the effect of a transformation on a particular figure. This Unit attempts to give mathematically precise descriptions of transformations while accommodating students' natural instinct to visualize the figures moving. Thus, in many cases, students are asked to study a figure and its image without considering the effect of the transformation on other points. However, the *moved* figure is always referred to as the image of the original, and the vertices of the image are often labeled with primes or double primes to indicate that they are indeed different points.

An interesting question is, "For which transformations are there points that remain fixed?" These are called *fixed points*. The image of each such point is simply the point itself. For a reflection, the points on the line of reflection are fixed points. For a rotation, the only fixed point is the center of rotation. For a translation, all points have images with new locations, so there are no fixed points. Point C is a fixed point in the reflection and rotation below.

Reflection

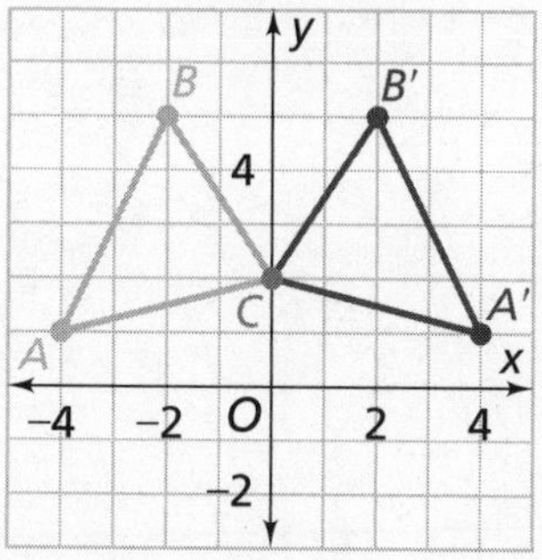

Rotation

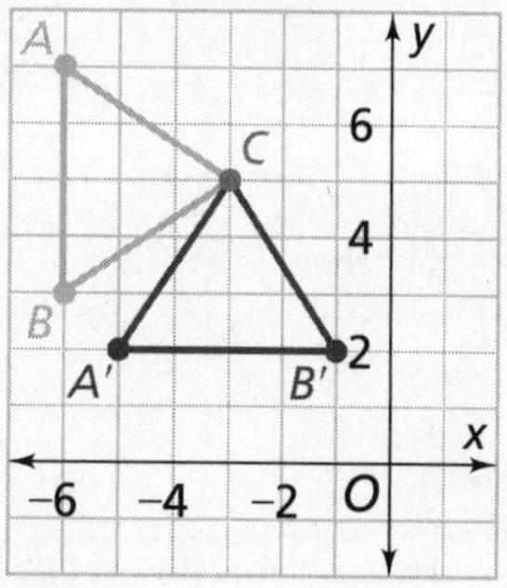

Congruent Figures

The discussion of distance-preserving transformations leads naturally to the idea of congruence. Two figures are congruent if they have the same size and shape. Intuitively, this means that you could "move" one figure exactly onto the other by a combination of symmetry transformations (rigid motions). In the language of transformations, two figures are congruent if there is a combination of distance-preserving transformations (symmetry transformations) that maps one figure onto the other. Several problems ask students to explore this fundamental relationship among geometric figures.

The question of *proving* whether two figures are congruent is explored informally. An important question is what minimum set of equal measures of corresponding sides and/or angles will guarantee that two triangles are congruent. It is likely that students will discover the following triangle congruence theorems that are usually taught and proved in high school geometry. This engagement with the ideas in an informal way will help make their experience with proof in high school geometry more understandable.

- Side-Side-Side

If the three sides of one triangle are congruent to three corresponding sides of another triangle, the triangles will be congruent (in all parts).

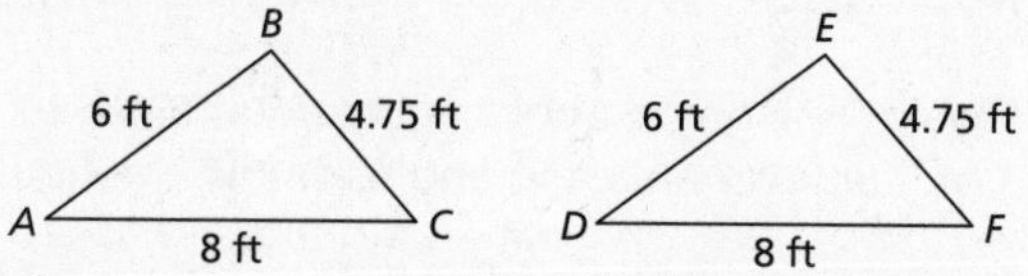

This condition is commonly known as the Side-Side-Side or SSS Postulate.
In the diagram above, $\overline{AB} = \overline{DE}$, $\overline{BC} = \overline{EF}$, and $\overline{AC} = \overline{DF}$.
So $\triangle ABC \cong \triangle DEF$ by the SSS Postulate.

continued on next page

- Side-Angle-Side

If two sides and the included angle of one triangle are congruent respectively to two sides and the included angle of another triangle, the triangles will be congruent (in all parts).

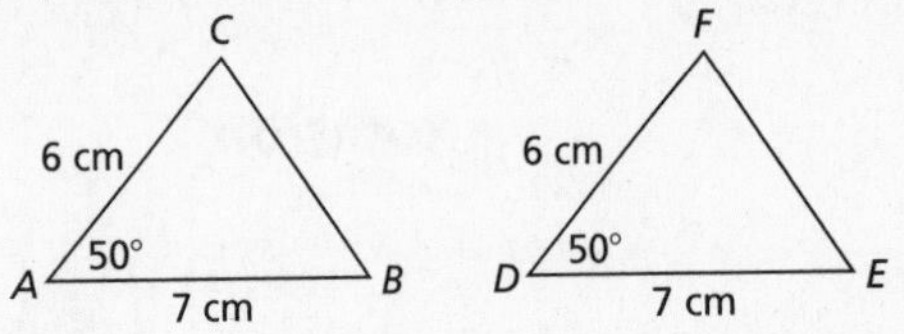

This condition is commonly known as the Side-Angle-Side or SAS Postulate.
In the diagram above, $\overline{AB} \cong \overline{DE}$, $\angle A \cong \angle D$, and $\overline{AC} \cong \overline{DF}$.
So $\triangle ABC \cong \triangle DEF$ by the SAS Postulate.

- Angle-Side-Angle

If two angles and the included side of one triangle are congruent respectively to two angles and the included side of another triangle, the triangles will be congruent (in all parts).

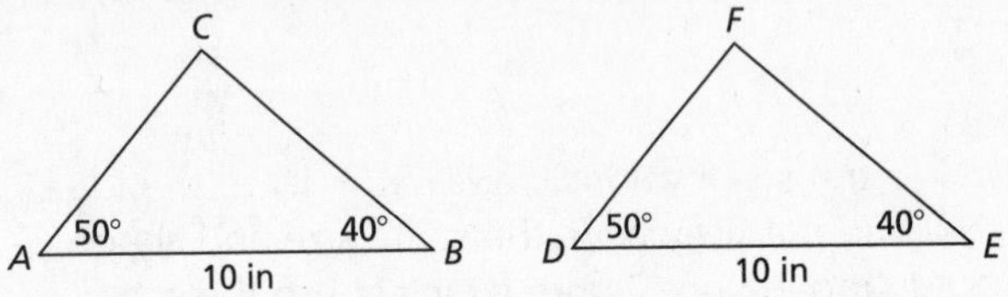

This condition is commonly known as the Angle-Side-Angle or ASA Postulate.
In the diagram above, $\angle A \cong \angle D$, $\overline{AB} = \overline{DE}$, and $\angle B \cong \angle E$.
So $\triangle ABC \cong \triangle DEF$ by the ASA Postulate.

Students should also find that Angle-Angle-Angle and Side-Side-Angle do not guarantee congruence. Angle-Angle-Angle guarantees similarity, or the same shape, but not the same size. With Side-Side-Angle, in some cases there are two possibilities, so you cannot know for certain that you have congruence.

In a right triangle, with the right angle and any two corresponding sides given, you can use the Pythagorean Theorem to find the third side. This gives two sides and the included angle, or three sides. Either combination is enough to know that two right triangles are congruent.

Reasoning From Symmetry and Congruence

Symmetry and congruence give us ways of reasoning about figures that allow us to draw conclusions about relationships of line segments and angles within the figures.

For example, suppose that $\overleftrightarrow{AM}$ is a line of reflection symmetry for triangle ABC; the measure of $\angle CAM$ is 37°; the length of $\overline{CB} = 6$; and the length of $\overline{AM} = 4$.

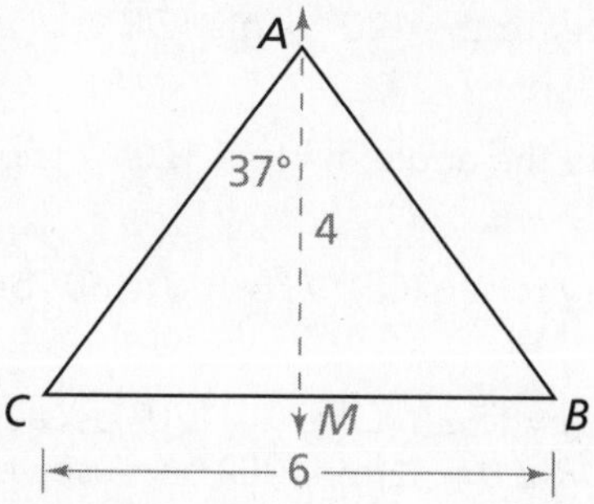

As a consequence of the line symmetry, you can say that

- Point C is a reflection of point B.
- Point A is the reflection of point A.
- Point M is the reflection of point M.
- $\overline{AC}$ is a reflection of $\overline{AB}$, which means that their lengths are equal.
- $\overline{CM}$ is a reflection of $\overline{BM}$, so each has length 3.
- $\overline{AM}$ is the reflection of $\overline{AM}$.
- $\overline{CB}$ is perpendicular to $\overleftrightarrow{AM}$, so $\angle AMC$ and $\angle AMB$ are right angles.
- $\angle BAM \cong \angle CAM$, so each angle measures 37°.
- $\angle C \cong \angle B$, and each angle measures $180° - (90° + 37°) = 53°$ (by the fact that the sum of the angles of a triangle is 180°).

In the Grade 7 Unit *Shapes and Designs*, students explored the angles made by a transversal cutting a pair of parallel lines. For some of the reasoning in this Unit, students will probably need to use ideas of vertical angles, supplemental angles, and alternate interior angles from *Shapes and Designs*. Those results are revisited and proven in this Unit as well.

In the diagram below, lines L_1 and L_2 are parallel lines cut by transversal L_3, and one angle measures 120°. From this, you can deduce all the other angle measures.

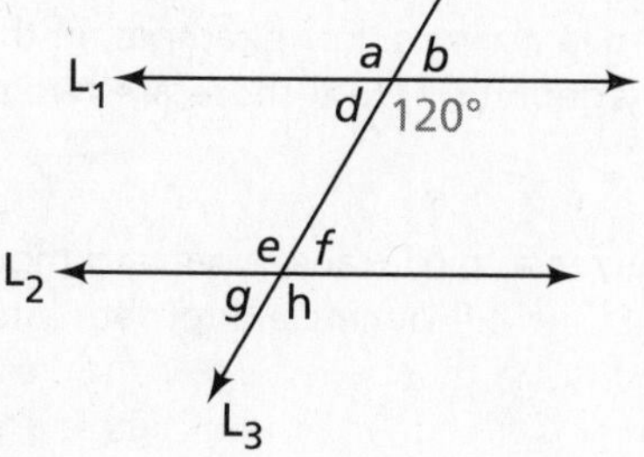

- $\angle d = 60°$ because it is supplementary to the 120° angle.
- $\angle a = 120°$ because it is supplementary to $\angle d$ (OR $\angle a = 120°$ because vertical angles are equal).

continued on next page

- $\angle b = 60°$ because it is supplementary to the 120° angle (OR $\angle b = \angle d = 60°$ because vertical angles are equal).
- $\angle h = 120°$ because you can translate the angle marked 120° along the transversal L_3 and match $\angle h$.
- $\angle f = 60°$ because it is supplementary to $\angle h$ (OR $\angle f = \angle d = 60°$ because alternate interior angles are equal).
- $\angle e = 120°$ because it is supplementary to $\angle f$ (OR $\angle$ = 120° because alternate interior angles are equal OR $\angle e = \angle h = 120°$ because vertical angles are equal).
- $\angle g = 60°$ because it is supplementary to $\angle h$ (OR $\angle g = \angle f = 60°$ because vertical angles are equal).

Suppose another angle measure and line L_4 are added to the diagram. We are not given that line L_4 is parallel to line L_3.

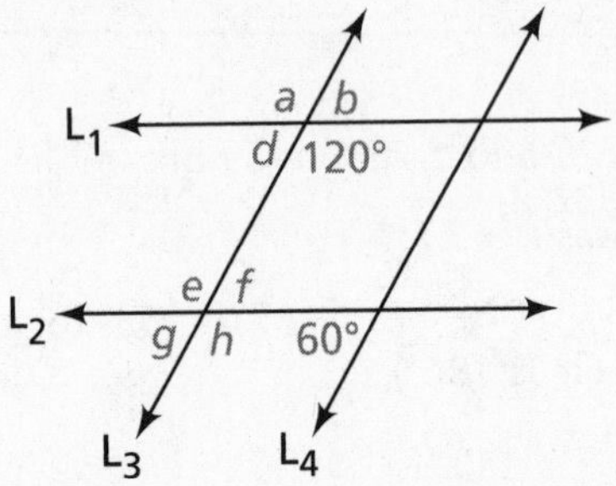

If $\angle g = 60°$ is translated along the transversal L_2, it will exactly match the angle marked 60°. So L_3, which is a side of $\angle g$, must be parallel to line L_4.

That is, you can use the ideas of transformations and the relationships among the angles formed when a transversal intersects two lines to determine whether or not the lines are parallel.

The relationships among parallel lines and their respective transversals can help especially when reasoning about parallelograms. For example, in the parallelogram shown below, you know, by definition, that there are two pairs of parallel lines and transversals.

Adding a diagonal to the parallelogram gives a third transversal and more congruent angles. That is, $\angle 1 = \angle 2$ and $\angle 3 = \angle 4$ because alternate interior angles are equal.

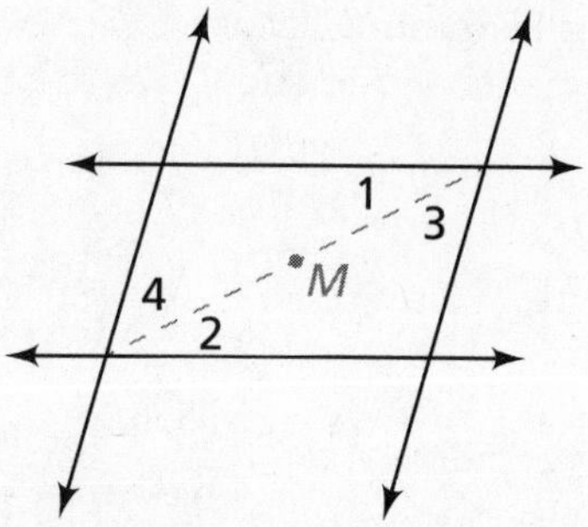

You can rotate the parallelogram about the midpoint *M* of the diagonal to show that the diagonal divides the parallelogram into two congruent triangles.
Note: ASA gives the same conclusion.

This reasoning from parallel lines cut by a transversal, combined with congruence and symmetry, leads to further results about parallelograms:

A. If *ABCD* is a parallelogram, then opposite sides are congruent.

B. If opposite sides of a quadrilateral are congruent, then it must be a parallelogram. **Note:** This is the converse of Statement A. The converse reverses the two parts of a logical statement.

C. The diagonals of a parallelogram bisect each other.

D. If the diagonals of a quadrilateral bisect each other, then that figure must be a parallelogram. **Note:** This is the converse of Statement C.

Similar reasoning with translations helps to prove that matching two pairs of corresponding sides and the pair of included angles in two triangles is enough to show that the triangles are congruent.

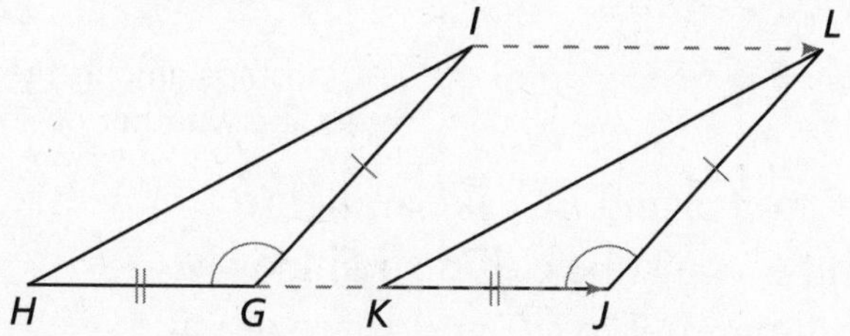

In the diagram above, if you translate triangle *HGI* so that $\angle G \rightarrow \angle J$, then you also have the following:

- $\overline{GI} \rightarrow \overline{JL}$ because $\overline{GI} \parallel \overline{JL}$ and $\overline{GI} \cong \overline{JL}$
- $\overline{HG} \rightarrow \overline{KJ}$ because $\overline{HG} \parallel \overline{KJ}$ and $\overline{HG} \cong \overline{KJ}$

continued on next page

As with all translations of a segment, a parallelogram *GJLI* will be formed. To complete the rest of the congruence statements and to show that the triangles are congruent, check the following:

- $\overline{HI} \rightarrow \overline{KL}$
- $\angle H \rightarrow \angle K$
- $\angle I \rightarrow \angle L$

Since $\angle H \rightarrow \angle K$ and $\angle I \rightarrow \angle L$ under this translation, $\overline{HI} \rightarrow \overline{KL}$ and $\overline{HI} \parallel \overline{KL}$. Therefore, $\angle H \cong \angle K$ because they are corresponding angles of parallel lines cut by a transversal. Finally, since the sum of the measures of the angles of a triangle is 180°, $\angle I \cong \angle L$. To conclude, given that two sides and the included angle of one triangle are congruent to the corresponding parts of another triangle, *all* corresponding parts of the triangles must be congruent.

In addition to the above applications, you can also use ideas from transformational geometry to prove that the sum of the angles of a triangle is 180°.

Start with triangle *ABC* and angles 1, 2, and 3. Rotate the triangle 180° about the midpoints of $\overline{AB}$ and $\overline{BC}$.

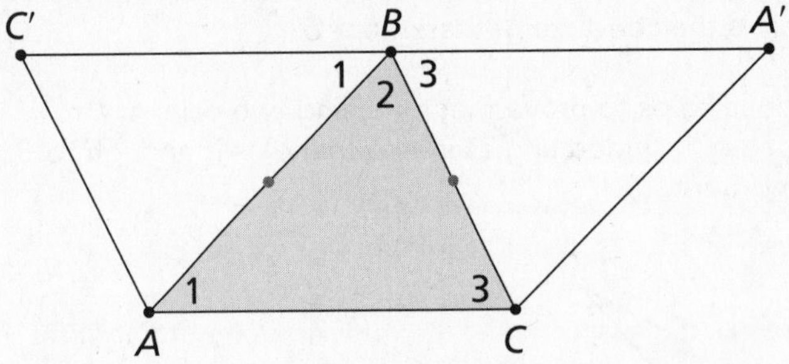

Then $\overline{A'B}$ is parallel to $\overline{AC}$, and $\overline{BC'}$ is parallel to $\overline{AC}$. Points A', B, and C' must be collinear since $\overline{A'B}$ and $\overline{BC'}$ are both parallel to $\overline{AC}$ and share a common point B. So, $\overline{A'C'}$ is a straight line through point B. Thus, $\angle 1 + \angle 2 + \angle 3 = 180°$.

You can also use Euclidean geometry to prove that the sum of the angles of a triangle is 180°.

Start with triangle ABC. Add a line m through point B that is parallel to $\overline{AC}$.

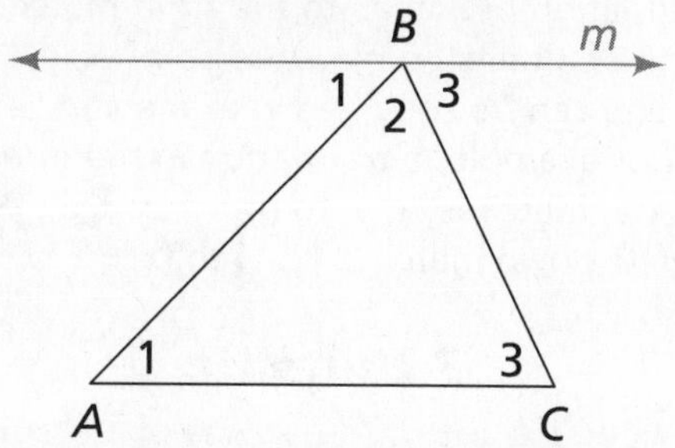

The angles marked "3" are congruent because alternate interior angles are equal. The angles marked "1" are congruent for the same reason. Thus, $\angle 1 + \angle 2 + \angle 3 = 180°$ because they form a straight angle.

Coordinate Rules for Symmetry Transformations

In Investigation 3, we return to transformations and look at transformations of figures on a coordinate plane.

Reflections

Students write rules for describing reflections of figures drawn on a coordinate grid. The rules tell how to find the image of a general point (x, y) under a reflection. For example, a reflection in the y-axis matches (x, y) to $(-x, y)$; a reflection in the x-axis matches (x, y) to $(x, -y)$; and a reflection in the line $y = x$ matches (x, y) to (y, x).

Reflection in the *y*-axis

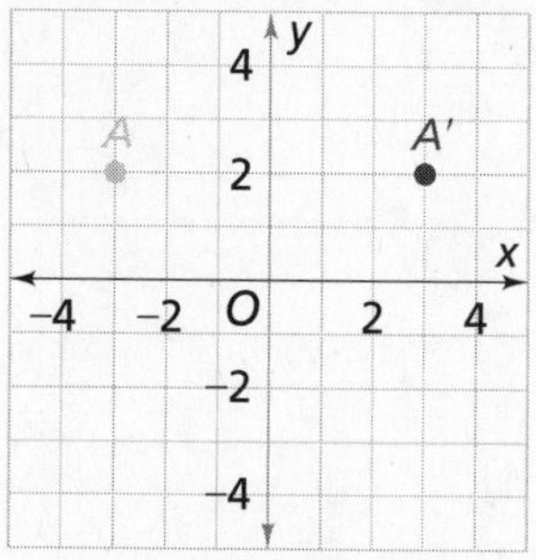

$(x, y) \rightarrow (-x, y)$

Reflection in the *x*-axis

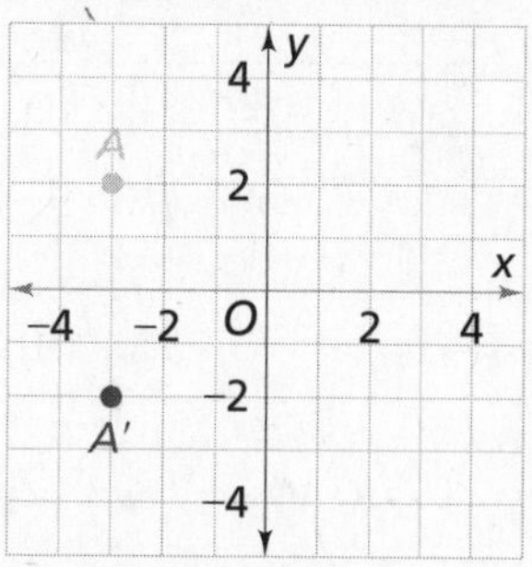

$(x, y) \rightarrow (x, -y)$

Reflection in the Line *y* = *x*

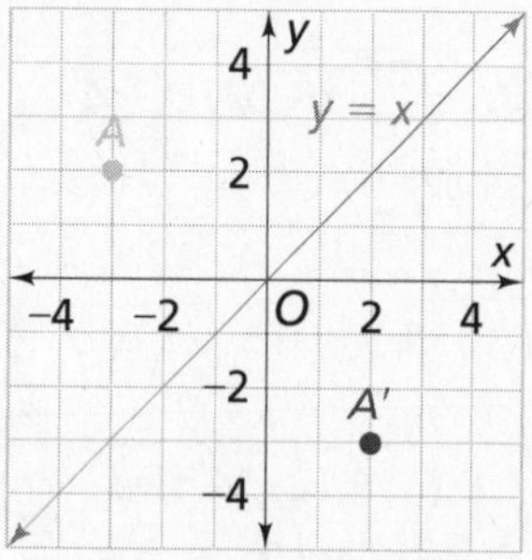

$(x, y) \rightarrow (y, x)$

continued on next page

Translations

A translation can also be specified by a rule for locating the image of a general point (x, y). For example, a horizontal translation of 3 units to the right matches (x, y) to $(x + 3, y)$, and a vertical translation of 3 units up matches point (x, y) to $(x, y + 3)$. A translation along an oblique line can be specified with the vertical and horizontal components of the slide. For example, a translation in the direction of the line $y = x$, 2 units right and 2 units up, matches (x, y) to $(x + 2, y + 2)$. A translation of 2 units to the right and 4 units down matches (x, y) to $(x + 2, y - 4)$.

3 Units Right

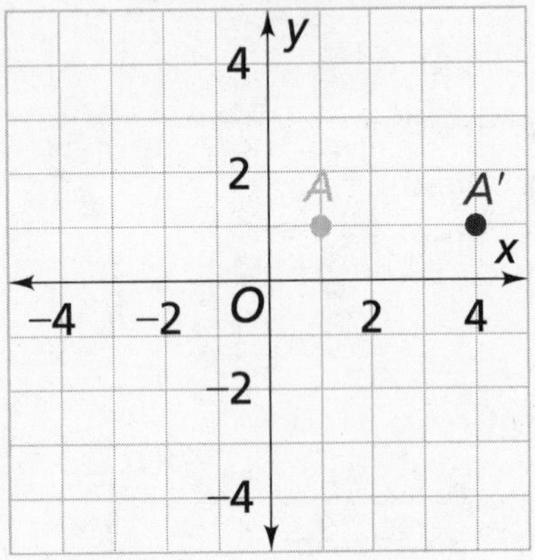

$(x, y) \rightarrow (x + 3, y)$

3 Units Up

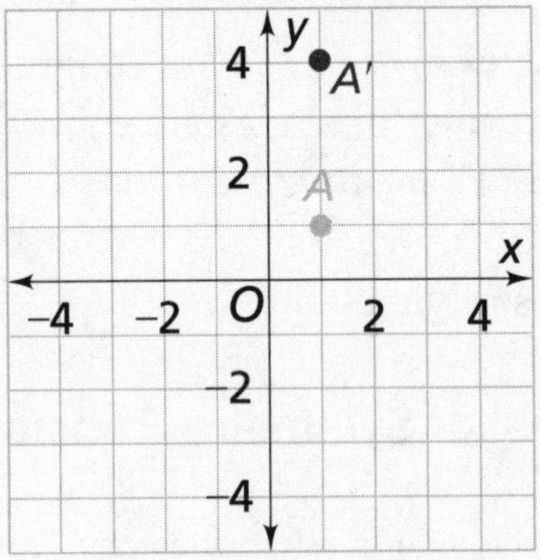

$(x, y) \rightarrow (x, y + 3)$

2 Units Right, 2 Units Up

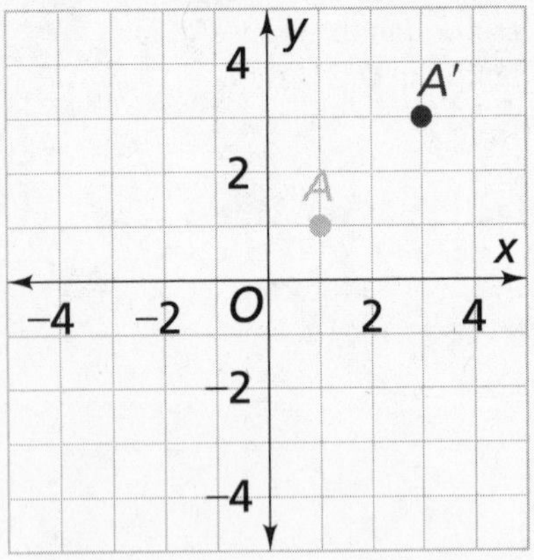

$(x, y) \rightarrow (x + 2, y + 2)$

2 Units Right, 4 Units Down

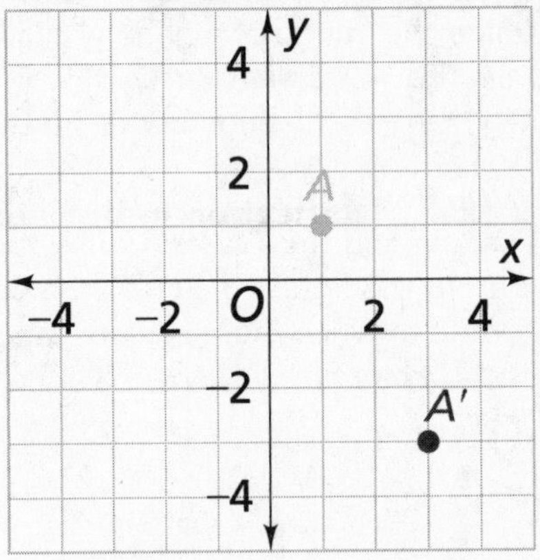

$(x, y) \rightarrow (x + 2, y - 4)$

Rotations

As with reflections and translations, students learn to specify certain rotations by giving rules for locating the image of a general point (x, y). For example, a rotation of 90° about the origin matches the point (x, y) to the image point $(-y, x)$, and a rotation of 180° about the origin matches (x, y) to $(-x, -y)$.

90° Rotation About (0, 0)

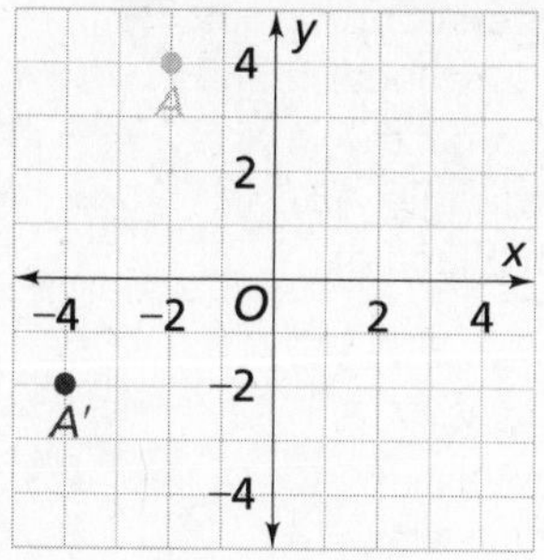

$(x, y) \rightarrow (-y, x)$

180° Rotation About (0, 0)

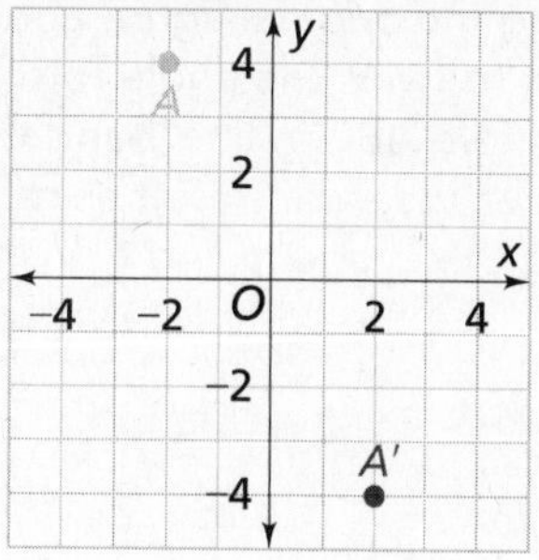

$(x, y) \rightarrow (-x, -y)$

As a consequence of using coordinate rules to define the results of transformations on points, students can verify observations they made previously about distances and slopes. For example, a 180° rotation of $\overline{AB}$ about a point C will result in an image $\overline{A'B'}$ that is parallel and congruent to $\overline{AB}$. This observation becomes very useful for proving further results.

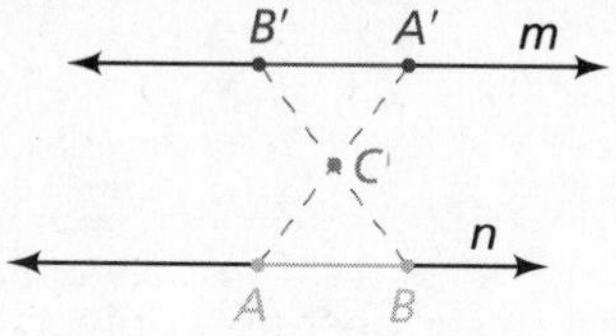

Combining Transformations

In very informal ways, students explore combinations of transformations. In a few instances in the ACE Extensions, students are asked to describe a single transformation that will give the same result as a given combination. For example, reflecting a figure in a line and then reflecting the image in a parallel line has the same result as translating the figure in a direction perpendicular to the reflection lines for a distance equal to twice the distance between the lines. Visit Teacher Place at mathdashboard.com/cmp3 to see the complete video.

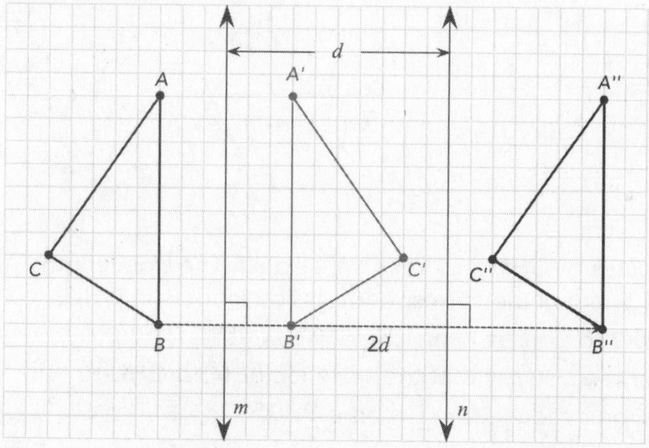

continued on next page

Reflecting a figure in a line and then reflecting the image in an intersecting line has the same result as rotating the original figure about the intersection point of the lines by an angle equal to twice the angle formed by the reflection lines. Notice that reflecting the triangle *ABC* in line 1 and then reflecting the image *A′B′C′* in line 2 does NOT give the same result as reflecting triangle *ABC* in line 2 first and then reflecting the image in line 1. Visit Teacher Place at mathdashboard.com/cmp3 to see the complete video.

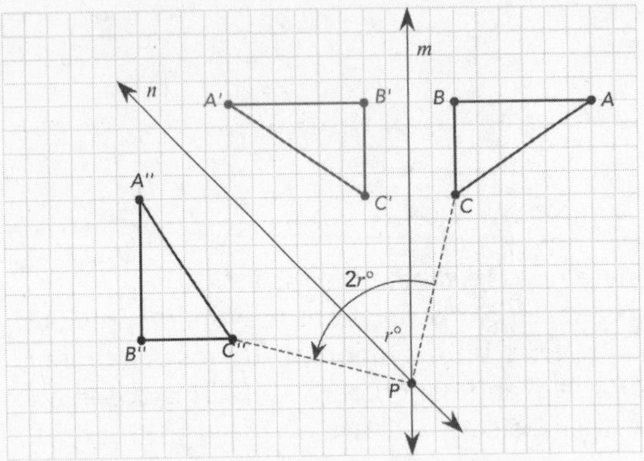

Similarity

In everyday language the word *similar* is used to suggest that objects or ideas are alike in some way. In mathematical geometry, the word *similar* is used to describe figures that have the same shape but different size. You can formally define the term with the concepts and language of transformations.

Two figures are similar if

- the measures of their corresponding angles are equal
- there is a constant factor, called the scale factor, with which the lengths of the sides of one figure can be multiplied by to give the lengths of the corresponding sides in the other figure

Parallelograms *GHIJ* and *VWXY* are similar.

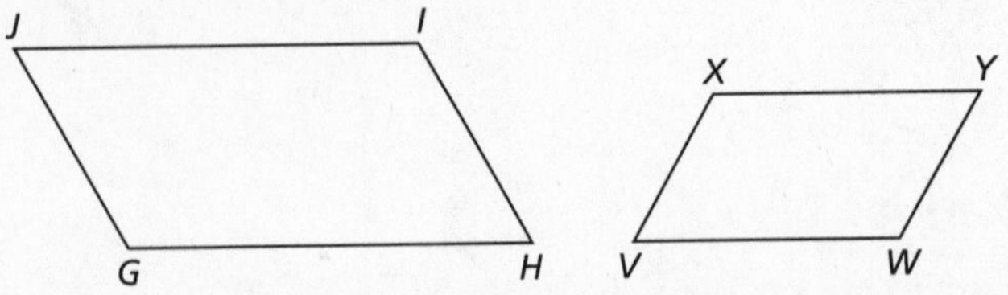

The corresponding angle measures of *GHIJ* and *VWXY* are equal. The side lengths in *VWXY*, when multiplied by 1.5, equal the corresponding side lengths in *GHIJ*. Thus, the scale factor from *VWXY* to *GHIJ* is $\frac{3}{2}$, or 1.5. *VWXY* stretches, or is enlarged, to become *GHIJ*. You can also say that the scale factor from *GHIJ* to *VWXY* is $\frac{1}{1.5}$, or $\frac{2}{3}$. *GHIJ* shrinks, or is reduced, to become *VWXY*.

Note: Congruent figures are a special case of similar figures with a scale factor of 1.

Dilations

A *dilation* with center P and scale factor $k > 0$ is a transformation of the plane (or space) that maps each point X to a point X' on ray PX so that $PX' = kPX$. The center point of any dilation maps to itself. The following diagram shows a dilation centered at P with scale factor $\frac{3}{2}$ that maps point A to point X, point B to point Y, and point C to point Z. The same diagram also shows how a dilation with scale factor $\frac{2}{3}$ maps point X to point A, point Y to point B, and point Z to point C.

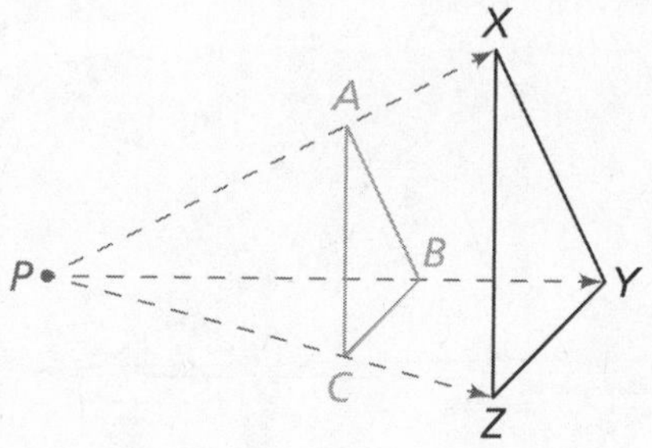

In everyday language, the word *dilation* usually suggests enlargement. However, in standard mathematical usage, the word dilation is used to describe either an enlargement or stretching action (scale factor greater than 1) or a reduction or shrinking action (scale factor between 0 and 1).

There are several very important properties of all dilation transformations. For any dilation with center P and scale factor k:

- If the dilation maps point X to point X' and point Y to point Y', then it maps segment XY onto segment $X'Y'$ and $X'Y' = kXY$.
- If the dilation maps $\angle ABC$ onto $\angle A'B'C'$, then the two angles are congruent.
- If the dilation maps polygon or circle F onto polygon or circle F', then the perimeter of F' is k times the perimeter of F and the area of F' is k^2 times the area of F.

Taken together, these properties explain how dilations preserve shapes of figures by preserving angle measures and proportional side length relationships among corresponding parts.

Coordinate Rules for Dilations

The coordinate rule to transform a figure to a similar image is $(x, y) \rightarrow (kx, ky)$ for some scale factor k. For example, if a figure is dilated by a scale factor of 4 about the origin, the coordinate rule is $(x, y) \rightarrow (4x, 4y)$. In general, if a figure is dilated by a scale factor of k about center (a, b), the coordinate rules are of the form $(x, y) \rightarrow (kx + a, ky + b)$. These coordinate rules are called *similarity transformations.*

Similar Figures

In geometry, you encounter two figures like triangles, rectangles, or trapezoids that seem to have the same shape but different size. Oftentimes, they are positioned so that you cannot see a simple dilation that would map one figure one onto the other. You first need to flip, turn, and/or slide the smaller figure onto the larger figure. For example, in triangles *ABC* and *XYZ* shown below, you can measure to check that:

$\angle X \cong \angle A$	$XY = 2 \cdot AB$
$\angle Y \cong \angle B$	$YZ = 2 \cdot BC$
$\angle Z \cong \angle C$	$ZX = 2 \cdot CA$

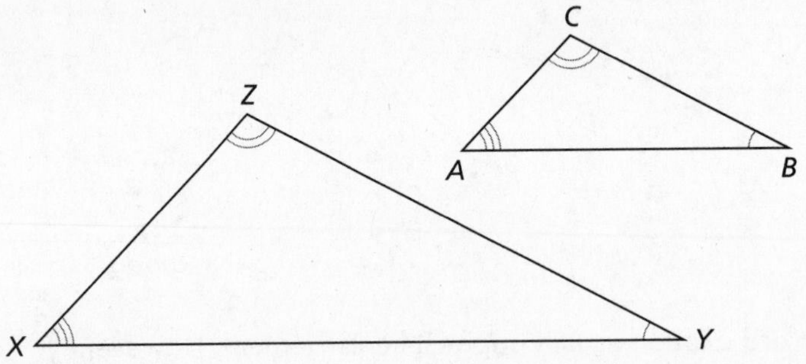

However, no simple dilation will map one of the triangles onto the other. You can use a sequence of translations to move the smaller triangle onto the larger triangle.

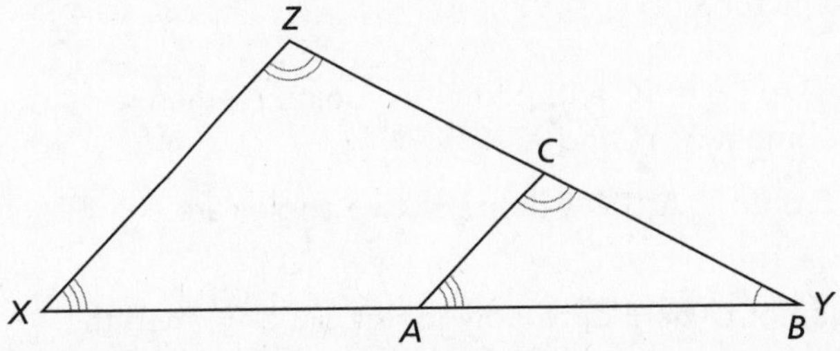

Then you can use a dilation centered at *Y* to transform triangle *ABC* exactly onto triangle *XYZ*, confirming that the original triangles are similar.

This illustrates the general definition of similarity for geometric figures: *Two figures are similar if there is a combination of one or more rigid motions and a dilation that transform one figure exactly onto the other.*

In the special case of triangles, it is not necessary to construct the sequence of rigid motions and dilation to confirm similarity. It turns out that critical knowledge about the measures of angles and sides of two triangles is sufficient to guarantee similarity. The most common conditions are:

- If two angles of one triangle are congruent to two corresponding angles of another, then the triangles are similar. (Angle-Angle)

Note: The congruence of two pairs of angles guarantees congruence of the third pair because the sum of angle measures in any triangle is 180°.

- If the ratios of the lengths of three pairs of corresponding sides in two triangles are equal, then the triangles are similar. (Side-Side-Side)

The SSS Similarity Theorem

The Side-Side-Side Similarity Theorem states that, if corresponding sides of two triangles are proportional, then the triangles are similar.

Take triangles *ABC* and *DEF* to have corresponding sides that are proportional, such that $\frac{AB}{DE} = \frac{AC}{DF} = \frac{BC}{EF}$.

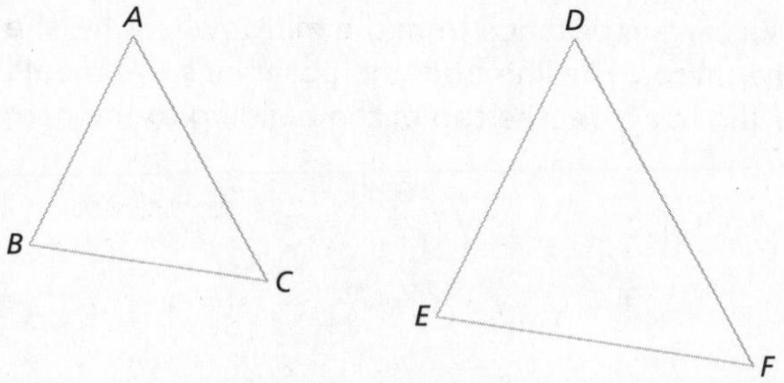

You can draw a line *QR* such that the line is equal in length to line *BC* and parallel to line *EF*.

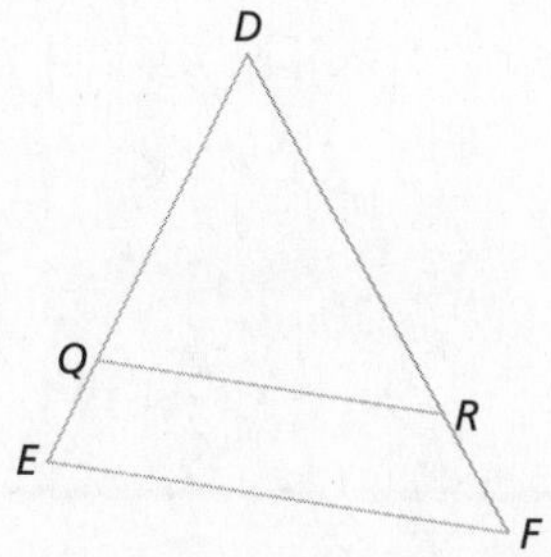

Since *QR* and *EF* are parallel, angles *Q* and *E* are congruent, as are angles *R* and *F*. So, triangles *DQR* and *DEF* are similar.

Since triangles *DQR* and *DEF* are similar, then $\frac{DQ}{DE} = \frac{DR}{DF} = \frac{QR}{EF}$.

We know that *AB* must be congruent to *DQ*, and *AC* must be congruent to *DR*. These facts result from the two proportions $\frac{AB}{DE} = \frac{AC}{DF} = \frac{BC}{EF}$ and $\frac{DQ}{DE} = \frac{DR}{DF} = \frac{QR}{EF}$, and the fact that $QR = BC$.

Since all corresponding line segments are congruent for triangles *ABC* and *DQR*, we can assume that the triangles are congruent by the Side-Side-Side Congruence Postulate. And, as similarity is transitive, since *DQR* is similar to *DEF*, its congruent triangle *ABC* must also be similar to *DEF*.

- If the ratios of lengths of two pairs of corresponding sides in two triangles are equal and the angles included in those sides are congruent, then the triangles are similar. (Side-Angle-Side)

continued on next page

When the scale factor of the dilation in a similarity transformation is equal to 1, the figures being compared are congruent. So, congruence is really a special case of similarity.

Applications of Similarity

You can use the relationships between corresponding parts of similar triangles to deduce unknown side lengths of one of the triangles. This application of similarity is especially useful in situations where you cannot measure a length or height directly.

For example, the diagram below shows a method for calculating the height of an object that you cannot reach with a ruler or tape measure. The observer places a mirror on the ground and stands a certain distance from the mirror where he/she sees the top of the building in the mirror. The line from the observer's eye meets the ground at the same angle as the line from the top of the building to the mirror.

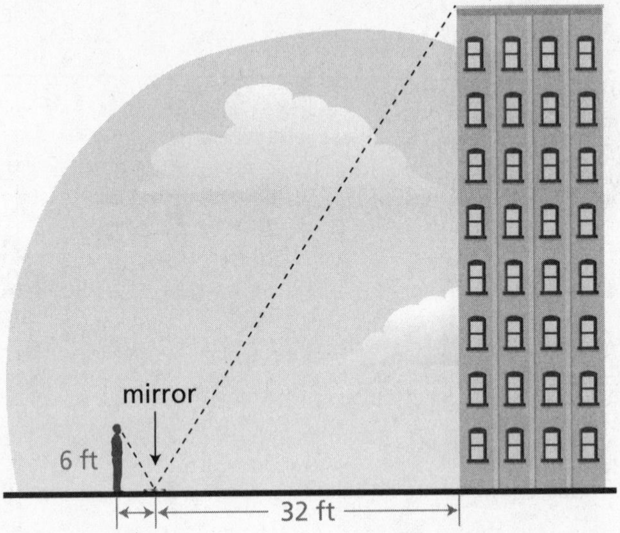

The two triangles outlined in the diagram are similar. You can measure the observer's height, his/her distance from the mirror, and the distance from the mirror to the base of the building, as shown. You can then use these measurements and proportional reasoning to find the height of the building x. That is, $\frac{x}{6} = \frac{32}{2}$. So, the height of the building is 92 feet.

Unit Introduction

Using the Unit Opener

Refer students to the three questions posed on the Looking Ahead page in the Student Edition. You may want to have a class discussion about these questions so students can start to think about the significance of symmetric details. However, it is not important to focus on finding the "correct" answers at this time. Each question is posed again in the Investigations when they have learned the mathematical concepts required to answer it. Ask your students to keep these questions in mind. As they work through the Investigations, they should think about how they might use the ideas they are learning to determine the answers.

Using the Mathematical Highlights

The Mathematical Highlights page in the Student Edition provides information to students, parents, and other family members. It gives students a preview of the mathematics and some of the overarching questions that they should ask themselves while studying *Butterflies, Pinwheels, and Wallpaper.*

As they work through the Unit, students can refer back to the Mathematical Highlights page to review what they have learned and to preview what is still to come. This page also tells students' families what mathematical ideas and activities will be covered as the class works through *Butterflies, Pinwheels, and Wallpaper.*

Unit Project

Introduction

Making a Wreath and Pinwheel is an optional assessment project for *Butterflies, Pinwheels, and Wallpaper*. This Unit Project focuses on rotational and reflection symmetry through origami, an incredibly rich and complex art form. However, there are some simple but amazing figures that even a beginner can produce successfully. The wreath and pinwheel that students make in this project show again how symmetry plays a fundamental role in such design.

Materials

- 8 paper squares of the same size (4 paper squares in each of 2 colors gives a nice result)
- scissors
- ruler

Assigning

Students can work on this project independently or with a partner. They will follow the directions in their books to make a wreath from squares of paper and then transform that wreath into a pinwheel. Figures made from origami paper are easier to manipulate, but regular-weight paper will work.

At the end of *Butterflies, Pinwheels, and Wallpaper*, each student should decide what form his or her project will take. They might choose a report, a poem, a story, or a poster. Suggest that students locate books about numbers in the library. Many books are available that could stimulate ideas. Stress that you expect them to use the vocabulary and concepts from the Unit to show everything they know about their favorite numbers and about what they have learned.

Providing Additional Support

Remind students that the more carefully they cut out the paper squares (which must be the same size), the better their results will be. Also, sharper folds will produce better results. The tricky part of this assembly is tucking one parallelogram into another and folding the tips into the valley. The tips must not "trap" the center part of the parallelogram into which they are being folded.

Grading

Suggested Scoring Rubric

A total of 50 points are possible for this project: 36 points for Exercise 1, 6 points for Exercise 2, and 8 points for Exercise 3.

Questions 1 and 2–6 points for each figure

- Identified all lines of reflection (3 pts)
- Identified the center and all angles of rotation (3 pts)

Question 3–8 points (The students should make at least 2 shapes.)

- Accurately identifies the shape of the center opening (4 pts)

Unit Project Answers

1. **a.** The square has four lines of symmetry (as indicated by the dashed fold lines in Directions section of the Student Edition) and rotational symmetry 90°, 180°, and 270° about its center.

   b. The "house" has one line of symmetry, a vertical line through the tip of the "roof," and no rotational symmetry.

   c. The "half-house" has no reflection symmetry and no rotational symmetry.

   d. The parallelogram has rotational symmetry of 180° about its center and no reflection symmetry.

   e. Answers will vary. Possible answer: For a wreath made from two alternating colors, students may say it has rotational symmetry 90°, 180°, and 270° about its center and no reflection symmetry. A single-color wreath has rotational symmetry 45°, 90°, 135°, 180°, 225°, and 270° about its center. The overall shape of the octagonal figure considered has eight lines of symmetry, but when the lines separating the individual pieces are taken into consideration, the figure does not have reflection symmetry. Acknowledge correct reasoning, with the knowledge that some students might choose to ignore the outlines of individual pieces in their search for symmetry.

   f. The pinwheel has no reflection symmetry. For a pinwheel made from two alternating colors, students may say it has rotational symmetry 90°, 180°, and 270° about its center. A single-color pinwheel has rotational symmetry 45°, 90°, 135°, 180°, 225°, 270°, and 315° about its center.

2. The two-winged pinwheel has no reflection symmetry and one rotational symmetry, 180° about its center.

3. Answers will vary. Possible answer: The center can take many shapes, including regular and nonregular quadrilaterals, hexagons, and octagons.

Looking Ahead

How could you move the wallpaper design so that it looks the same after the move?

Suppose you want to measure the distance across a pond from point *A* to point *B*. **How** could you locate points *C*, *D*, and *E* so that $AB = DE$?

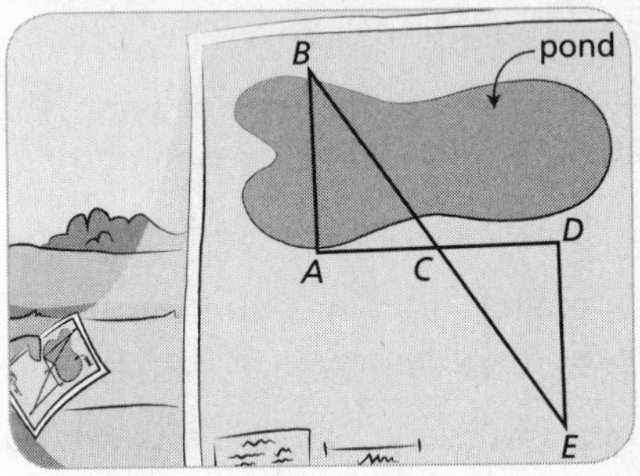

What coordinate rule for translation would "move" Mug 1 to the position of Mug 2?

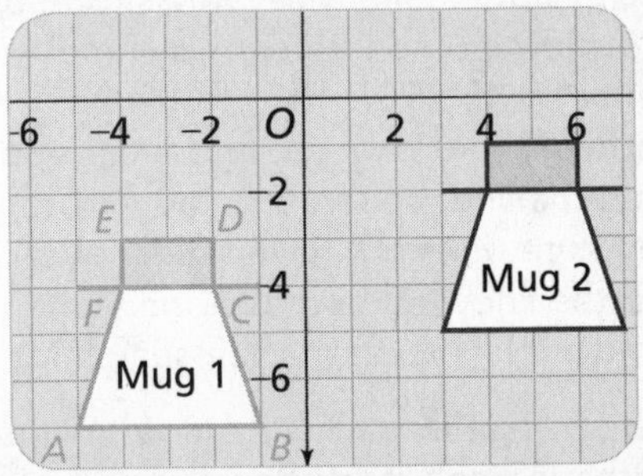

Notes

Geometric shapes give structure and style to natural and man-made objects that you see and use every day. To create and understand useful designs, it is helpful to know ways of making and describing shapes. In this Unit, you will develop your knowledge about symmetry, transformations, congruence, and similarity—four of the most important tools for thinking about geometric shapes.

Notes

Mathematical Highlights

Butterflies, Pinwheels, and Wallpaper

In *Butterflies, Pinwheels, and Wallpaper,* you will learn how to

- Identify figures that have different kinds of symmetry
- Describe types of symmetry using reflections, rotations, and translations
- Use symmetry transformations to compare the size and shape of figures to see whether they are congruent or similar
- Identify congruent and similar triangles and quadrilaterals efficiently
- Use properties of congruent and similar triangles to solve problems about shapes and measurements

ASK YOURSELF

When you encounter a new problem, it is a good idea to ask yourself questions. In this Unit, you might ask questions such as:

How can I use symmetry to describe the shape and properties of figures in a design or a problem?

What figures in a pattern are congruent?

What parts of congruent figures will be matched by a congruence transformation?

What figures in a problem are similar?

Notes

Common Core State Standards

Mathematical Practices and Habits of Mind

In the *Connected Mathematics* curriculum you will develop an understanding of important mathematical ideas by solving problems and reflecting on the mathematics involved. Every day, you will use "habits of mind" to make sense of problems and apply what you learn to new situations. Some of these habits are described by the *Common Core State Standards for Mathematical Practices* (MP).

MP1 Make sense of problems and persevere in solving them.

When using mathematics to solve a problem, it helps to think carefully about

- data and other facts you are given and what additional information you need to solve the problem;
- strategies you have used to solve similar problems and whether you could solve a related simpler problem first;
- how you could express the problem with equations, diagrams, or graphs;
- whether your answer makes sense.

MP2 Reason abstractly and quantitatively.

When you are asked to solve a problem, it often helps to

- focus first on the key mathematical ideas;
- check that your answer makes sense in the problem setting;
- use what you know about the problem setting to guide your mathematical reasoning.

MP3 Construct viable arguments and critique the reasoning of others.

When you are asked to explain why a conjecture is correct, you can

- show some examples that fit the claim and explain why they fit;
- show how a new result follows logically from known facts and principles.

When you believe a mathematical claim is incorrect, you can

- show one or more counterexamples—cases that don't fit the claim;
- find steps in the argument that do not follow logically from prior claims.

Notes

MP4 Model with mathematics.

When you are asked to solve problems, it often helps to

- think carefully about the numbers or geometric shapes that are the most important factors in the problem, then ask yourself how those factors are related to each other;
- express data and relationships in the problem with tables, graphs, diagrams, or equations, and check your result to see if it makes sense.

MP5 Use appropriate tools strategically.

When working on mathematical questions, you should always

- decide which tools are most helpful for solving the problem and why;
- try a different tool when you get stuck.

MP6 Attend to precision.

In every mathematical exploration or problem-solving task, it is important to

- think carefully about the required accuracy of results: is a number estimate or geometric sketch good enough, or is a precise value or drawing needed?
- report your discoveries with clear and correct mathematical language that can be understood by those to whom you are speaking or writing.

MP7 Look for and make use of structure.

In mathematical explorations and problem solving, it is often helpful to

- look for patterns that show how data points, numbers, or geometric shapes are related to each other;
- use patterns to make predictions.

MP8 Look for and express regularity in repeated reasoning.

When results of a repeated calculation show a pattern, it helps to

- express that pattern as a general rule that can be used in similar cases;
- look for shortcuts that will make the calculation simpler in other cases.

You will use all of the Mathematical Practices in this Unit. Sometimes, when you look at a Problem, it is obvious which practice is most helpful. At other times, you will decide on a practice to use during class explorations and discussions. After completing each Problem, ask yourself:

- What mathematics have I learned by solving this Problem?
- What Mathematical Practices were helpful in learning this mathematics?

Notes

Unit Project

Making a Wreath and a Pinwheel

Origami is the Japanese art of paper folding. In this project, you will make an origami wreath and then transform your wreath into a pinwheel.

Materials

- 8 paper squares of the same size (4 paper squares in each of 2 colors gives a nice result)
- Scissors
- Ruler

Directions

The wreath is made by connecting eight folded squares. Follow these instructions to fold each square:

- Fold a paper square to make the creases as shown.

Notes

- Fold down the top corners of the square to make a "house." Then, fold the house in half so that the flaps are on the inside.

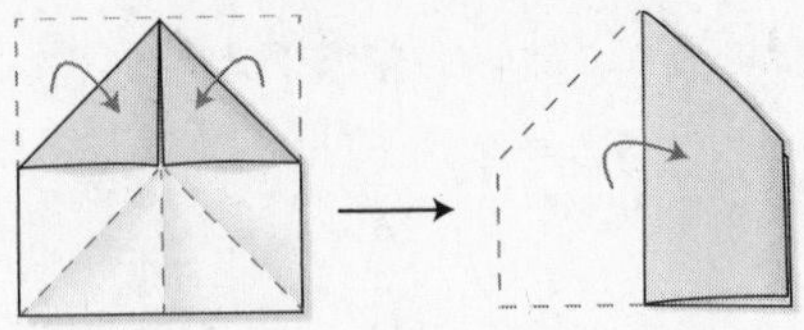

- Hold the "half-house" at its point, and push the bottom corner in along the folds to make a parallelogram.

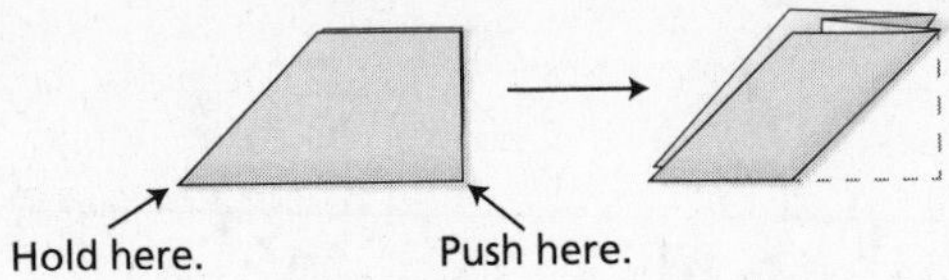

Follow these steps to connect the eight pieces:

- Position two of the folded pieces as shown on the left below. (If you used different colors, use one piece of each color.) Slide the point of the right piece into the folded pocket of the left piece.

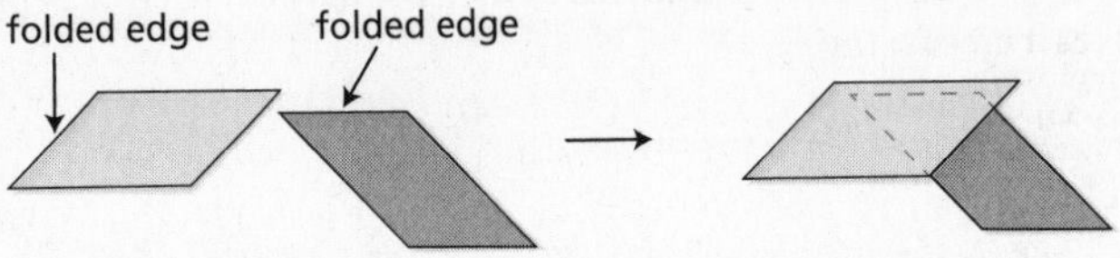

- Fold down the tips that extend over the inserted piece and tuck them into the valley formed by the folds of the inserted piece.

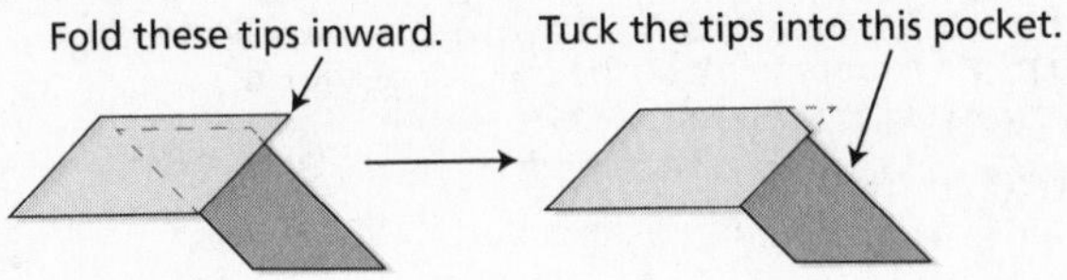

Notes

- Follow the steps on the previous page to attach the remaining folded pieces.
- Complete the wreath by connecting the last piece to the first piece, being careful to fold each flap over only one layer.
- To make a pinwheel, gently slide the sides of the wreath toward the center.

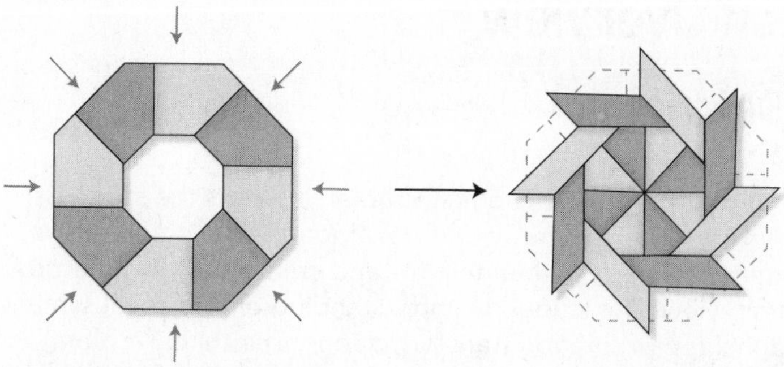

Study the drawings in the instructions for making the origami wreath and the pinwheel. Look for symmetries in the figures made at each stage.

1. Describe the reflectional and rotational symmetries of each figure.

a. the square **b.** the "house" **c.** the "half-house"

d. the parallelogram **e.** the wreath **f.** the pinwheel

2. Slide your pinwheel back into a wreath shape. If you gently push on a pair of opposite sides, you will get a pinwheel with only two "wings." Describe the reflectional and rotational symmetries of this figure.

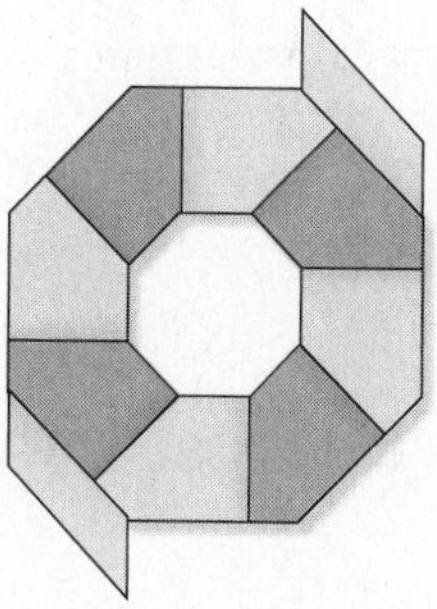

3. Slide your pinwheel back into a wreath shape. Gently push on opposite sides of the pinwheel to produce other shapes. Look at the shape of the center opening. What shapes can you make by pushing on the sides of the wreath?

Notes

Investigation 1

PLANNING

Symmetry and Transformations

Investigation Overview

Investigation Description

This Investigation has four Problems. The first Problem reviews the students' understanding of mirror or line symmetry and develops the definition of line reflection transformations. They will then test for and create such symmetries. The second Problem reviews the students' understanding of rotational symmetry and develops the definition of rotation transformations. The third Problem develops the idea of translations and translational symmetry. The fourth Problem summarizes basic properties of shapes that are preserved by these rigid motion transformations, or transformations that preserve shape and size.

Investigation Vocabulary

- angle of rotation
- basic design element
- center of rotation
- line of symmetry
- line reflection
- reflectional symmetry
- rotation
- rotational symmetry
- symmetry
- transformation
- translation
- translational symmetry

Mathematics Background

- Types of Symmetry
- Making Symmetric Designs
- Symmetry Transformations

Planning Chart

Content	ACE	Pacing	Materials	Resources
Problem 1.1	1–7, 19–20, 30–35	1 day	**Labsheet 1.1** Questions A–C Diagrams rulers, angle rulers or protractors, miras or mirrors	**Teaching Aid 1.1A** Getting Ready **Teaching Aid 1.1B** A Basic Design Element • Transformations
Problem 1.2	8–10, 21–26, 29	1½ days	**Labsheet 1.2** Question B rulers, angle rulers or protractors, tracing paper	**Teaching Aid 1.2A** Finding the Center **Teaching Aid 1.2B** Where is the Center? • Transformations
Problem 1.3	11–13, 27, 36	1 day	**Labsheet 1.3** Questions A and B Diagrams rulers, angle rulers or protractors, tracing paper	• Transformations
Problem 1.4	14–18, 28, 37–39	1½ days	**Labsheet 1.4** Transformation Properties **Labsheet 1ACE:** Exercises 14–17 (accessibility) rulers, angle rulers or protractors	• Tessellations
Mathematical Reflections		½ day		
Assessment: Check Up 1		½ day		• Check Up 1

Goals and Standards

Goals

Transformations Describe types of transformations that relate points by the motions of reflections, rotations, and translations; and methods for identifying and creating symmetric plane figures

- Recognize properties of reflection, rotation, and translation transformations
- Explore techniques for using rigid motion transformations to create symmetric designs
- Use coordinate rules for basic rigid motion transformations

Mathematical Reflections

Look for evidence of student understanding of the goals for this Investigation in their responses to the questions in *Mathematical Reflections*. The goals addressed by each question are indicated below.

1. How would you explain to someone how to make a design with

a. reflectional symmetry?

b. rotational symmetry?

c. translational symmetry?

Goal

- Explore techniques for using rigid motion transformations to create symmetric designs

2. How are points and their images related by each of these geometric transformations?

a. reflection in line m

b. rotation of $d°$ a bout point P

c. translation with distance and direction set by the segment from point X to point Y

Goal

- Recognize properties of reflection, rotation, and translation transformations

3. How do reflections, rotations, and translations change the size and shape of line segments, angles, and/or polygons, if at all?

Goal

- Recognize properties of reflection, rotation, and translation transformations

Standards

Common Core Content Standards

8.G.A.1 Verify experimentally the properties of rotations, reflections, and translations. *Problems 1, 2, 3, and 4*

8.G.A.1a Lines are taken to lines, and line segments to line segments of the same length. *Problems 1, 2, 3, and 4*

8.G.A.1b Angles are taken to angles of the same measure. *Problems 1, 2, 3, and 4*

8.G.A.1c Parallel lines are taken to parallel lines. *Problem 3 and 4*

Facilitating the Mathematical Practices

Students in *Connected Mathematics* classrooms display evidence of multiple Common Core Standards for Mathematical Practice every day. Here are just a few examples of when you might observe students demonstrating the Standards for Mathematical Practice during this Investigation.

Practice 1: **Make sense of problems and persevere in solving them.**

Students are engaged every day in solving problems and, over time, learn to persevere in solving them. To be effective, the problems embody critical concepts and skills and have the potential to engage students in making sense of mathematics. Students build understanding by reflecting, connecting, and communicating. These student-centered problem situations engage students in articulating the "knowns" in a problem situation and determining a logical solution pathway. The student-student and student-teacher dialogues help students not only to make sense of the problems, but also to persevere in finding appropriate strategies to solve them. The suggested questions in the Teacher Guides provide the metacognitive scaffolding to help students monitor and refine their problem-solving strategies.

Practice 3: **Construct viable arguments and critique the reasoning of others.**

In Problem 1.3, the students write a definition for the translation of given points. They know that a slide or translation transformation matches each point to its image. Some students will use the information to argue that if the image of two points is under translation, the distance between the points is equal to the distance between the two original points. Other students may argue that if a line connects each set of points, the two lines should have the same slope because a translation does not change the orientation of points on any figure. Working as group, the students will discuss their assumptions and develop an accurate definition.

Students identify and record their personal experiences with the Standards for Mathematical Practice during the Mathematical Reflections at the end of the Investigation.

PROBLEM 1.1

Butterfly Symmetry

Line Reflections

Problem Overview

Focus Question What does it mean to say that a figure has flip or reflectional symmetry? How is each point related to its image under transformation by reflection in a line?

Problem Description

The overarching goal of this Problem is to review the students' understanding of symmetry. From that concept, they develop the idea of transformations that "move" figures to new positions without the figures changing their size or shape. This is the foundation of congruence as prescribed in the Common Core State Standards.

Problem Implementation

Let students work in groups of 2–4.

Labsheet 1ACE: Exercise 1 (accessibility) is provided as an example of how to modify ACE Exercises to provide additional scaffolding for students who may need additional guidance on this Problem.

Materials

- **Labsheet 1.1:** Questions A–C Diagrams
- **Teaching Aid 1.1A:** Getting Ready
- **Teaching Aid 1.1B:** A Basic Design Element

rulers

angle rulers or protractors

miras or mirrors

Using Technology

If the students have access to a computer, they may find it helpful to use **Transformations** to answer the Questions of this Problem. This activity may also help to reduce the amount of class time reserved for drawing designs. **Note:** The default setting of this activity includes a grid and axes, but there is the option to remove them.

Vocabulary

- basic design element
- line of symmetry
- line reflection
- reflectional symmetry
- symmetry
- transformation

Mathematics Background

- Types of Symmetry
- Making Symmetric Designs
- Symmetry Transformations

At a Glance and Lesson Plan

- At a Glance: Problem 1.1 Butterflies, Pinwheels, and Wallpaper
- Lesson Plan: Problem 1.1 Butterflies, Pinwheels, and Wallpaper

Launch

Launch Video

This animation shows the symmetry in reflection, rotation, and translation. Each type is treated separately using a snowflake, a pinwheel, and wallpaper. Visit Teacher Place at mathdashboard.com/cmp3 to see the complete video.

You can show this animation to introduce students to the concept of symmetry in this Problem. Then you can pose the suggested questions and finish the Launch with Presenting the Challenge.

Connecting to Prior Knowledge

You might consider launching the Investigation and this Problem by asking students to describe what they see as similarities and differences among the three designs pictured in the Student Edition (or others of your choosing). Then focus more specifically on the transformation idea by asking the questions in the Student Edition. You could use **Teaching Aid 1.1A: Getting Ready** to guide this discussion. **Teaching Aid 1.1B: A Basic Design Element** provides possible answers. Students have worked with line symmetry in elementary grades (specifically Grade 4, according to the Common Core State Standards) and with line and rotational symmetry in the Grade 7 Unit *Shapes and Designs*. The focus here is more on the transformation of a basic design element that makes the design, and less on the overall design.

Suggested Questions

- What is the basic element for the butterfly shape? (The basic element consists of one wing and half the body.)
- Where is the line of symmetry? (It is the vertical line through the midway of the body.)
- Imagine that you blinked, just as someone flipped the butterfly over. Why would the butterfly look unchanged when you looked again? (The two halves are identical so I wouldn't be able to tell the difference between them.)
- What is the basic element for the pinwheel? (Answers will vary; but most students will point out the triangle that is repeated 8 times.)
- How many copies do you need to make the complete pinwheel? (I need 7 copies of an original triangle.)
- Where is the center of rotation? (This may be a new idea for students, but they are likely to intuit the center. They will work with rotations in more detail in Problem 1.2, so a further discussion is not needed at this time.)
- Imagine that you blinked, just as someone turned the pinwheel. Why would the pinwheel look unchanged when you looked again? (The 8 triangles are identical. As long as the pinwheel is turned through $\frac{1}{8}$ of a turn, it will look the same.)
- What is the basic element for the wallpaper design? (the bicyclist)
- What is the direction and distance of the translation? (This may be a new idea for students. They will work with translations in more detail in 1.3. At this point, students might say something like "down and right, or up and right.")
- Imagine that you blinked, just as someone slid the wallpaper design. Why would the wallpaper look unchanged when you looked again? (The bicycles are identical, so I wouldn't be able to tell the difference between them. Students might point out that you can tell the piece of wallpaper has moved if you have some reference for where the edges were originally. This is one of the ways that translations are different from other rigid motions: here we have to imagine that the design goes on forever. Students will have a chance to think about this further in Problem 1.3.)

Presenting the Challenge

A segue into Problem 1.1 might be accomplished by asking students how they could demonstrate the symmetry of the pentagon *ABCDE* in the introduction. If any of the flip, mirror, or fold techniques are not mentioned, you could ask students how those methods might demonstrate the symmetry. Then tell students that they are going to find a mathematical technique and exact instructions for describing and creating line symmetries. They will do this by focusing on pairs of symmetric points. Point out the notation: A and A' are a symmetric pair, because A' is the image or reflection of A in line m. (The vocabulary "in line m" may feel a little awkward at this point; it relates to the idea of line m acting like a mirror and A' is the reflection of A in that mirror.) Tell the students that by the end of the Problem, they will be able to answer the following questions:

- What is the relationship between each pair of symmetric points and the line of symmetry?
- How can you use that relationship to draw designs with line symmetry?

Explore

Providing for Individual Needs

Shapes like the butterfly have what is called bilateral, mirror, flip, line, or reflectional symmetry. The key idea is that there is a line that cuts the figure into identical halves so that each point on one half has a matching image point on the other half. If a line segment connects any point and its image, the line of symmetry is the perpendicular bisector of that line segment. This principle can be used to match each point with its image, to locate a line of symmetry when symmetric points are easy to identify, and to construct symmetric figures. Those are the ideas developed in the three parts of this Problem.

While it is desirable to have students do actual drawing and measuring experiments to discover the basic ideas, some teachers have found that student drawing and measuring skills can make such experimental work very time consuming. For this reason, Questions B and C simply ask the students to explain how they might do the required drawing. The answers to the questions do not explicitly require a sketch of the design. However if you value the drawing activity, you can make a local adjustment of the Problem to require this work. To reduce the drawing time, **Labsheet 1.1: Questions A–C Diagrams** provides a copy of the figures for Questions A–C. Some students may spend most of their drawing time on measuring each line segment accurately. They might find it helpful to work on this Problem electronically with geometry software.

For Question A, if students do not immediately see that the line of symmetry bisects BB', CC', and DD', you may want to ask the following questions.

Suggested Questions

- You have measured all the segments AA', BB', CC', DD', and EE'. Which one is the longest? Why is that? (DD'; D is farthest from the line of symmetry.)
- How far is D from the line of symmetry compared to how far is D' from the line of symmetry? Why does that make sense? (Each point and its image must be the same distance from the line of symmetry so that if we flipped or folded the design, each point would change places with its image.)
- Which points are in the same location as their images? Why is that? (A and E; these points are on the line of symmetry.)

For Question B, if students try drawing the line of symmetry without joining points to images, you may want to discuss the importance of this step:

- I see you guessed where the line of symmetry would be. How can you check that the line is correct? (I can fold the design in half, or place a mirror along the line of symmetry.)
- If you think your line of symmetry could be improved upon, would it help to join points to their images, as in Question A? (Yes; because I could find the midpoint of each line segment that joins the points to their image. If all the midpoints of these line segments are on the line of symmetry I drew, then it's accurate.)

For Question C, ask students the following:

- How did you measure the distance from the line of symmetry to K'? (Observe whether students have realized that you have to draw a segment perpendicular to the line of symmetry in order to accurately find image locations. If they have not realized this, then join a point to the proposed image and ask them what would happen if we folded along the line n.)
- What shape is the original figure? Is the image the same shape? (The original figure is a trapezoid, so the image is also a trapezoid.)

You may have to work on Question C part (2) as a class, because students might not intuitively make the connection that if $K \rightarrow K'$ and $L \rightarrow L'$, then $KL \rightarrow K'L'$. This is one of the very useful properties of transformations, or rigid motions, so it is important to call this to their attention. During the discussion, the student should come to the understanding that images of points actually "carry along" the line segments that join the points.

Planning for the Summary

What evidence will you use in the summary to clarify and deepen understanding of the Focus Question?

What will you do if you do not have evidence?

Summarize

Orchestrating the Discussion

After working on this Problem, the students should be able to answer the Focus Questions. You could prompt the discussion of these questions by referring to Question C.

Suggested Questions

- What steps did you have to take to find the images of points *J*, *K*, *L*, *M*? (First, I measured the distance from each point to the line of symmetry. Then, I continued the length of each line segment until it measured the same distance on the other side of the line of symmetry.)
- What do you notice about *JJ'* and *KK'*? (They are parallel to each other and perpendicular to the line of symmetry.)
- In mathematics, when you talk about a distance from a point to a line, the distance is assumed to be the perpendicular distance. Why is this important? (If you measured from a point to each point on a line, you would a different distance every time. However, the perpendicular distance is the shortest distance and is unique.)
- What do you notice about *JK* and *J'K'*? (These line segments are the same length.)
- How do you know that the shape of the original figure, and its image, is a trapezoid? (The original figure is a trapezoid because it has exactly one pair of parallel lines, *JM* and *KL*. Because the image is under a rigid motion, *J'M'* and *K'L'* are also parallel lines.)
- Reflection is called a transformation, or rigid motion, because it preserves certain properties of the original figure. What properties of trapezoid *JKLM* is preserved in trapezoid *J'K'L'M'*? What is not preserved? (The length of the segments and the angle measures are preserved but the orientation is not preserved.)
- Can we start with any figure and make a design with reflectional symmetry? Do we have to choose a particular line of symmetry? (Yes; any original figure and its reflection image make a symmetric design. Likewise, any line can be used as the line of symmetry, and it may be on or off the original figure.)
- If you draw a figure and a line of reflection on a piece of paper, every point on the paper has an image on the other side of the line of reflection. You can think of the piece of paper as a plane that goes on forever. When there is a line reflection, every point in the plane has an image point. You can picture a copy of the plane flipping in the line of reflection, while carrying the figure with it. Are any points unmoved by a line reflection? (Yes; only the points on the line of reflection.)

Check for Understanding

Display two simple figures, like the ones below:

- Which figure has flip or reflectional symmetry?
- Which points are paired by the symmetry?
- How can the line of symmetry be located?

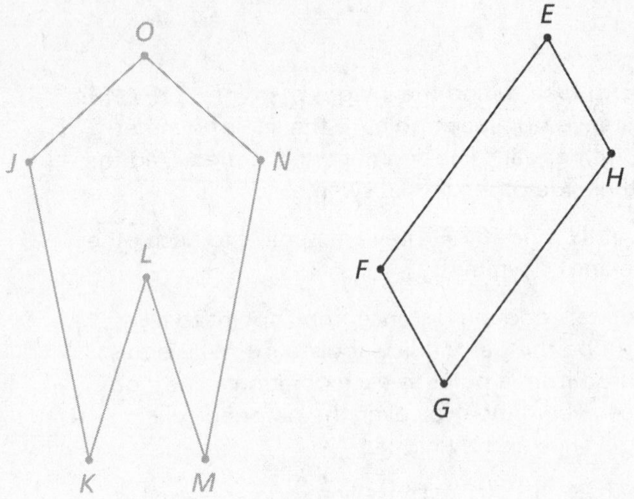

Reflecting on Student Learning

Use the following questions to assess student understanding at the end of the lesson.

- What evidence do I have that students understand the Focus Question?
  - Where did my students get stuck?
  - What strategies did they use?
  - What breakthroughs did my students have today?
- How will I use this to plan for tomorrow? For the next time I teach this lesson?
- Where will I have the opportunity to reinforce these ideas as I continue through this Unit? The next Unit?

ACE Assignment Guide

- **Applications:** 1–7
- **Connections:** 19–20
- **Extensions:** 30–35

PROBLEM 1.2

In a Spin

Rotations

Problem Overview

Focus Question What does it mean to say that a figure has turn or rotational symmetry? How is each point related to its image under transformation by rotation?

Problem Description

This Problem reviews and extends the students' understanding of rotational or turn symmetry and develops the definition of a rotational transformation.

Problem Implementation

Let students work in groups of 2–4.

Materials

- **Labsheet 1.2:** Question B
- **Teaching Aid 1.2A:** Finding the Center
- **Teaching Aid 1.2B:** Where is the Center?

rulers

angle rulers or protractors

tracing paper

Using Technology

If the students have access to a computer, they may find it helpful to use **Transformations** to answer the Questions of this Problem. This activity may also help to reduce the amount of class time reserved for drawing designs. **Note:** The default setting of this activity includes a grid and axes, but there is the option to remove them.

Vocabulary

- angle of rotation
- center of rotation
- rotation
- rotational symmetry

Mathematics Background

- Making Symmetric Designs
- Symmetry Transformations

At a Glance and Lesson Plan

- At a Glance: Problem 1.2 Butterflies, Pinwheels, and Wallpaper
- Lesson Plan: Problem 1.2 Butterflies, Pinwheels, and Wallpaper

Launch

Connecting to Prior Knowledge

You might choose to start the work on this Problem by asking students how the pinwheel is different from the butterfly in Problem 1.1. Display **Teaching Aid 1.1B: A Basic Design Element** and ask them to explain how the pinwheel has its own kind of symmetry.

Suggested Questions

- What angle of rotation would rotate one of the triangles so that the image helps to make this symmetric design? (45°; Students might need to measure this, so their guesses could be inaccurate.)
- How many copies do you need to make? (7 copies of the original triangle, which indicates that a 45° turn counterclockwise, or 360 ÷ 8, would "move" the original triangle to the location of an adjacent image. Repeating this rigid motion 7 times would complete the design.)
- Is there a different basic design element that you could copy? (Taking two triangles together would give us a different basic design element. I would have to copy this 3 times. The rotation angle would be 90°, or 360 ÷ 4. I could take 4 triangles together as a basic design element, and rotate that element 180° around the center of the pinwheel.)

Presenting the Challenge

If you want to leave the Problem open for exploration, you might remind the students that they found a relationship between a point, its image, and the line of symmetry. They then used this relationship to draw figures with line symmetry. In this Problem the challenge is to do the same for figures with rotational symmetry.

Suggested Questions

- How is each point X related to its image point X', the center of the rotation O, and the angle of rotation? ($OX = OX'$ and the measure of $\angle XOX'$ is equal to the angle of rotation.)

Specific parts of Problem 1.2 will expand on the details of this answer.

Explore

Providing for Individual Needs

The parts in Questions A of this Problem can be answered with measurements of angles in the given figures and with logical analysis. To help students see that different angles of rotation are possible, you might ask about the basic design element.

Suggested Questions

- You said you "moved" *A* to *G*. How much of a turn is that? (The turn is 90°.)
- How many rotations will it take for *A* to "move" back to the starting position? (It will take 4 rotations.)
- So, what part of the design would you have to copy 3 times so that the basic design element and the 3 copies make the complete design? (I would have to copy 2 large triangles and 2 adjacent small triangles.)
- Is there a basic design element you could have copied 7 times so that the original element and the 7 copies would make the complete design? (No; because the longer points of the star have to match the larger triangles and there are only 4 of them.)
- You are not actually making drawings, but you can imagine *A* "moving" to location *G*. Can you trace that with your finger? (Yes; because point *A* "moves" along the arc of a circle as it rotates to *G*. Some students might not see this so, it may be helpful for them to lay a protractor on the figure. They will then follow the shape of the arc with the edge of the protractor from point *A* to point *G*.)

Comparing the ideas of rotation with reflection might be helpful for students because the "movement" with reflection is a straight line from point to image. For example, from point *A* "moves" to point *E* by rotation of 180° about *O* or under reflection in line segment *GC*. In Question B, using tracing paper to make a copy and rotating the copy should make this path clear.

Question B asks about procedures for constructing a design that has rotational symmetry. It also asks for two drawings (or sketches), with different angles of rotation. If students are having trouble understanding the relationship between a figure and its image after a rotation, you may want to hand out **Labsheet 1.2: Question B**. It provides the basic design element and they can use tracing paper to help them understand the motion involved.

In Question B, the students are encouraged to find other ways of making symmetric designs. Most students will choose a center of rotation on the figure, at point *P* or *Q*. You may want to explain that other centers of rotation are possible by displaying **Teaching Aid 1.2A: Finding the Center** and **Teaching Aid 1.2B: Where is the Center?** The discussion can be focused on ways to find an unknown center of rotation. These Teaching Aids can also be used in the Summary.

- What is the center for your rotation? How do you use this? (All methods involve drawing a line segment from the center to a point on the original. This line specifies the radius of the circle, or the constant distance between the point and the center as the point moves the along the arc of the circle.)

Students might copy the basic deign element on tracing paper and use a protractor to make the desired angle with the radius. Next, they would hold the tracing paper at the center point and rotate it to a new position. The last step is to copy the image of basic design element on the tracing paper. Other students might use a line segment from the center of rotation to a point on the figure as the focus of the transformation. This line segment acts as one side of the required angle and the center is a vertex. Using a protractor, they would measure the angle or rotation and then draw another line segment that is the image of the original line segment on the figure. This method would have to be repeated for each point on the original figure to make accurate images of the basic design element. A third method that students might choose is using a compass. They decide on the points of the figure they want to use and the center of rotation. Next, they draw arcs of a circle with a radius set to match the distance from a center to each point on the original figure. To draw the image in its proper place, they would measure the angle of rotation specified.

- Can you keep track of the way point *R* is moving as you rotate the tracing paper? (Yes; it "moves" along the arc of a circle with a constant distance from the center of rotation.)
- How many copies do you have to make? How can you predict the number of copies needed? (It depends on the angle of rotation. For example, an angle of 120 degrees requires 2 copies of the basic design element plus the original element because $360 \div 120 = 3$.)
- Can you choose any point for the center of rotation? (Students are likely to choose *P* or *Q*, but other points are possible, including points not on the figure. Refer to Teaching Aids 1.2A and 1.2B.)

Planning for the Summary

What evidence will you use in the summary to clarify and deepen understanding of the Focus Question?

What will you do if you do not have evidence?

Summarize

Orchestrating the Discussion

Ask students to share their drawings from Question B. One possibility is shown here.

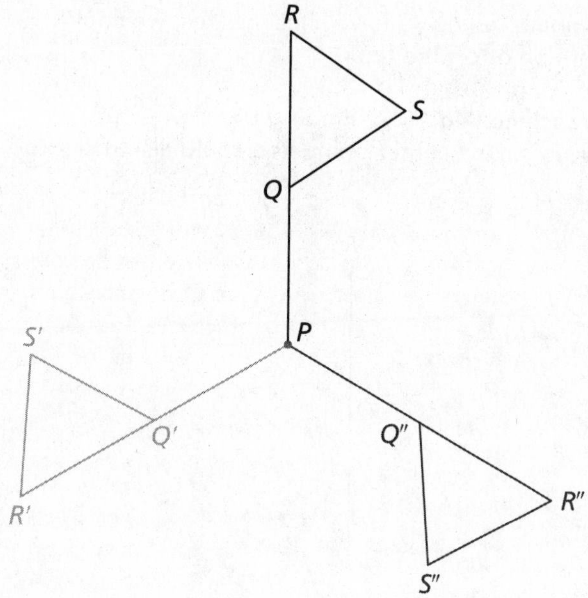

Suggested Questions

- What are the center of rotation and angle of rotation for this design? (The center is point *P*, and the angle of rotation is 120 degrees.)
- As you rotate the basic design element around *P* to make an image, what point is the image of point *R*? Can you show the path that *R* moves along? (The image of *R* is point *R*′ and *R*″. It "moves" along the arc of a circle (with radius equal to the measure of *PR*).)
- What point is the image of point *Q*? Point *S*? (Point *Q*′ and *Q*″ is the image of *Q*, and point *S*′ and *S*″ is the image of *S*.)
- Are points *Q* and *S* "moving" along the same circle as *R* in this rotation? (No; because the radii of the circles they "move" along are different. The angle is the same, and the center is the same, but *Q*, *R*, and *S* are different distances from the center of rotation *P*. (From closest to farthest, the order is *Q*, *S*, then *R*.))
- When you rotate *Q* around *P* and *R* around *P*, what happens to *QR*? (*QR* "moves" to the location of *Q*′*R*′ and *Q*″*R*″. This question is important for students who may not make this connection on their own.)
- Rotation is a type of transformation, or rigid motion, because it preserves certain properties of the basic design element. What do you think is preserved in Question C? What is not preserved? (The lengths of segments and the measure of angles are preserved, but the orientation of the basic design element is not preserved.)

- Suppose you draw a figure on paper and make a copy on tracing paper. If you rotate the copy about a center of rotation, every point on the original paper has an image after the rotation. You can think of the piece of paper as a plane that goes on forever. When you do a rotation, every point on the plane has an image point. Picture the copy of the plane rotating and carrying the figure with it. Are any points unmoved by a rotation? (Yes; only the point that is the center of rotation.)
- Are there any other center points we could have chosen? (Yes; we could have chosen any center point on or off the figure.)

Note: You may want to display **Teaching Aid 1.2A: Finding the Center** to demonstrate other possible choices for the center point. You could also use it to prompt a class discussion.

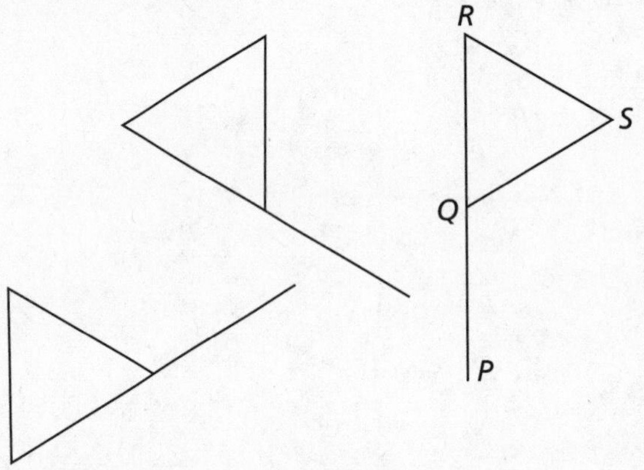

- Does it look like the drawing could be completed to make a symmetric design? What difficulty would you have in completing this? (It looks like we would need 5 copies of the basic design element plus the original element. The difficulty is in figuring out the location of the center point and the angle of rotation.)
- Can you guess where the center might be? (Let students guess and encourage them to trace the arcs formed by the movement of points on the original. They could also draw line segments that connect the corresponding image points. This would help them see the type of polygon that could be made with the line segments. Then they could measure the angles at the vertices of the polygon to find the angle of rotation for the design. The center of rotation is the center of the polygon.)

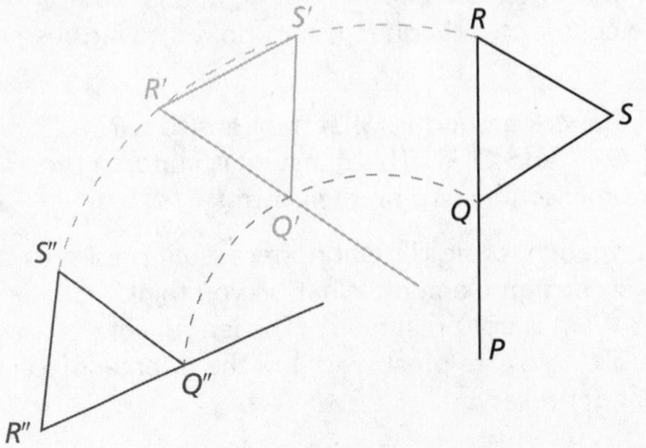

- How do these arcs help us figure out where the center is? (Students may not have an answer at this time. This question is a preview of a future discussion that will occur later in the Unit.)

Note: If you join the segment RR' you have drawn a chord of the circle. The center is somewhere on the perpendicular bisector of this chord. Likewise, the center is on the perpendicular bisector of $Q'Q''$, so the intersection point of the two perpendicular bisectors gives the desired center.

Discuss definitions produced by students in response to Question D. You might record each suggestion and let students critique them until they are satisfied with the final result. Refer to the answer for Question D.

Reflecting on Student Learning

Use the following questions to assess student understanding at the end of the lesson.

- What evidence do I have that students understand the Focus Question?
  - Where did my students get stuck?
  - What strategies did they use?
  - What breakthroughs did my students have today?
- How will I use this to plan for tomorrow? For the next time I teach this lesson?
- Where will I have the opportunity to reinforce these ideas as I continue through this Unit? The next Unit?

ACE Assignment Guide

- **Applications:** 8–10
- **Connections:** 21–26
- **Extensions:** 29

PROBLEM 1.3

Sliding Around

Translations

Problem Overview

Focus Question What does it mean to say that a figure has slide or translational symmetry? How is each point related to its image under transformation by translation?

Problem Description

The objective of this Problem is to develop the students' understanding of slide or translational symmetry and the work involved with this type of transformation.

Problem Implementation

Let students work in groups of 2–4.

Materials

- **Labsheet 1.3:** Questions A and B Diagrams

rulers

angle rulers or protractors

tracing paper.

Using Technology

If the students have access to a computer, they may find it helpful to use **Transformations** to answer the Questions of this Problem. This activity may also help to reduce the amount of class time reserved for drawing designs. **Note:** The default setting of this activity includes a grid and axes, but there is the option to remove them.

Vocabulary

- translation
- translational symmetry

Mathematics Background

- Making Symmetric Designs
- Symmetry Transformations

At a Glance and Lesson Plan

- At a Glance: Problem 1.3 Butterflies, Pinwheels, and Wallpaper
- Lesson Plan: Problem 1.3 Butterflies, Pinwheels, and Wallpaper

Launch

Launch Video

This animation shows Tory and Jayden hanging wallpaper with a design that has translation symmetry. The characters show how shifting a piece of wallpaper can align the pattern with an adjacent piece of wallpaper. This concept is used to keep the translational symmetry across the two pieces of wallpaper. Visit Teacher Place at mathdashboard.com/cmp3 to see the complete video.

You can show this animation to introduce the Problem. Then you can continue the Launch by Presenting the Challenge.

Connecting to Prior Knowledge

You might choose to launch the work on this Problem similar to the way it is done in Problems 1.1 and 1.2. Start with an open question asking the students to describe how each point of a basic design element "moves" under a translation that preserves appearance of the wallpaper design.

The definition of translational symmetry is complex by the fact that there is no bounded figure with this kind of symmetry (whereas it is much easier to imagine such a figure with reflectional or rotational symmetry). If one asks whether a bounded piece of wallpaper looks the same after it has been slid left, right, up, or down, the honest answer will usually be, "No." This is because that finite sample of the pattern will not be in the same position as before the transformation. For this reason, when talking technically about translational symmetry, it is customary to insert the caveat, "Imagine that the design continues without end in all directions (or that the design has unlimited strip patterns in two specified directions)." Once that technical ground rule is established, students will feel more comfortable discovering the properties translational symmetry.

Presenting the Challenge

Before the students start to work in their groups, you can ask the questions in the Student Edition.

Suggested Questions

- How would you explain the exact translation that creates an image of a basic design element? (A complete answer for this question is not necessary at this time. The specifics will come from the Problem. At this point, you may simply pose the question or give students the opportunity to give their initial ideas. Possible ideas may include figuring out the distance that the basic design element "moved." They may also say that the direction of the slide is needed.)
- How many images of the basic design element would you have to make so that the completed design has translational symmetry? (If you have not already talked about this idea, this is an opportunity to say that that a design with translational symmetry must look the same after a translation. In order to achieve this, the dimensions of the design must be infinite or go on forever. If the dimensions were fixed, the slide or translation would be noticeable.)

After this discussion, the students can work on the specific tasks of the Problem that ask them to explore several different examples of translations.

Explore

Providing for Individual Needs

For Question A, in order to help students discover the defining properties of slides or translations, it is helpful for them to connect corresponding vertices of a polygon and its translation image. **Labsheet 1.3: Questions A and B Diagrams** allows students to discover that those connecting segments are all the same length and parallel to each other. As they continue to explore the properties of translation, they will discover that the corresponding segments are also parallel to each other. This is different from the result of a reflection or rotation of a segment.

Suggested Questions

- You noticed that GG', HH', and JJ' are all the same length so the distance of the translation is constant. What else is the same about GG', HH', and JJ'? (Students might say the orientation or the slope of the segments. Encourage them to see that these segments are parallel.)
- There are a lot of parallel line segments as a result of this translation: GG', HH', JJ', etc. What else do you notice about the original figure and its image? (Students might say the image is the same size and shape as the original figure. Encourage them to be explicit about what they mean by size and shape.)

- When you say the image is the same size and shape, what do you mean? (The sides are the same length and the angles are the same size. (You can push the students to give more details by asking about the perimeter and area of the figure.))
- Looking at segments *GM* and *G′M′*, what else do you notice about the figure and its image? Why does this happen? (The segments are parallel. The students' explanations about why corresponding sides are parallel are likely to be incomplete. You might encourage them to recall their knowledge of parallel lines cut by a transversal.)
- You say that angle G is the same size as angle *G′*. Does that have anything to do with your claim that GM is parallel to *G′M′*? (*GG′* is a transversal, cutting *GM* and *G′M′* at G and *G′*. Students explored parallels and transversals in the Grade 7 Unit Shapes and Designs. If there are congruent angles in corresponding positions at the intersection of a transversal *t* with two other lines *m* and *n*, then *m* and *n* are parallel.)

In Question B, we revisit the idea of parallel segments created by a translation. Watch for student strategies that can be usefully shared in the Summary.

- What does that arrow tell you about the translation needed? How can you apply the same translation to all points on the polygon? (Students may have various strategies for copying the direction and distance shown, and applying it to all vertices of the polygon. Encourage them to think about angle and parallel lines. They might trace the polygon and the arrow, lay a ruler or straight edge along the original translation arrow, and slide the tracing so that the traced arrow moves along the edge of the ruler. This will preserve the direction. They might also use the reference line method. They start by drawing a vertical line that intersects the left end of the arrow. Then, they measure the angle from the arrow to the vertical line. Next, they use tracing paper to draw the polygon and draw vertical lines through each vertex. Now they can take each vertical line on the polygon and line it up with the vertical line on the arrow. The image of each vertex will be made at the right end of the arrow to preserve the distance and direction of the translation.)

You may want to work on part (4) of Question B as a class in the summary. Student may not make the connection that if you "move" *A* and *B* the same distance and direction, then you will also "carry" along all the intermediate points on the line segment *AB*. This is an important and useful idea, so it needs to be explicitly stated. However, it is not necessary to make this topic the main focus of the discussion.

Planning for the Summary

What evidence will you use in the summary to clarify and deepen understanding of the Focus Question?

What will you do if you do not have evidence?

Summarize

Orchestrating the Discussion

The main point of the summary is to agree on a definition of translation. There are also other points that need to be made explicit for everyone. Having the students share their strategies for Question B will help to bring out all these points.

Suggested Questions

- What equal segments does your strategy create? What parallel segments? (The distances translated are all equal and parallel. The segments of the original figure and its images are also the same lengths and parallel.)

- How is translational symmetry like or unlike reflectional and rotational symmetry? (Similar to reflection and rotational symmetry, a basic design element is needed. This time, however, you need to think about making an infinite number of images, unlike one image in reflectional symmetry or a fixed number of images in rotational symmetry. For reflections, the instructions for the transformation depend on locating the line of symmetry. For rotations, the instructions include locating a center and fixing an angle. Translations require distance and direction.)

- What parallelograms do you see on the finished figure? ($ABB'A'$, $BCC'B'$, $EAA'E'$, etc. Two sides are parallel because they are the same distance and direction as the translation arrow, and two sides are the same distance and direction because one is the image of the other.)

- Translation is a type of rigid motion because it preserves certain properties of the original figure. What do you think is preserved in Question C? What is not preserved? (Translation preserves the lengths of segments, the measures of angles, and any parallel relationships. It also preserves the orientation of the figure, but not its original location.)

- If you draw a figure on a piece of paper, you can think of the piece of paper as a plane that goes on forever. When you do a translation, every point in the plane has an image point. You can picture a copy of the plane being translated and carrying the figure with it. Are there any points unmoved by a translation? (No; translation does not preserve the position of any point. **Note:** If the slide is 0 units, then no point moves. At this stage of development, you do not need to discuss this, but it may come up in class. A similar thing happens with a 0° rotation.)

Have the students share their responses for Question D to the class, and allow them to critique each other's answers until they are satisfied with the definition created. Refer to the answer for Question D.

Reflecting on Student Learning

Use the following questions to assess student understanding at the end of the lesson.

- What evidence do I have that students understand the Focus Question?
  - Where did my students get stuck?
  - What strategies did they use?
  - What breakthroughs did my students have today?
- How will I use this to plan for tomorrow? For the next time I teach this lesson?
- Where will I have the opportunity to reinforce these ideas as I continue through this Unit? The next Unit?

ACE Assignment Guide

- **Applications:** 11–13
- **Connections:** 27
- **Connections:** 36

PROBLEM

1.4 Properties of Transformations

Problem Overview

Focus Question How, if at all, will the shape, size, and position of a figure change after each of the transformations—reflection, rotation, or translation?

Problem Description

This Problem addresses the properties of figures that are preserved after a reflection, a rotation, or a translation. If students are thinking about each transformation in its physical sense, some of the answers are obvious. If they think about the relationship of points to their images, the core results are a bit less obvious. For example, if two points are mapped to their images across a line of reflection, why is it obvious that their images should be the same distance apart?

Problem Implementation

Let students work in groups of 2–4.

Materials

- **Labsheet 1.4:** Transformation Properties
- **Labsheet 1ACE:** Exercises 14–17 (accessibility)
- **Check Up 1**

rulers

angle rulers or protractors

Using Technology

Students can use **Tessellations** to create their own symmetric design and describe all the possible reflection, rotation, or translation symmetries they see in their figure.

Vocabulary

There are no new glossary terms introduced in this Problem.

Mathematics Background

- Types of Symmetry
- Making Symmetric Designs
- Symmetry Transformations

At a Glance and Lesson Plan

- At a Glance: Problem 1.4 Butterflies, Pinwheels, and Wallpaper
- Lesson Plan: Problem 1.4 Butterflies, Pinwheels, and Wallpaper

Launch

Connecting to Prior Knowledge

Refer to the graphic in the Student Edition to start a discussion.

Suggested Questions

- What is the shape of the original figure? (a trapezoid)
- How do you know what kind of transformation has been applied? (From the left to right, the transformations shown are reflection, rotation, and translation.)
- What are the details you should give to describe each transformation? (Reflection requires the line of symmetry; Rotation requires the center and angle of rotation; Translation requires the distance and direction of the rigid motion.)
- How can you check you have described the correct transformation? (I can make a trace of the figure and follow the directions I wrote. If the traced copy "moves" to the location of the image, then the transformation is correct.)

Presenting the Challenge

Tell students that the ideas and details they summarize here will be useful in Investigations 2, 3, and 4. For example, they learn that accurately describing a transformation that "moves" one figure to the location of another is a way of showing that the two figures are congruent. It is not enough to say that the figures look the same.

Labsheet 1.4: Transformation Properties gives students the opportunity to collect together all the information gleaned in Problems 1.1, 1.2, and 1.3.

Note: Students have to find the center of a rotation in Question A. In Investigation 2 students will use a sequence of transformations to "move" one shape on to another to check for congruence. The sequence can be done in more than one order, so finding the center of a rotation does not have to be the first step. A translation can "move" a point on one shape to the corresponding point on the other shape and this location would be the center of rotation. For this reason, you may choose to downplay the work for finding the center of rotation. However, students might enjoy the challenge of figuring out how the center relates to the segments joining points to images.

Explore

Providing for Individual Needs

For Question A, students should be able to independently find the line of symmetry or the distance and direction of translation. However, they may need help finding the center of a rotation.

Suggested Questions

- What seems to be the angle of rotation for the middle transformation? How do you know? (90°; *WZ* is at a right angle to *W′Z′*.)
- How can we go about finding the center of the rotation? Would sketching the arcs followed by *X* as it "moves" to *X′*, and *Y* as it "moves" to *Y′*, help? (Students might suggest guessing the measure of the angle and checking to see if it's correct. This process will help make better guesses for the center of rotation.)
- We are trying to find a point *O* so that *OX* and *OX′* are the same distance, and *OY* and *OY′* are the same. Suppose we join *XX′* and *YY′*. Do these segments suggest where to look for point *O*? (The center is at the intersection of the perpendicular bisectors of *XX′* and *YY′*. **Note:** See the diagram in the answer to Question A or the **Teaching Aid 1.2A: Finding** the Center for a visual representation of finding the center of rotation.)

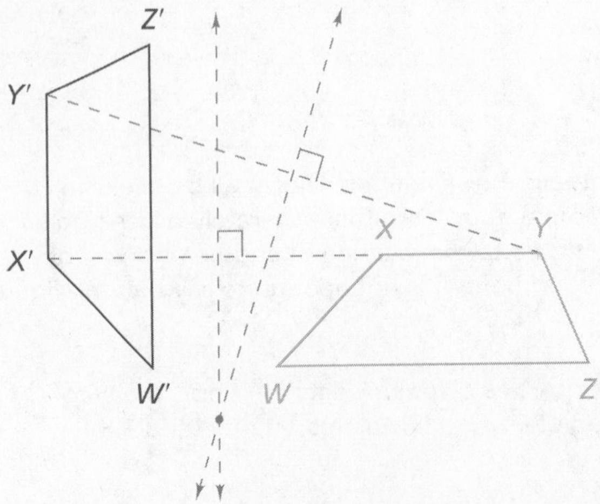

Some students may need more direction to complete Question A because they haven't yet developed tips or shortcuts for identifying a transformation. Provide them with **Labsheet 1ACE: Exercises 14–17** (accessibility) for practice on more examples.

In Question B, the question of which points or lines are "unmoved" by various transformations is non-trivial. Students have thought about this before in the context of each kind of transformation. In the examples shown in the Problem, there are no apparent "unmoved" points or lines, unless we think about the transformation moving not just the trapezoid but also every point in the plane. That subtlety is probably best addressed in the summary discussion. You might want to assign each group the responsibility of leading the discussion by summarizing their findings for each part of the Problem.

Planning for the Summary

What evidence will you use in the summary to clarify and deepen understanding of the Focus Question?

What will you do if you do not have evidence?

Summarize

Orchestrating the Discussion

Review the students' answers of each part of Questions. The key result is that flips, turns, and slides all "move" lines onto lines, angles onto angles of the same size, and segments onto segments of the same length. Lines that are parallel in the original figure are "moved" onto parallel lines in the image figure. Line segments and their images are also parallel under translation. Area and perimeter are preserved by all three transformations.

Take this opportunity to discuss which points or lines are "unmoved." Students may say that no points are unmoved under the transformations shown. This is a subtle point so use your best judgement about whether this will confuse students, or excite them.

Suggested Questions

- When are points or lines "unmoved" under a reflection? (Points on the line of reflection or sides/segments that coincide with the line of symmetry would be "unmoved.")
- If we look at the completed diagram you made for the reflectional symmetry example, are there any points or lines "unmoved"? (Yes because if you think of the whole plane being reflected in the line of reflection, then points and segments on that line are "unmoved.")

- Let's look at the example of a rotation. Instead of only thinking about the trapezoid rotating around the center, imagine the whole plane is rotating around the center while carrying the trapezoid along with it. What points or lines are "unmoved"? (The center of rotation is "unmoved." **Note:** An "unmoved" line is one that goes through the center of rotation and maps on to itself by the angle of rotation 180°. This is not shown in the example.)
- Let's do the same thought experiment with the translation example. Imagine the entire plane is translated carrying along the trapezoid. What points or lines are unmoved? (All points, segments and lines are moved.)

Reflecting on Student Learning

Use the following questions to assess student understanding at the end of the lesson.

- What evidence do I have that students understand the Focus Question?
  - Where did my students get stuck?
  - What strategies did they use?
  - What breakthroughs did my students have today?
- How will I use this to plan for tomorrow? For the next time I teach this lesson?
- Where will I have the opportunity to reinforce these ideas as I continue through this Unit? The next Unit?

ACE Assignment Guide

- **Applications:** 14–18
- **Connections:** 28
- **Extensions:** 37–39
- **Labsheet 1ACE:** Exercises 14–17 (accessibility)

Mathematical Reflections

Possible Answers to Mathematical Reflections

1. a. A design has reflectional symmetry if it has two identical halves lying on either side of a line. When you fold along the line, the two halves of the design will be a mirror image of each other. In order to create this type of design, you need any basic element and any reflection line. You measure the distances from strategic points on the design element to the line of symmetry; then you measure the same distances on the other side of the line of symmetry to locate the image points. These distances have to be perpendicular to the line of symmetry, so the line of symmetry is equidistant from each point and its image. Joining the image points creates the image. Together, the original element and the image make the symmetric design.

b. A design has rotational symmetry if there is a fixed center point in which the design turns around by a given degree. When the turn is complete, the design looks exactly like it did before any transformation occurred. In order to create this type of design, you need a basic element and a center point, which can be on or off the figure. Then you decide on an angle of rotation, because the number of images needed depends on the angle size. For example, with an angle of rotation of 45 degrees, there will be 8 copies of the basic design element, 7 images plus the original element. For each strategic point, P, on the original element, you measure the distance from the center, OP, and draw OP' so $\angle POP' = 45$ degrees. Also, OP' is the same length as OP, and P' is the image of P. Connecting the image points gives a copy of the original element. To complete the design, you have to repeat the rotation, making images, until you are back at the original element. (In general, number of images equals $\frac{360}{d} - 1$, where d is the number of degrees in the angle of rotation. Rewriting the same equation, $d = \frac{360}{n+1}$, where n is the number of images of the basic design element. **Note:** The total number of copies, including the original element, is $\frac{360}{d}$.)

c. A design has translational symmetry if you can slide a portion of the design some distance in some direction so that the overall design looks unchanged. In order to create this type of design, you need a basic design element and a specified distance and direction. Then for each strategic point P on the basic design element, you draw a segment PP', where all the segments are the same length and parallel to the direction specified. You then connect the image points to make the image of the basic design element. You repeat this, technically, an infinite number of times, in both directions to complete the design.

2. Points and their images are related by geometric transformations as follows:

a. Reflection in line m "moves" each point X to the location of point X' so that m is the perpendicular bisector of segment XX'.

b. Rotation of $d°$ about point P "moves" each point X to the location of point X' so that $XP = X'P$ and the measure of $\angle XPX'$ is $d°$.

c. Translation with distance and direction set by the segment from point X to point X' "moves" each point A to a point A' located so that $AA' = XX'$ and segment $\overline{AA}$ is parallel to segment $\overline{XX}$.

3. Reflections, rotations, and translations do not change the size and shape of line segments, angles, and/or polygons.

Possible Answers to Mathematical Practices Reflections

Students may have demonstrated all of the eight Common Core Standards for Mathematical Practice during this Investigation. During the class discussion, have students provide additional Practices that the Problem cited involved and identify the use of other Mathematical Practices in the Investigation.

One student observation is provided in the Student Edition. Here is another sample student response.

> In Problem 1.3, we explored several translations. It makes sense that the translation arrows connecting points to images are all parallel, because they are going in to the same direction and distance. Then we noticed there were other parallel lines; each segment and its image are parallel. The picture of a shape and its image connected by translation arrows looks like a lot of overlapping parallelograms.
>
> **MP7: Look for and make use of structure.**

Investigation 1

Symmetry and Transformations

Symmetry is one of the most important and appealing features of shapes. Artists use symmetry to make designs that are pleasing to the eye. Architects use symmetry to make buildings balanced. Symmetry is also found in the structure of animals, plants, and everyday objects.

Common Core State Standards

8.G.A.1 Verify experimentally the properties of rotations, reflections, and translations:

8.G.A.1a Lines are taken to lines, and line segments to line segments of the same length.

8.G.A.1b Angles are taken to angles of the same measure.

8.G.A.1c Parallel lines are taken to parallel lines.

Notes

The butterfly, the pinwheel, and the piece of wallpaper, shown on this page and the next, illustrate three familiar forms of symmetry.

The butterfly has *reflectional symmetry*. You can make the butterfly design by reflecting, or flipping, a **basic design element** in a *line of symmetry* to make an image, or copy. The basic design element and its image form a design with reflectional symmetry.

- What is the basic design element for the butterfly design?
- Where is the line of symmetry?

The pinwheel has *rotational symmetry*. You can make the pinwheel design by rotating, or turning, a basic design element about a *center of rotation* to make one or more images. The basic design element and its images form a design with rotational symmetry.

- What is the basic design element for the pinwheel design?
- How many copies do you need to complete the symmetric design?
- Where is the center of rotation?

Notes

The wallpaper design has *translational symmetry*. You can make the wallpaper design by translating, or sliding, a basic design element several times a certain distance and direction to make images. The basic design element and its images form a design with translational symmetry.

- What is the basic design element for the wallpaper design?
- What is the direction and distance of the translation?

The completed designs each have a different kind of symmetry. If you blinked just as someone flipped the butterfly design over the line of symmetry, the butterfly would look unchanged when you looked again. If you blinked just as someone turned the pinwheel 90 degrees about its center, the pinwheel would look unchanged when you looked again.

- If you blinked just as someone slid the wallpaper design, would the wallpaper look unchanged?

1.1 Butterfly Symmetry
Line Reflections

The butterfly shape has line or **reflectional symmetry.** You can make a design of your own with reflectional symmetry. Begin by drawing a basic design element and a **line of symmetry.** Then fold along the line, or use tracing paper, to locate the mirror images of key points.

The geometric operation, or **transformation,** that flips a figure and matches each point to an image point is called a **line reflection.** To identify the image of a point P, you can use prime notation (P'). You read P' as "P prime."

Notes

For example, you can make the symmetric figure below by reflecting pentagon *ABCDE* in line *m* to form $A'B'C'D'E'$. Together, the pentagons form a symmetric design.

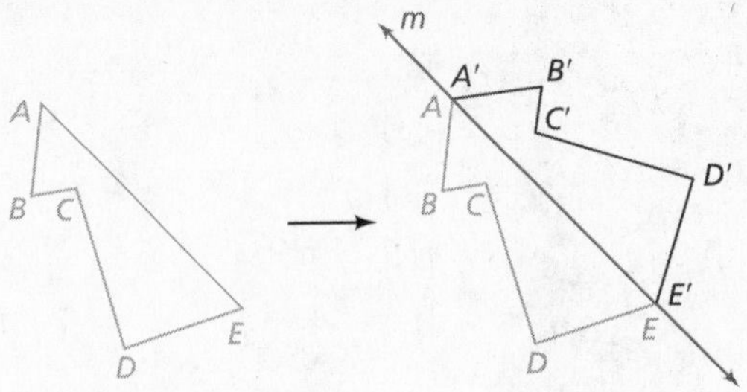

- What is the relationship between each pair of symmetric points and the line of symmetry?
- How could you use that relationship to draw figures with line symmetry, without folding, tracing, or using a mirror?

To see how line reflections match parts of symmetric designs, it helps to do some drawing, folding, and measuring experiments. Using drawing tools, such as a ruler, an angle ruler, or a protractor, will help you discover important ideas about reflections.

Problem 1.1

A Copy pentagon *ABCDE*, its image, $A'B'C'D'E'$, and the line of reflection, *m*.

1. Draw segments connecting each vertex of pentagon *ABCDE* to its image on pentagon $A'B'C'D'E'$.
2. Measure lengths and angles to see how the line of reflection is related to each segment you drew in part (1).
3. Describe the patterns in your measurements from part (2).
4. Which points are in the same location as their image under this reflection?

Notes

Problem 1.1 continued

B The design below has reflectional symmetry. How could you use only a pencil, a ruler, and an angle ruler or protractor to locate the line of symmetry?

C **1.** How could you use what you learned in Questions A and B to locate vertices J', K', L', and M', the images of vertices *J, K, L,* and *M* under a reflection in line *n*?

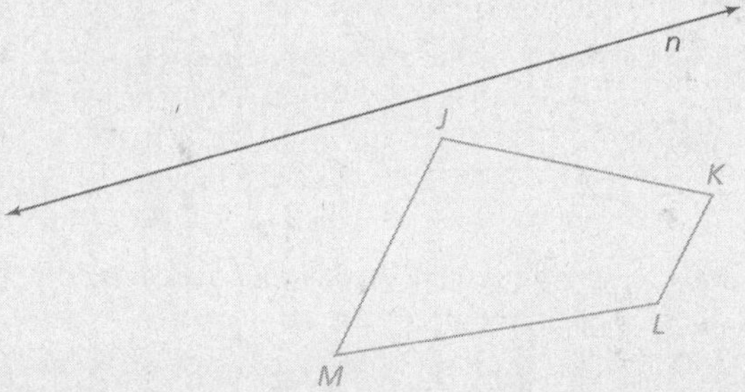

2. Is segment $K'L'$ the image of segment *KL*? In other words, when you reflect the points *K* and *L* to find points K' and L', does this reflection carry with it all the points between *K* and *L*, and locate them on segment $K'L'$? Explain.

3. Are the properties of the original quadrilateral *JKLM* preserved in its image $J'K'L'M'$? Explain.

D Use your results from Questions A–C to complete this sentence: A reflection in line *m* matches each point *X* on a figure to an image point X' so that . . .

ACE Homework starts on page 18.

Notes

1.2 In a Spin
Rotations

The pinwheel design below has **rotational symmetry.** The transformation that turns a figure about a fixed point and matches each point to an image point is called a **rotation** about the **center of rotation.**

- What **angle of rotation** would rotate a basic design element so that the image makes the complete symmetric design?
- Is there a different basic design element and angle of rotation that you could use to make the complete symmetric design?

In most problems involving rotations, you are only interested in how key points of a design move. However, like line reflections, rotations match each point to an image point.

How is each point X related to its image point X', the center of rotation O, and the angle of rotation?

Using drawing tools, such as a ruler, angle ruler, or protractor, will help you discover important ideas about rotations.

Notes

Problem 1.2

A The compass star below has eight points that are labeled and a center of rotation *O*.

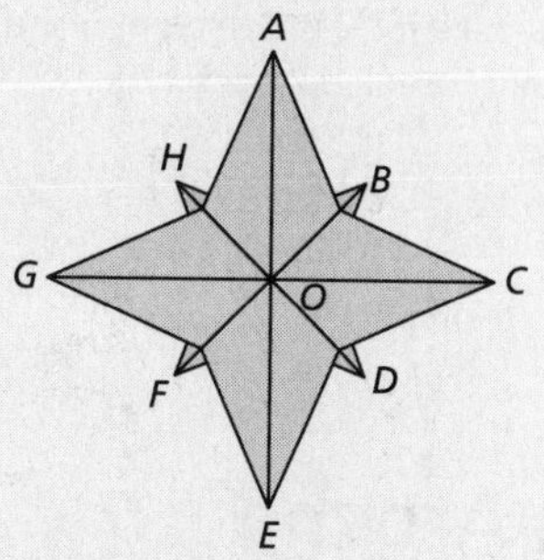

1. What is the smallest counterclockwise rotation (in degrees) that will rotate the star to a new position in which it looks unchanged?
2. **a.** Match each point on the compass star with the point that represents its image after the rotation in part (1).

   b. What is the image of segment *AO*? Of segment *HO*?
3. Describe the paths of points *A* and *H* on the compass star as they "move" from their original positions to their images.
4. Describe the relationship among any point *X*, its image, and the center of the compass star after the rotation in part (1).
5. Can you flip the compass star without changing its appearance? If so, what is the line of symmetry?

B Use the "flag" at the right as the basic design element. Using drawing tools, make designs that have rotational symmetries with the given angle of rotation.

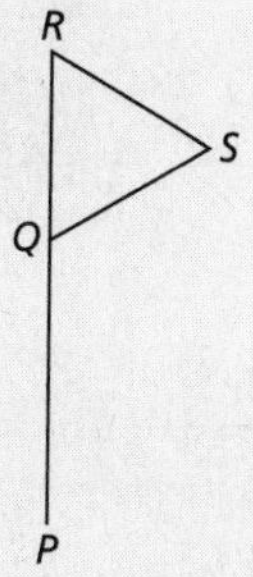

- In each case, specify the center of the rotation.
- If possible, find different ways to complete each of these tasks. Sketch the symmetric designs that would result from each strategy.

1. 120° counterclockwise
2. 90° counterclockwise

continued on the next page >

STUDENT PAGE

Notes

Problem 1.2 continued

C How is making a design with rotational symmetry like or unlike making a figure with reflectional symmetry?

D Use your results from Questions A–C to complete this sentence: A rotation of d degrees about point O matches each point X on a figure to an image point X' so that . . .

ACE Homework starts on page 18.

1.3 Sliding Around
Translations

The wallpaper design below has neither reflectional symmetry nor rotational symmetry. However, it has a basic design element that repeats in a pattern. Suppose the wallpaper extended in all directions. Then you could slide the paper in several directions without changing what the eye would see.

Figures with the property of the wallpaper design have **translational symmetry.** The transformation that slides a figure and matches each point to an image point is called a **translation.**

? How could you describe a translation that matches the basic design element to an image?

Notes

Translations match a point on the plane to an image point. For reflections, you learned how each point and its image relate to the line of symmetry. For rotations, you learned how each point and its image relate to the center of rotation. In this Problem, you will learn how each point X is related to its image point X' after a translation.

Problem 1.3

A **1.** Diagrams 1 and 2 show polygon *GHJKLM* and its image under two different translations. On a copy of the diagrams:

- Locate and label the images G', H', J', K', L', and M' so that G' is the image of G, H' is the image of H, and so on.
- Draw segments from each vertex of *GHJKLM* to its image.
- Describe patterns relating the segments GG', HH', etc.

Diagram 1

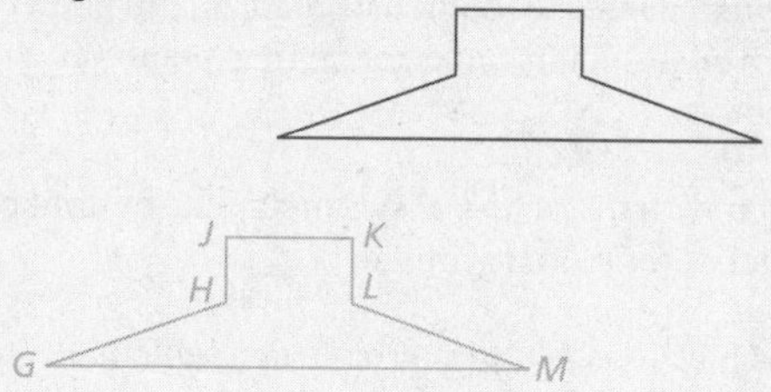

Diagram 2

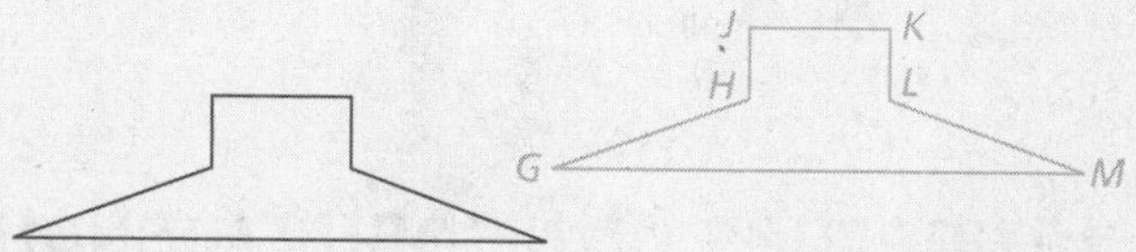

2. If you wanted to make a complete design with translational symmetry, how many images would you have to make?

continued on the next page >

Notes

Problem 1.3 continued

B Will drew a polygon and then drew an arrow to specify the distance and direction of a slide. How could you draw the image of the polygon under the specified translation?

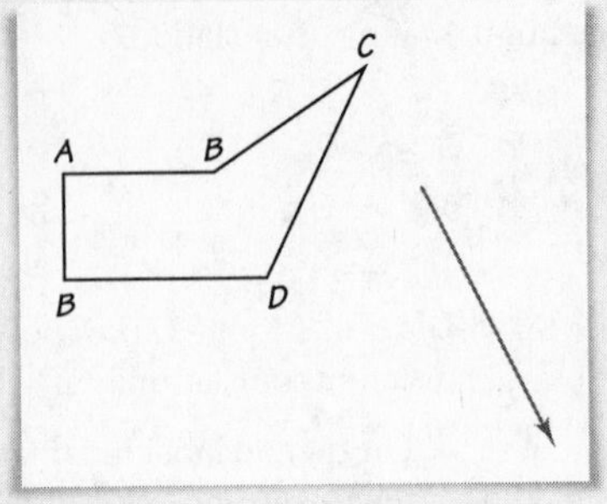

1. How do the corresponding vertices of the polygon and its image relate to each other? That is, what is the relationship between points A and A', points B and B', and so on?
2. How do the corresponding sides and angles of the polygon and its image relate to each other?
3. What shape is polygon $ABB'A'$? Explain.
4. Does the translation that matches point A to point A' and point B to point B' also match all the points on segment AB to points on segment $A'B'$? Explain.

C How is making a design with translational symmetry like or unlike making a design with reflectional or rotational symmetry?

D Use your results from Questions A–C to complete this sentence: A translation matches any two points X and Y on a figure to points X' and Y' so that . . .

ACE Homework starts on page 18.

1.4 Properties of Transformations

Reflections, rotations, and translations are useful in making symmetric designs from a basic design element. You can also use these ideas to show how one shape can be "moved" to fit onto another. To do so, it helps to know in advance what will change and what will stay the same.

Notes

The diagrams below show trapezoid *WXYZ* "moved" by a flip, turn, or a slide.

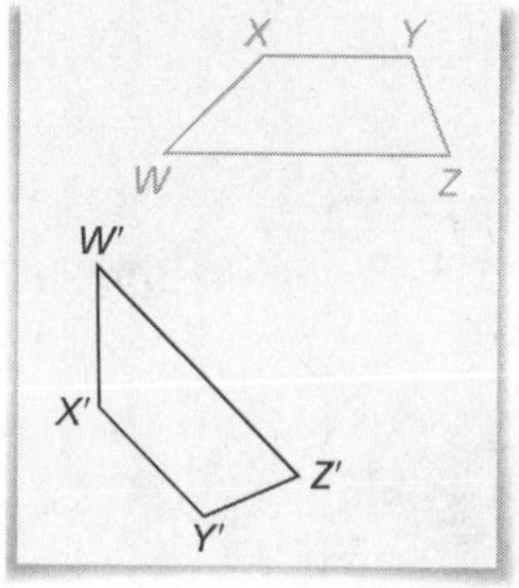

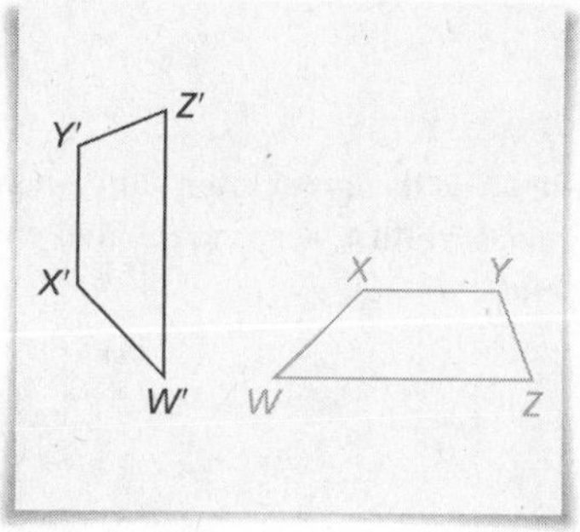

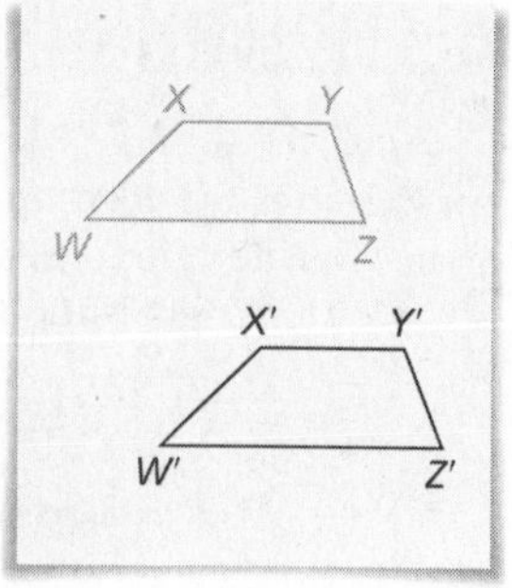

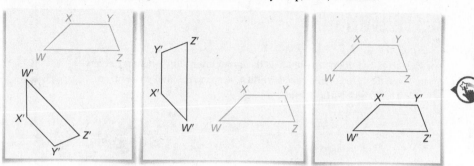

- What transformations were used?
- How can you describe the details of each transformation?
- How is the shape, size, and position of the trapezoid affected?

In this Problem, you will summarize important ideas from Problems 1.1, 1.2, and 1.3. You will use these ideas in later Investigations.

Problem 1.4

Use the transformations of trapezoid *WXYZ* shown above.

A Describe each transformation with as much detail as you can. For example, give the reflection line, or the center of the rotation, or the direction and distance of the translation. Draw diagrams to support your answer.

B Suppose a reflection, a rotation, or a translation matches points W and W', points X and X', points Y and Y', and points Z and Z'. In each case,

1. What distances are equal?
2. What angles are equal?
3. What line segments are parallel?
4. Which points and/or lines are "unmoved," if any?
5. Which properties of the original figure are preserved? Which properties change?

ACE Homework starts on page 18.

Notes

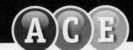

Applications

For Exercises 1–4, identify the basic design element and all symmetries of the given design. For Exercises 3 and 4, assume the design continues to the left and right without end.

1. 

2. 

3. 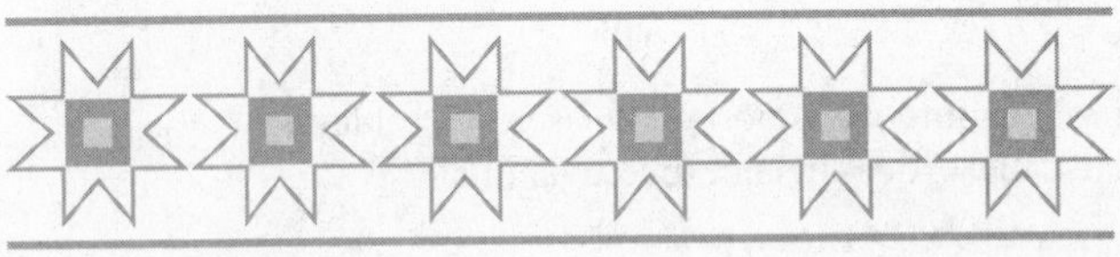

4. 

Notes

5. On a copy of the diagram below, draw the image of triangle *ABC* after a reflection in line *m*. Describe how the vertices of the image relate to the corresponding vertices of the original triangle and the line of reflection.

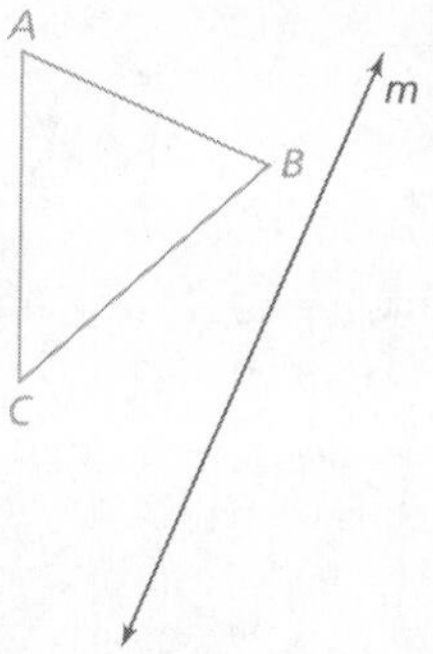

6. Quadrilateral *A′B′C′D′* is a reflection image of quadrilateral *ABCD*.

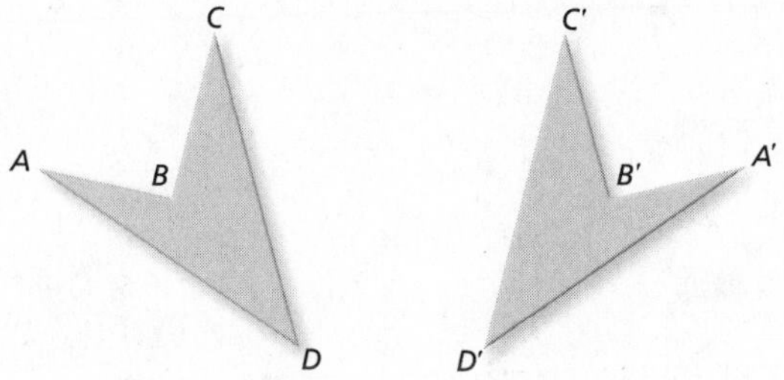

a. On a copy of the diagram, draw the line of reflection. Explain how you found it.

b. Describe the relationship between a point on the original figure and its image on *A′B′C′D′*.

7. Use the diagram at the right.

a. On a copy of the diagram, draw the image of polygon *PQRST* after a reflection in line *n*.

b. Does the resulting design have reflectional symmetry? Explain why or why not.

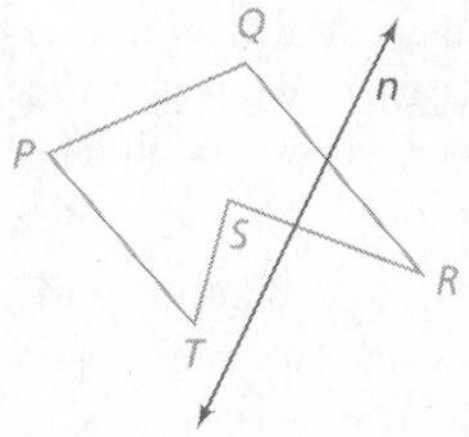

Notes

8. Use triangle *XYZ* below.

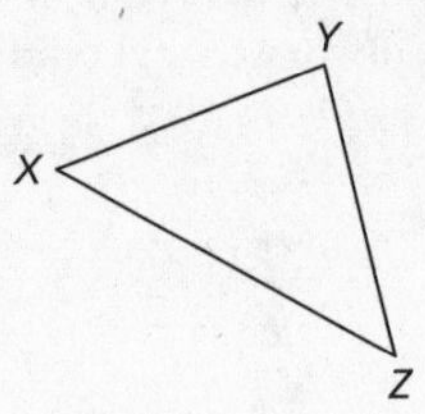

a. On a copy of the diagram, draw the image of the triangle after a counterclockwise rotation of 90° about point *Z*.

b. Describe how each vertex of the image relates to the corresponding vertex on the original triangle.

9. Use triangle *XYZ* and point *R* below.

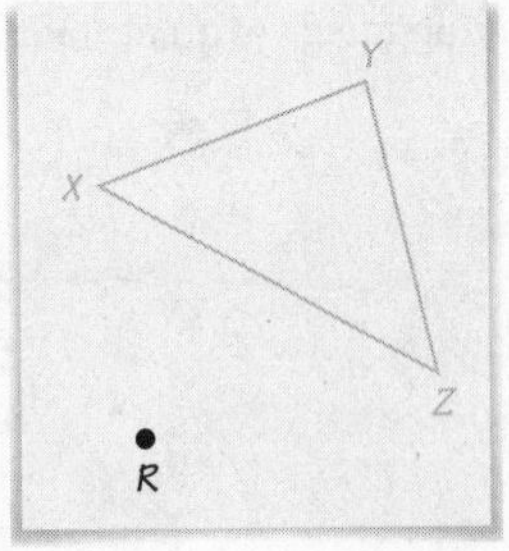

a. On a copy of the diagram, draw the image of the triangle after a counterclockwise rotation of 90° about point *R*.

b. Describe how each vertex of the image relates to the corresponding vertex on the original triangle.

10. Use polygon *FGHJK* at the right.

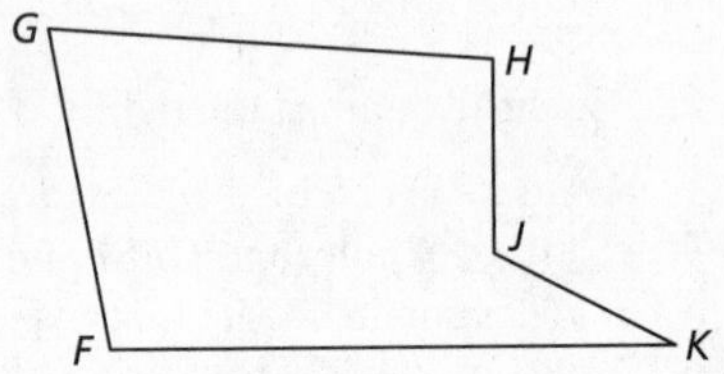

a. On a copy of the diagram, draw the image of the polygon after a counterclockwise rotation of 180° about point *K*.

b. Describe how each vertex of the image relates to the corresponding vertex on the original polygon.

Notes

11. Use triangle *PQR* and the arrow shown below.

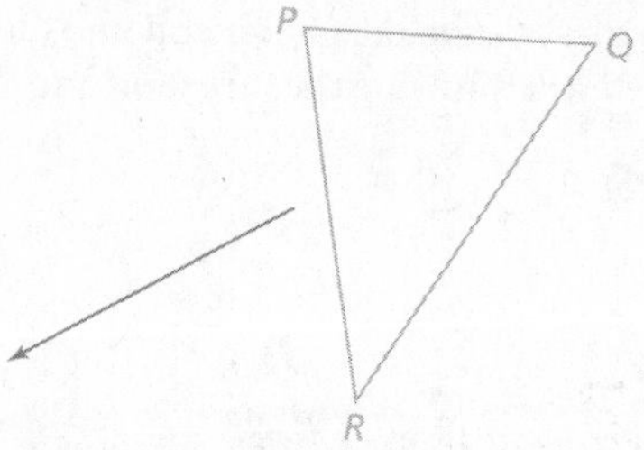

a. On a copy of the diagram, translate the triangle as indicated by the arrow.

b. Describe how each vertex of the image relates to the corresponding vertex on the original triangle.

12. The diagram at the right that shows a triangle and its image under a translation.

a. On a copy of the diagram, label the vertices of the two triangles *ABC* and $A'B'C'$, respectively, to indicate the correspondence of vertices by the translation.

b. Draw lines with an arrowhead at one end connecting pairs of corresponding vertices and explain what those lines have in common.

13. Use copies of the figure below for parts (a)–(c).

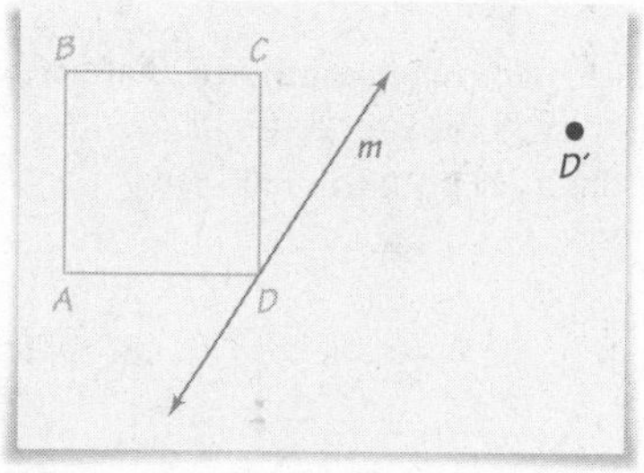

a. Draw the image of square *ABCD* under a reflection in line *m*.

b. Draw the image of square *ABCD* under a 45° counterclockwise rotation about point *A*.

c. Draw the image of square *ABCD* under a translation that matches point *D* to point D'.

Notes

Exercises 14–17 each give a figure and its image under a flip, turn, or slide. In each case, name the type of transformation used. For a flip, sketch the line of reflection. For a turn, locate the center and find the angle of rotation. For a slide, draw a line showing the direction and distance of the translation.

14.

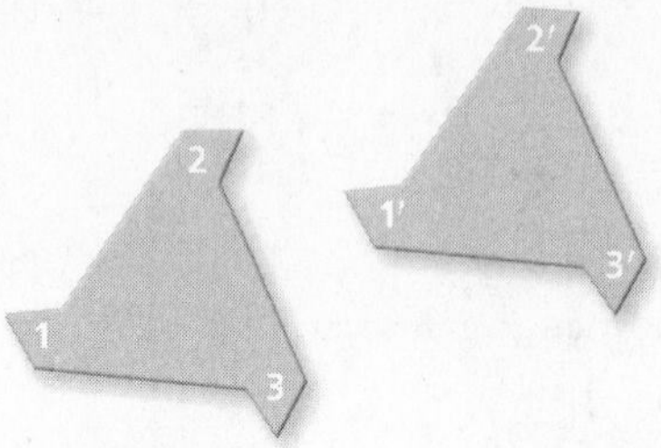

15.

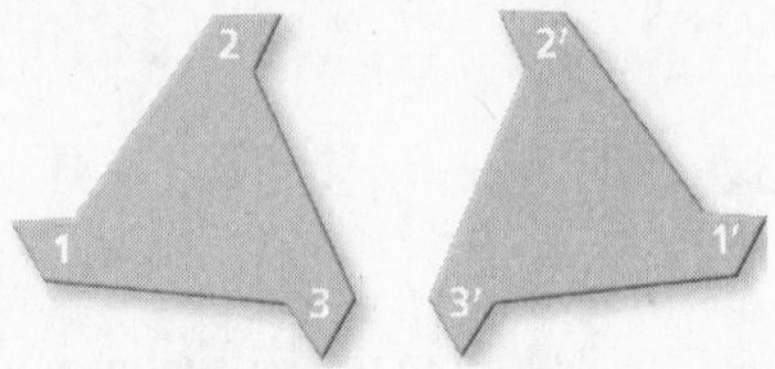

16.

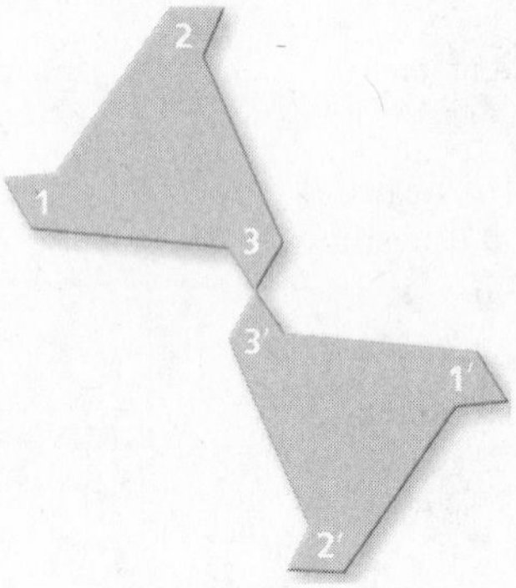

17.

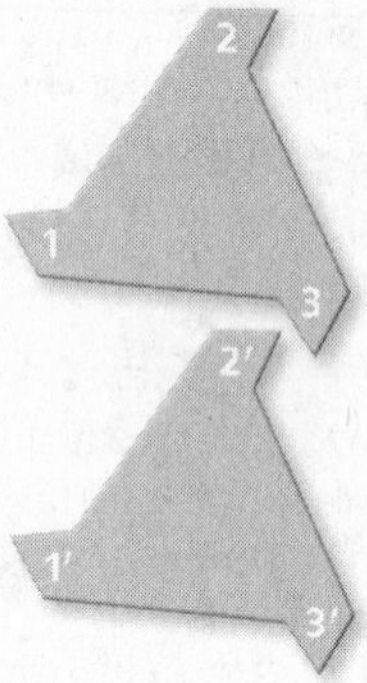

18. Quadrilateral *PQRS* is the image of parallelogram *ABCD* after a reflection and a translation. List all the properties of quadrilateral *PQRS* that you can infer from this fact.

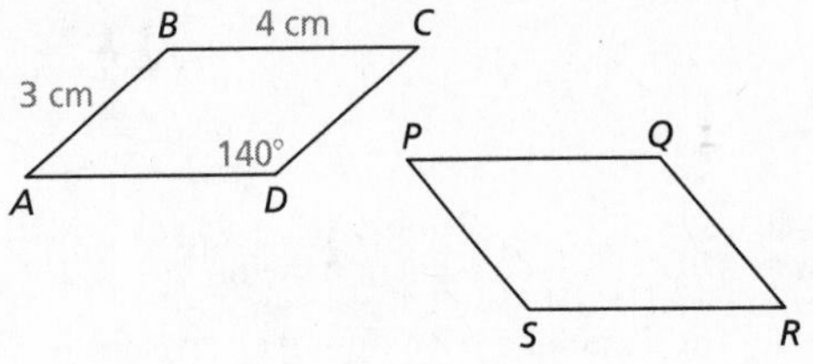

Notes

Connections

19. What symmetries does each capital letter have, if any?

A B C D E F G H I J K L M N O P Q R S T U V W X Y Z

20. What symmetries does the rim have?

For Exercises 21–26, draw an example of each type of polygon. Draw all the lines of symmetry. If the polygon has rotational symmetry, identify the center and angle of rotation.

21. nonsquare rectangle
22. nonrectangular parallelogram
23. isosceles triangle
24. equilateral triangle
25. nonsquare rhombus
26. isosceles trapezoid

27. The rectangular prism and cylinder shown at the right both have a height of 4 centimeters. The diameter of the base of the cylinder is also 4 centimeters. Each figure is filled with a layer of centimeter cubes (some partial).

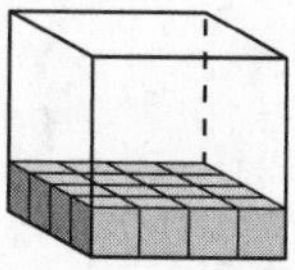

Rectangular Prism

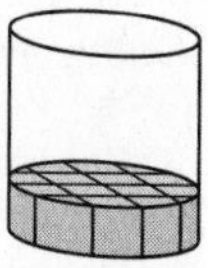

Cylinder

   a. Describe the symmetries of the prism and the cylinder.
   b. How many layers of cubes will it take to fill the prism?
   c. What is the volume of the prism?
   d. How many cubes do you need to make one layer covering the bottom of the cylinder?
   e. What is the volume of the cylinder?

Notes

28. What kinds of symmetries do the following mathematical objects have?

a. a number line

b. a coordinate graph showing all four quadrants

c. the graph of a quadratic function such as $y = x^2$

d. the commutative properties of addition and multiplication

Extensions

29. Draw a rectangle like *ABCD* shown below and mark a point *P* outside of the rectangle.

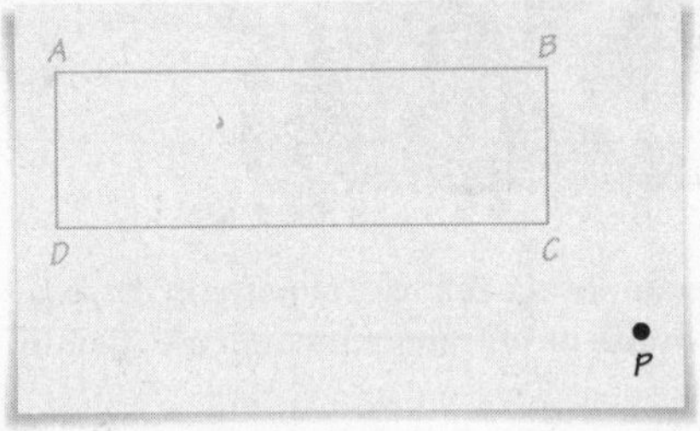

a. Draw and label the image $A'B'C'D'$ of the rectangle under a counterclockwise rotation of 90° about point *P*.

b. Describe the path each vertex of the rectangle travels in the rotation.

c. Copy and complete the tables. Find the measurements indicated in the tables.

PA	PA′	∠APA′
■	■	■

PB	PB′	∠BPB′
■	■	■

PC	PC′	∠CPC′
■	■	■

PD	PD′	∠DPD′
■	■	■

Notes

d. Describe any patterns in the tables that relate the vertices of the original rectangle, the vertices of the image rectangle, and the center of rotation.

e. How would your answer to part (d) change if the angle of rotation were 120° instead of 90°?

The designs in Exercises 30–34 are actually first names. Describe the symmetries in each name. Then, write the name in standard lettering.

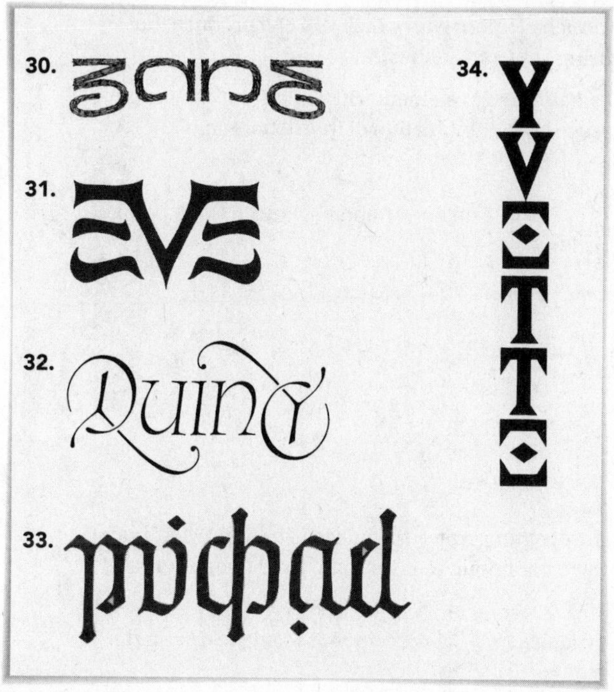

35. Use the artistic technique illustrated in Exercises 30–34 to write your own name.

Notes

36. In this Investigation, you studied designs with reflectional, rotational, and translational symmetries. The design below is a bit different from those with the basic symmetries. Assume that the pattern continues to the left and right without end.

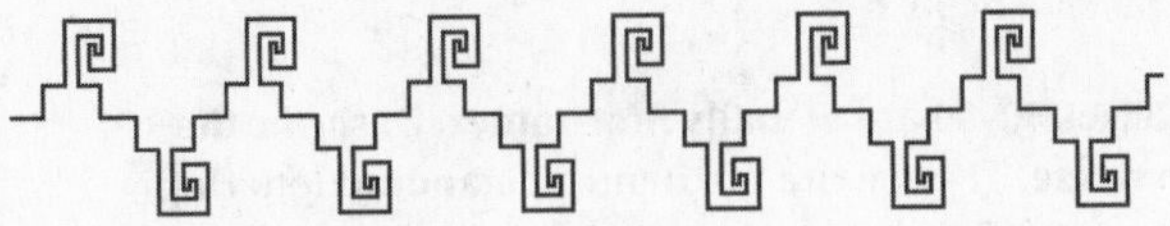

a. Trace a basic design element with which you can produce the whole figure using only translations.

b. Trace a smaller basic design element with which you can produce the whole figure using a combination of translations and line reflections.

37. Triangle *MBK* has its vertices on lines ℓ and n. Vertex *B* is the point of intersection of the lines.

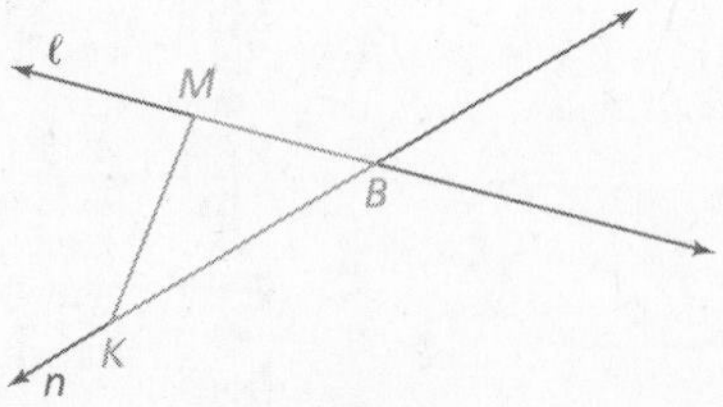

a. On a copy of the diagram, sketch the image of triangle *MBK* under a rotation of 180° about point *B*. Locate and label image points M', B', and K'.

b. What angle in triangle $M'B'K'$ corresponds to angle *MBK* in the original triangle?

c. Make a conjecture about the angles formed where the two lines intersect. Test the conjecture with several other examples and see if you can find reasons for the pattern you observe.

Notes

38. Use a copy of the diagram below. Reflect triangle ABC over line ℓ. Label the image $A'B'C'$. Then, reflect triangle $A'B'C'$ over line m. Label the image $A''B''C''$.

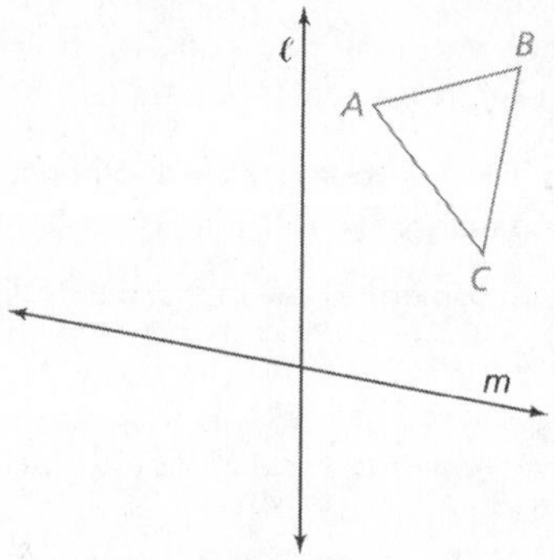

a. Can you "move" triangle ABC exactly onto triangle $A''B''C''$ with a single flip, turn, or slide? If so, describe the transformation.

b. Experiment with reflecting figures in two intersecting lines. Make a conjecture based on your findings.

39. In the diagram below, lines a and b are parallel. On a copy of the diagram, reflect triangle EFG in line a. Label the image $E'F'G'$. Then, reflect triangle $E'F'G'$ in line b. Label the image $E''F''G''$.

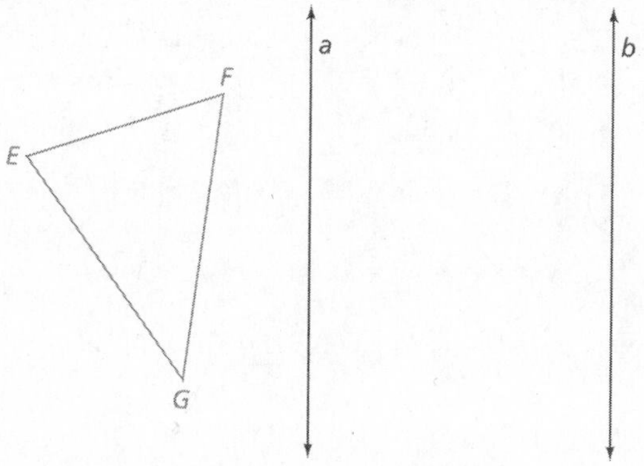

a. Can you "move" triangle EFG exactly onto triangle $E''F''G''$ with a single flip, turn, or slide? If so, describe the transformation.

b. Experiment with reflecting figures in two parallel lines. Make a conjecture based on your findings.

Notes

Mathematical Reflections 1

In this Investigation, you used geometric transformations to describe and construct symmetric figures. The following questions will help you summarize what you have learned.

Think about these questions. Discuss your ideas with other students and your teacher. Then write a summary of your findings in your notebook.

1. **How** would you explain to someone how to make a design with
   - **a.** reflectional symmetry?
   - **b.** rotational symmetry?
   - **c.** translational symmetry?
2. **How** are points and their images related by each of these geometric transformations?
   - **a.** reflection in line m
   - **b.** rotation of $d°$ about point P
   - **c.** translation with distance and direction set by the segment from point X to point X'
3. **How** do reflections, rotations, and translations change the size and shape of line segments, angles, and/or polygons, if at all?

Notes

Common Core Mathematical Practices

As you worked on the Problems in this Investigation, you used prior knowledge to make sense of them. You also applied Mathematical Practices to solve the Problems. Think back over your work, the ways you thought about the Problems, and how you used Mathematical Practices.

Nick described his thoughts in the following way:

In Problem 1.1, we used rulers to measure distances between points and their images so we could locate the line of symmetry of a design.

We also used rulers to measure the distance between each vertex of a figure and a given reflection line so we could find the image.

It turns out that you have to make sure that the distance from a point to the line is a perpendicular distance. If you do not check this with a protractor, the image is not accurate.

Common Core Standards for Mathematical Practice
MP5 Use appropriate tools strategically.

- What other Mathematical Practices can you identify in Nick's reasoning?
- Describe a Mathematical Practice that you and your classmates used to solve a different Problem in this Investigation.

Notes

Investigation 2

PLANNING

Transformations and Congruence

Investigation Overview

Investigation Description

This Investigation has three Problems. The first Problem introduces the concept that figures with the same size and shape can be matched in a way that shows corresponding sides, angles, and vertices. The second Problem develops the students' understanding of the ways in which the congruence of two triangles can be confirmed by transforming one onto the other. The third Problem develops the idea that the congruence of triangles can be determined without any transformation, but by matching the measures of three strategically chosen parts of each triangle.

Investigation Vocabulary

- congruent figures

Mathematics Background

- Congruent Figures

Planning Chart

Content	ACE	Pacing	Materials	Resources
Problem 2.1	1–4, 27–29	1 day	**Labsheet 2.1** Question D **Labsheet 2ACE:** Exercises 1–4 (accessibility) tracing paper, rulers, angle rulers or protractors	**Teaching Aid 2.1** Kaleidoscope Designs • Transformations
Problem 2.2	5, 6, 13–18, 30–32, 36–39	1 day	**Labsheet 2.2** Questions A–F **Labsheet 2ACE:** Exercise 39 (accessibility) tracing paper, rulers, angle rulers or protractors	
Problem 2.3	7–12, 19–26, 33–35, 40	1½ days	**Labsheet 2.3** Questions C–E rulers, angle rulers or protractors	**Teaching Aid 2.3** Congruence Criteria
Mathematical Reflections		½ day		
Assessment: Partner Quiz		½ day		• Partner Quiz

Goals and Standards

Goals

Congruence and Similarity Understand congruence and similarity and explore necessary and sufficient conditions for establishing congruent and similar shapes

- Recognize that two figures are congruent if one is derived from the other one by a sequence of reflection, rotation, and/or translation transformations
- Recognize that two figures are similar if one can be obtained from the other by a sequence of reflections, rotations, translations, and/or dilations
- Use transformations to describe a sequence that exhibits the congruence between figures
- Use transformations to explore minimum measurement conditions for establishing congruence of triangles
- Use transformations to explore minimum measurement conditions for establishing similarity of triangles
- Relate properties of angles formed by parallel lines and transversals, and the angle sum in any triangle, to properties of transformations
- Use properties of congruent and similar triangles to solve problems about shapes and measurements

Mathematical Reflections

Look for evidence of student understanding of the goals for this Investigation in their responses to the questions in *Mathematical Reflections*. The goals addressed by each question are indicated below.

1. How can you find a sequence of flips, turns, and slides to "move" one figure exactly onto another to show that they are congruent?

   Goals
   - Recognize that two figures are congruent if one is derived from the other one by a sequence of reflection, rotation, and/or translation transformations
   - Use transformations to describe a sequence that exhibits the congruence between figures

2. What information about the sides and angles of two triangles will guarantee you can "move" one triangle onto the other?

   Goal
   - Use transformations to explore minimum measurement conditions for establishing congruence of triangles

3. How could you convince someone that two given triangles are *not* congruent?

   Goal
   - Recognize that two figures are congruent if one is derived from the other one by a sequence of reflection, rotation, and/or translation transformations

Standards

Common Core Content Standards

8.G.A.1 Verify experimentally the properties of rotations, reflections, and translations. *Problems 1 and 2*

8.G.A.1a Lines are taken to lines, and line segments to line segments of the same length. *Problems 1 and 2*

8.G.A.1b Angles are taken to angles of the same measure. *Problems 1 and 2*

8.G.A.2 Understand that a two-dimensional figure is congruent to another if the second can be obtained from the first by a sequence of rotations, reflections, and translations; given two congruent figures, describe a sequence that exhibits the congruence between them. *Problems 1, 2, and 3*

Facilitating the Mathematical Practices

Students in *Connected Mathematics* classrooms display evidence of multiple Common Core Standards for Mathematical Practice every day. Here are just a few examples of when you might observe students demonstrating the Standards for Mathematical Practice during this Investigation.

Practice 1: **Make sense of problems and persevere in solving them.**
Students are engaged every day in solving problems and, over time, learn to persevere in solving them. To be effective, the problems embody critical concepts and skills and have the potential to engage students in making sense of mathematics. Students build understanding by reflecting, connecting, and communicating. These student-centered problem situations engage students in articulating the "knowns" in a problem situation and determining a logical solution pathway. The student-student and student-teacher dialogues help students not only to make sense of the problems, but also to persevere in finding appropriate strategies to solve them. The suggested questions in the Teacher Guides provide the metacognitive scaffolding to help students monitor and refine their problem-solving strategies.

Practice 8: **Look for and express regularity in repeated reasoning.**
After experimenting with the transformations in Investigation 1, the students compare the original figure and its image. They look for clues to help them determine which transformation they should test for first. For example, when they see the orientation of the figure is the same, they may automatically reason that the image is under translation. If the base of the original figure is transformed to the side of the image, they may test for rotation first. Similarly, if they can picture a mirror being in between the original figure and its image, they may reason that the design must have reflectional symmetry. The patterns in the designs in Investigation 1 helped them to develop their own reasoning to describe symmetry, which also helps them test for congruency in Investigation 2.

Students identify and record their personal experiences with the Standards for Mathematical Practice during the Mathematical Reflections at the end of the Investigation.

PROBLEM
2.1 Connecting Congruent Polygons

Problem Overview

Focus Question What does it mean to say that two geometric shapes are congruent to each other? How could you show congruence with movable copies of the figures?

Problem Description

The overarching goal of this Problem is to develop the idea that two figures are congruent if and only if one can "move" onto the other by a sequence of reflections, rotations, and/or translations. To discuss congruence from this perspective, one needs some standard language for corresponding points, sides, and angles, and the symbol for the congruence relationship. These important preliminaries of the Investigation are addressed in this Problem.

Problem Implementation

Let students work in groups of 2–4.

Materials

- **Labsheet 2.1:** Question D
- **Labsheet 2ACE:** Exercises 1–4 (accessibility)
- **Teaching Aid 2.1:** Kaleidoscope Designs

angle rulers or protractors

rulers

tracing paper

Using Technology

If the students have access to a computer, they may find it helpful to use **Transformations** to answer the Questions of this Problem. This activity may also help to reduce the amount of class time reserved for drawing designs. **Note:** The default setting of this activity includes a grid and axes, but there is the option to remove them.

Vocabulary

- congruent figures

Mathematics Background

- Congruent Figures

At a Glance and Lesson Plan

- At a Glance: Problem 2.1 Butterflies, Pinwheels, and Wallpaper
- Lesson Plan: Problem 2.1 Butterflies, Pinwheels, and Wallpaper

Launch

Launch Video

To help students visualize the repetition of a basic design element, this animation shows a character describing the patterns seen in a kaleidoscope. The description provides a good model for students to use to describe basic design elements and the symmetry of an element within a design. Visit Teacher Place at mathdashboard.com/cmp3 to see the complete video.

You can use this animation in addition to studying the kaleidoscope patterns in the Student Edition to introduce the Problem. After showing the animation, continue by asking the suggested question in Connecting to Prior Knowledge.

Connecting to Prior Knowledge

You might consider launching the Problem by asking students to study each of the given kaleidoscope designs and identify the basic design element. They should explain how a transformation strategy could be used to replicate that basic design element and complete the full figure. Use **Teaching Aid 2.1: Kaleidoscope Designs** to facilitate the discussion.

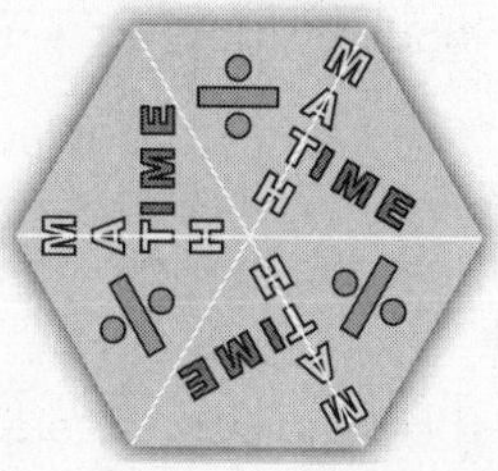

Suggested Questions

- What transformations have been used to make these designs? (The first graphic can be made by rotating a triangle around the midpoint. Five copies of the triangle are made, and the angle of rotation is 60°. The second graphic also uses a triangle as the basic design element. It is reflected in one side to make a new basic design element that has the shape of a rhombus. The rhombus shape is then rotated 120° around the midpoint. Likewise, the third graphic is made from a rhombus that is rotated 120° around the midpoint.)

Presenting the Challenge

Before students start to work on Problem 2.1, you may want to inspect the given quadrilaterals, *ABCD* and *PQRS*, as a class. Explain that since the text says *ABCD* and *PQRS* are congruent, they must have corresponding sides of the same length and corresponding angles of the same measure.

Suggested Questions

- How do you know which sides are the same length? Which angles are the same measure? (Students might not identify corresponding sides correctly because the orientation of the figures is different. Discuss proposed matches and listen to explanations. It is not important to correct the students' responses at this time. Matching the corresponding parts of the figure is part of the work in this Problem.

Tell students that to visually match up sides and angles, it helps to imagine a series of transformations that "move" one polygon onto the other. The goal is to make the correct match and name the exact transformations.

Explore

Providing for Individual Needs

The questions of this Problem introduce notational conventions for describing congruence. Some students will take more time than others to match congruent sides. Point out that it helps to notice the relative positions of these sides. Have tracing paper and **Labsheet 2.1: Question D** available. Watch for students who make incorrect matches and use the opportunity to discuss their reasons. They should be taking advantage of the shortest sides, longest sides, etc.

Suggested Questions

- I see that you have matched *AB* to *QR*. Are these the longest sides in each figure? (No.)
- Notice that *QR* is adjacent to *PQ*, the shortest side. Is *AB* also adjacent to the shortest side in the other figure? (No; so I can say that *AB* and *QR* are not corresponding sides.)

- Would it help to start with the short sides and match them? (Yes; *CD* matches *PQ*, so they are corresponding sides. However, I need to figure out whether $C \rightarrow P$ or $C \rightarrow Q$.
- The angles at *P* and *Q* look very similar to the angles at *C* and *D*. How can we figure out the corresponding angles? (Students can take advantage of positional clues, such as that *QR* is longer than *PS* and *AD* is longer than *BC*, so the angle between *CD* and *AD* matches the angles between *PQ* and *QR*. **Note:** You may want to add the included angle to the conversation for describing this situation. This will appear in Problem 2.3, but you can discuss it now if it seems helpful.)

For Question D, you might ask:

- Can you use your tracing to be sure that your answers for Questions A, B, and C are correct? (Yes; if I label the tracing.)
- What transformations did you use? (Students might slide and turn the copy simultaneously. Encourage them to separate these movements. Since finding the center of a rotation takes more time than finding a line of symmetry or slide direction, students are likely to slide $C \rightarrow P$, or some other matched pair of vertices, and then turn *ABCD* onto *PQRS* until $CD \rightarrow PQ$.

Watch for alternative transformation sequences and share them during the summary.

Planning for the Summary

What evidence will you use in the summary to clarify and deepen understanding of the Focus Question?

What will you do if you do not have evidence?

Summarize

Orchestrating the Discussion

If students were working on this Problem in groups, it will be useful to check their answers to Questions A–C. When you finish checking the details of each Question, you could revisit the Focus Question and have selected students or groups explain their transformation sequences.

For Question D, ask:

Suggested Questions

- Why did some people start with a slide? (Once matching vertices have been figured out, sliding is the simplest option of the three transformations.)

- Did anyone start by rotating the polygon? If you did, how did you find the center and angle of rotation? (Yes; I had to join points to images, find perpendicular bisectors, and then find the center. Lastly, I had to measure an angle.)
- Did anyone rename *PQRS*? If you did, how did the new name tell you how sides and angles are matched? (Yes; I renamed it *RSPQ*. This matches $\angle R$ to $\angle A$, $\angle S$ to $\angle B$, etc. It also matches side *RS* to side *AB*, side *SP* to side *BC*, etc.)
- What do you mean when you say side *RS* corresponds to side *AB*, or $\angle S$ corresponds to $\angle B$, etc.? (I am identifying the congruent parts of congruent figures. Their lengths and measures are the same, and they are located in corresponding positions. Students might use the language of transformations and say that if side *RS* is "moved" through a series of transformations, the image is side *AB*.)
- Would you say that side *RS* corresponds to side *BA*? (Yes; because the lengths are the same.)

Reflecting on Student Learning

Use the following questions to assess student understanding at the end of the lesson.

- What evidence do I have that students understand the Focus Question?
  - Where did my students get stuck?
  - What strategies did they use?
  - What breakthroughs did my students have today?
- How will I use this to plan for tomorrow? For the next time I teach this lesson?
- Where will I have the opportunity to reinforce these ideas as I continue through this Unit? The next Unit?

ACE Assignment Guide

- **Applications:** 1–4
- **Connections:** 27–29
- **Labsheet 2ACE:** Exercises 1–4 (accessibility)

PROBLEM
2.2

Supporting the World

Congruent Triangles I

Problem Overview

Focus Question How much information do you need to decide that two triangles are congruent? How do you plan the transformations that "move" one triangle onto another?

Problem Description

This Problem reviews and extends the students' understanding of establishing congruence by a sequence of reflections, rotations, and/or translations. The work on this topic is done using triangles.

Problem Implementation

Let students work in pairs.

Materials

- **Labsheet 2.2:** Questions A–F
- **Labsheet 2ACE:** Exercise 39 (accessibility)

tracing paper

rulers

angle rulers or protractors

Vocabulary

There are no new glossary terms introduced in this Problem.

Mathematics Background

- Congruent Figures

At a Glance and Lesson Plan

- At a Glance: Problem 2.2 Butterflies, Pinwheels, and Wallpaper
- Lesson Plan: Problem 2.2 Butterflies, Pinwheels, and Wallpaper

Launch

Launch Video

This animation shows a sequence of transformations that move quadrilateral *ABCD* onto another quadrilateral *PQRS*. Because the two quadrilaterals match after the sequence of transformations, the quadrilaterals are congruent. Visit Teacher Place at mathdashboard.com/cmp3 to see the complete video.

Show this animation to introduce the Problem. You can continue the Launch by using Connecting to Prior Knowledge and focusing on congruence in triangles.

Connecting to Prior Knowledge

To launch this Problem, remind the students of what they learned in the Grade 7 Unit *Shapes and Designs* about the importance of triangles in building structures. Then, pose the question of how one could go about establishing that two triangles are identical in shape and size.

Presenting the Challenge

Review the directions that apply to each part of this Problem. You could use Question A and **Labsheet 2.2: Questions A–F** as a reference to ask:

Suggested Questions

- Do the two triangles look congruent? How do you know? (Students should mention congruent sides and angles. They should check for congruence by measuring or tracing.)
- Did you measure all sides and angles? (Students will probably only measure a subset of sides or angles before deciding that the triangles are congruent. Part of the work on this Problem is about developing a sense of what needs to be checked. For this reason, it is not important to comment on the students' ideas at this point.)
- Can you slide triangle *ABC* onto triangle *XYZ*? Why or why not? (No; because the orientation is different, so a rotation is also needed.)
- If you decide to do the slide first, how far is the slide and in what direction? (One possibility is $C \rightarrow X$.)

- If you decide to do a rotation, what details should you give? (I should give the center and angle of rotation.)

After this discussion, the class is now set to finish Question A and complete other parts of the Problem.

Explore

Providing for Individual Needs

The class may find it helpful to have access to transparencies or tracing paper. Encourage each group to test their transformation ideas with physical movements of triangles. You should also remind them to write down their transformation plans for the pairs of congruent triangles. When the students identify a pair of triangles as noncongruent, press them to explain their reasoning behind that decision.

For Question B, the students should give the details for the necessary reflection. Have them demonstrate their ideas as they describe them.

Suggested Questions

- I see you flipped your tracing paper of triangle *DEF* over. What line of symmetry are you thinking of? (Any line perpendicular to a line that includes *EF* and *ST* is convenient. The line of symmetry could pass through *E*, *F*, or the point midway between *F* and *S*.)
- After you flip your tracing over this line do you need any other transformations? (It depends on where the line of symmetry is located.)

For Question D, the students should also give the details for the necessary slide, rotation, and reflection.

- What did you do first in Question D? (Students might start with a counterclockwise rotation of 90° about *K*. Then, apply a slide that transforms $K \rightarrow N$. This matches *KJ* to *NO*. Lastly, a reflection in $\frac{\overline{KJ}}{NO}$ completes the sequence of transformations. Other orders are possible.)

The triangles in Questions C and E are not congruent. Push students to explain why the triangles are not identical in shape and size.

- How can you be sure that the triangles in Question C are not congruent? Did you measure all the angles and sides? (Students should realize that finding all the measures is not necessary. Sides might be flipped or reoriented, but if you measure two sides of each triangle and there are no matches between the triangles, then the triangles cannot be congruent. You could also measure the longest side of each triangle. If they do not match, then the triangles cannot be congruent.)

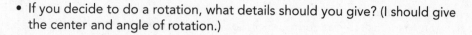

- If the angles of the two triangles in Question E match each other, why do you say that the triangles are not congruent? (Some students might refer back to the Grade 7 Unit *Stretching and Shrinking* and say that the triangles are scale copies of each other. Other students may measure sides or trace one of the triangles to show that the side lengths are different. They may also find that the areas are different. These are all important ideas to discuss in the summary.)

Planning for the Summary

What evidence will you use in the summary to clarify and deepen understanding of the Focus Question?

What will you do if you do not have evidence?

Summarize

Orchestrating the Discussion

Different groups of students can demonstrate their sequences of transformations for Questions A, B, D, and F, using **Labsheet 2.2: Questions A–F**. After each demonstration, ask:

Suggested Questions

- Did another group use a different order? Did that make any difference to the details of your transformations? (Yes; it usually makes a difference. For example, in Question B, if you reflect triangle *DEF* in a line perpendicular to *EF* through *E*, then the subsequent translation will be $E \rightarrow T$. Another option is to reflect triangle *DEF* in a line perpendicular to *EF* through *F*. Then, the translation is still $E \rightarrow T$, but this will be a shorter distance because of this line of symmetry is closer to triangle *STU*.
- Did you measure all the sides and angles before you decided the triangles were congruent? Or did you use shortcuts? (Students are likely eyeballing the figures and measuring some parts for confirmation. At this point, we do not expect students to say that you only have to measure a certain combination of sides and angles. This reasoning will appear in Problem 2.3, so it is important to alert students that some shortcuts are valid and some are not. For example, measuring all the angles would not distinguish between the noncongruent triangles in Question E. However, measuring one pair of angles in Question C would show that only one of the triangles has a right angle.)
- How should you name the triangles to show the corresponding congruent parts? Explain. (For Questions A, B, D, and F: $\triangle ABC \cong \triangle ZYX$, $\triangle DEF \cong \triangle UTS$, $\triangle JKL \cong \triangle ONM$, and $\triangle ABC \cong \triangle RQP$. Push students to use names for the triangles that show the correspondence, and to use the language of congruence and correspondence.

For the pairs of noncongruent triangles, ask:

- How did you know that the triangles in Question C are not congruent? (Students might say they measured sides, or they might say they checked angles *W* and *H*; one of these angles looks like a right angle.)
- How many sides do you have to measure to know that a pair of triangles are not congruent? (Three sides must be measured.)
- How do you know the triangles in Question E are not congruent? How are they different? (They are scale copies of each other. One triangle is larger than the other.)
- What is the least number of parts you would have to measure to be sure that a pair of triangles are not congruent? (Students might have different answers for this; see answers in the Explore.)

At this point in the Investigation, it is not necessary to make formal statements of the most common congruence criteria (all three sides congruent, two sides with an included angle congruent, two angles with an included side congruent, and two angles and an adjacent side congruent). However, you may want to observe how students are thinking about the ways in which certain combinations of side and angle measurements determine the shape of a triangle.

Note: Tracing, using transformations, or measuring and comparing parts is not a rigorous proof of congruence. However, these strategies do illustrate how transformations could be used as a starting point. This will be further discussed in Problem 2.3.

Reflecting on Student Learning

Use the following questions to assess student understanding at the end of the lesson.

- What evidence do I have that students understand the Focus Question?
  - Where did my students get stuck?
  - What strategies did they use?
  - What breakthroughs did my students have today?
- How will I use this to plan for tomorrow? For the next time I teach this lesson?
- Where will I have the opportunity to reinforce these ideas as I continue through this Unit? The next Unit?

ACE Assignment Guide

- **Applications:** 5, 6, 13–18
- **Connections:** 30–32
- **Extensions:** 36–39
- **Labsheet 2ACE:** Exercise 39 (accessibility)

PROBLEM 2.3

Minimum Measurement

Congruent Triangles II

Problem Overview

Focus Question What is the smallest number of side and/or angle measurements needed to conclude that two triangles are congruent?

Problem Description

The goal of this Problem is to develop the students' understanding of using transformations to determine congruence of two triangles, with less than complete measurement information about the figures. The most familiar such congruence criteria are all three sides congruent (Side-Side-Side), two sides with an included angle congruent (Side-Angle-Side), two angles with an included side congruent (Angle-Side-Angle), and two angles and an adjacent side congruent (Angle-Angle-Side). It is not intended that students perform transformations using tracing paper or other tools, but rather that they reason about why a subset of congruent criteria would guarantee that a transformation is possible or impossible, in all such cases. **Note:** In High School Geometry, these congruent criteria are abbreviated SSS, SAS, ASA, AAS, respectively.

Problem Implementation

Let students work in groups of 2–4.

Materials

- **Labsheet 2.3:** Questions C–E
- **Teaching Aid 2.3:** Congruence Criteria
- **Partner Quiz**

rulers

angle rulers or protractors

Vocabulary

There are no new glossary terms introduced in this Problem.

Mathematics Background

- Congruent Figures

At a Glance and Lesson Plan

- At a Glance: Problem 2.3 Butterflies, Pinwheels, and Wallpaper
- Lesson Plan: Problem 2.3 Butterflies, Pinwheels, and Wallpaper

Launch

Launch Video

This is a fun animation that depicts the use of congruent and similar triangles in bridge design. The discussion centers around whether triangles are congruent if they share the same side or if all three angles are equivalent. Visit Teacher Place at mathdashboard.com/cmp3 to see the complete video.

Show this animation to spark a discussion of the congruent triangles shown in the introduction to the Problem. Continue the discussion by using Connecting to Prior Knowledge.

Connecting to Prior Knowledge

Before the students start working on this Problem, you may want to discuss the congruent triangles *ABC* and *PQR* pictured in the introduction. Ask them to explain what the term *corresponding* means in order to make sure the context of the Problem is clear to the entire class.

Suggested Questions

- How do you visually recognize the corresponding pairs of sides? Pairs of angles? (Students might talk about applying transformations so that a copy of one triangle fits onto the other triangle. Push them to point out the parts of the triangles that help them recognize the way one matches the other.)
- Which side of triangle *PQR* should match with *AC*? How do you know that? (*PR* matches *AC* because it's the longest side in each triangle.)
- Which angle is the largest angle in triangle *ABC*? Where is the corresponding angle in triangle *PQR* located? (The largest angle is $\angle B$, which is opposite the longest side, *AC*. The corresponding angle is $\angle Q$, which is also opposite the longest side, *PR*.)

Refer back to Problem 2.2:

- Did you need to measure all parts of each triangle before you were confident that they could be matched by a sequence of transformations? (Students may say that they only checked the lengths of sides because they learned in the Grade 7 Unit *Shapes and Designs* that three side lengths define a unique triangle. At this point, allow them to describe the different combinations they used. Then, tell the students that they will have an opportunity to verify their ideas in Problem 2.3.)
- How do you show that two triangles are NOT congruent? Do you have to measure all the sides and angles? (From Problem 2.2 and the Grade 7 Unit *Stretching and Shrinking*, students should realize that measuring angles alone is not sufficient.)

Presenting the Challenge

This Problem makes use of an important mathematical proof strategy—using counterexamples to disprove claims. It might be productive to begin Question A as a class so that students have a model of the sort of evidence to look for or construct to disprove a claim. The students can use **Labsheet 2.3: Questions C–E** to complete the Problem.

Suggested Questions

- If I tell you that I have drawn two triangles, and each of them has a longest side length of 3 inches, might the triangles be congruent? Must they be congruent? (Give students a short time to discuss this in their groups and then ask for answers.)
- Suppose I say, "Triangles *ABC* and *PQR* are congruent because *AB* and *PQ* are corresponding sides where $AB = PQ$." How can you prove that this statement is not true? (Draw an example where $AB = PQ$ but *AC* and *PR* are different lengths.)
- One counterexample is enough to disprove that a statement is always true. If you cannot draw a counterexample, does that mean that the claim is always true? (If no one can draw a counterexample, then the claim may still be false. But sometimes an individual may not be able to think of a counterexample, though one does exist. There is a difference between saying, "I cannot think of a counterexample," and "There is no counterexample.")

Tell students that the focus of this Problem is to make convincing arguments about why a given claim is always true or not always true. They can use counterexamples or reason about transformations.

Explore

Providing for Individual Needs

As students tackle the parts in Questions A–C, it will be an automatic response for them to simply answer *yes* or *no*. As they work, monitor the answers they write down to see that each yes or no answer includes a brief explanation. It should address why they believe the given information will (or will not) assure that one triangle can be "moved" onto the other.

In Question C, it is important that the students give thorough explanations for their answers. It is not enough to draw triangles that satisfy the conditions. For this reason, it will be helpful to ask them questions that lead them in the right direction while they're working. You may also want to ask the students to record their arguments for sharing in the Summary.

Suggested Questions

- For Question C part (1), how would you describe the matching information about sides and angles? What transformations "move" triangle *GHI* onto triangle *JKL*? (We have two pairs of matching angles, and also a matching pair of sides between the angles [included sides]. Translate a copy of *GHI*, so that $H \rightarrow K$, and then rotate around *K*, until the angles at *H* and *K* coincide.)
- How can you be sure that this will work for any size of angles at *H* and *K*? (It is given that angle *H* is congruent to angle *K* so, after a sequence of transformations, the directions of the sides of angle *H* will match the directions of the sides of angle *K*. It is also given that $GH = JK$, so after the same sequence of transformations, *G* will "move" onto *J* and *GH* will "move" onto *JK*. Lastly, it is given that angles *G* and *J* are congruent. Since we have already matched *GH* and *JK*, we also have the directions of sides *IG* and *LJ* matched. These facts are not dependent upon the size of the angles, but their location in comparison to the location of the congruent sides.)
- You have explained how the direction of side *HI* has to match the direction of side *KL*, and how the direction of side *IG* has to match the direction of side *LJ*. How can you be sure that the lengths will also match? (After the sequence of transformations described, *I* would have to be matched to a point on *KL*, because we know the directions of the sides *HI* and *KL* coincide. Likewise, *I* would be matched to a point on *LJ* because there can only be one point that is on both *KL* and *LJ*. For this reason, *I* matches the point *L*. **Note:** Students may not make this connection on their own, but it is a good idea to encourage them to consider why they can assert that $I \rightarrow L$.
- For Question D part (1), how would you describe the matching information? Does Amy's reasoning convince you that all corresponding sides and angles must match? (It is given that two pairs of sides and a pair of included angles match. Student answers will vary, but they should include that Amy failed to explain why a translation will "move" $H \rightarrow K$, $G \rightarrow J$, and $I \rightarrow L$. She should have added that if two pairs of sides and the vertices that join them match, then the other two pairs of vertices and the third pair of sides should also match.)

- Suppose the given congruent angles were smaller than shown. Would Amy's (or your) reasoning still be valid? (Yes; because the description of the transformations does not depend on the size of the angles (or the sides).)
- For Question D part (2), what are the two parallelograms? How do we know that these quadrilaterals have parallel sides? (The two parallelograms are *GJLI* and *HKLI*. We know that $HI \parallel KL$ and $HK \parallel IL$, because that is the direction of the translation, which has the same effect on every vertex. $GI \parallel JL$ because $\angle G$ and $\angle J$ are congruent, and they are the corresponding angles for two lines cut by a transversal. We also know that $GI = JL$ because of the translation that "moves" $G \rightarrow J$ and $I \rightarrow L$. Lastly, $HI \parallel KL$ because translations "move" segments to parallel segments.
- What do we know about parallelograms that might identify equal sides and angles? (Opposite sides of a parallelogram are parallel and congruent.)
- For Question E part (1), what additional information would you need to decide that the given triangles are congruent? (Any pair of corresponding congruent sides would make all the information sufficient enough to show that the triangles are congruent. It would be the same combination of matching parts as the pairs of triangles in Question C part (1).)

For Question E part (2), encourage students to prepare an argument for why some other combination of three pairs of corresponding parts will guarantee that two triangles are congruent. One combination that students should suggest is all three sides congruent. This condition can be a challenge to justify using a sequence of transformations that "moves" one triangle onto another. However, students have met this condition before in the Grade 7 Unit *Shapes and Designs* where they found that three specific side lengths define a unique triangle. Then, this idea was revisited in the Grade 8 Unit *Looking for Pythagoras*, where they used it to justify the converse of the Pythagorean Theorem. The other combinations of three measurements they might describe are Side-Angle-Side, Angle-Side-Angle, and Angle-Angle-Side. Refer to the Summarize section and **Teaching Aid 2.3: Congruence Criteria**.

When most students have made good progress on Questions A–E part (2), you can have a summary discussion as a class about their results. Question E part (3) is an extra challenge for the students that are very interested in this topic, so it is not necessary to wait for all students to complete it before discussing their results on this Problem.

Going Further

In the case that you want to expand the discussion on Question E, you can pose the following question.

- Suppose we have triangles *ABC* and *PQR*, where $AB = PQ = 3$ inches, $AC = PR = 5$ inches, and $\angle B = \angle Q = 90°$. Is this enough information to guarantee the triangles are congruent? Explain. (The given information is two sides with a nonincluded angle congruent, or Side-Side-Angle. Since triangles *ABC* and *PQR* are right triangles, we can calculate that $BC = QR = \sqrt{5^2 - 3^2} = 4$. Therefore, this is a case where Side-Side-Angle leads to Side-Side-Side, which defines a unique triangle.

Planning for the Summary

What evidence will you use in the summary to clarify and deepen understanding of the Focus Question?

What will you do if you do not have evidence?

Summarize

Orchestrating the Discussion

This Problem is intended to present students with some specific examples of congruent (and noncongruent) triangles. The students will use the information from these examples to develop general conjectures. However, they will need to discuss their findings with the class as part of the learning process. Choose students or groups to present their arguments for Questions C, D, and E part (1) and encourage the class to critique the explanations. Teaching Aid 2.3 will help you discuss the students' conjectures for Question E part (3). The last three triangles all have two sides with a nonincluded angle congruent, but the last triangle is not congruent to the other two. This counterexample illustrates that Side-Side-Angle is not a trustworthy combination of matching measurements to guarantee congruence.

Suggested Questions

- In Question C part (1), which congruence criterion is described by the information provided? (It shows Angle-Side-Angle, which is two angles with an included side congruent.)
- In Question C part (2), which congruence criterion is described by the information provided? (It shows Side-Angle-Side, which is two sides with an included angle congruent.)
- What information is the group giving us about the pairs of triangles? Are you convinced that the argument presented by this group guarantees congruence? (Students are likely to argue Angle-Side-Angle, Side-Angle-Side, Side-Side-Side, and perhaps Angle-Angle-Side. They should see that Angle-Angle-Side is not really a distinct combination, because two pairs of congruent angles are given, and it is known that the sum of the angles must be 180°. They may also suggest that Side-Side-Angle is enough to guarantee congruence. This combination works sometimes but cannot be guaranteed to work with every situation. (Refer to the Going Further in the Explore section of this Problem.))

Reflecting on Student Learning

Use the following questions to assess student understanding at the end of the lesson.

- What evidence do I have that students understand the Focus Question?
  - Where did my students get stuck?
  - What strategies did they use?
  - What breakthroughs did my students have today?
- How will I use this to plan for tomorrow? For the next time I teach this lesson?
- Where will I have the opportunity to reinforce these ideas as I continue through this Unit? The next Unit?

ACE Assignment Guide

- **Applications:** 7–12, 19–26
- **Connections:** 33–35
- **Extensions:** 40

Mathematical Reflections

Possible Answers to Mathematical Reflections

1. There are a number of ways to devise a chain of flips, turns, and/or slides that will “move” one figure exactly onto another congruent figure. It certainly makes sense to start by identifying congruent parts of the two figures and the correspondence of vertices that is implied by that information. Then you can focus on a particular pair of corresponding sides or angles and determine the sequence of transformations that “move” one onto of the other.
2. There are three basic and widely useful criteria for establishing congruence of triangles without transformation motions. They are all three sides congruent (SSS), two sides with an included angle congruent (SAS), and two angles with an included side congruent (ASA) or two angles and an adjacent side congruent (AAS). In some cases, it is possible to show congruence with different information. For example, in a right triangle, the Pythagorean theorem allows one to deduce the length of a leg if one other leg and the hypotenuse are known. This case is an exception to the fact that Side-Side-Angle shows congruence, but this method is not effective. (Refer to the Going Further in the Explore section of Problem 2.3.)
3. To show that two triangles are not congruent, I start by measuring the sides and angles. If I find differences in the measurements, then I can imply noncongruence. For example, suppose that there are three pairs of congruent corresponding angles. If I find that the lengths of the corresponding sides are different, the triangles are not congruent.

Possible Answers to Mathematical Practices Reflections

Students may have demonstrated all of the eight Common Core Standards for Mathematical Practice during this Investigation. During the class discussion, have students provide additional Practices that the Problem cited involved and identify the use of other Mathematical Practices in the Investigation.

One student observation is provided in the Student Edition. Here is another sample student response.

In Problem 2.3, we had to explain why certain conditions were sufficient or insufficient to show that triangles are congruent. As I worked on each case, I found that certain methods of showing congruence are more accurate than others. For example, I used a counterexample to show that a statement is not always true. I also used my knowledge of transformations to show that the given conditions were sufficient. These strategies are more effective than using one example to show that a statement is always true. It is also more effecting than tracing to show that two specific triangles are congruent because I am making a statement about the sides and angles of the triangles.

MP3: Construct viable arguments and critique the reasoning of others.

Investigation 2

Transformations and Congruence

You can use reflections, rotations, and translations to arrange copies of a basic design element in a symmetric pattern, as in the kaleidoscope patterns shown below.

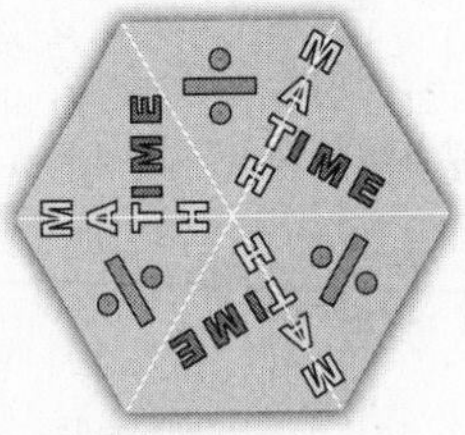

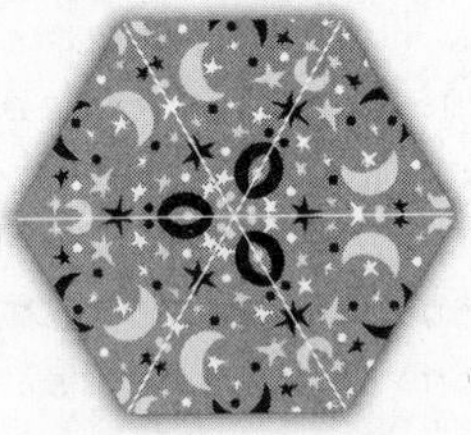

- Can you find the basic design element in each kaleidoscope pattern?
- What transformations could you use on the basic design element to make the symmetric patterns?

Two figures that have the same size and shape are **congruent.** If you can flip, turn, and/or slide one figure exactly onto the other, the figures must be congruent. In this Investigation, you will compare the size and shape of geometric figures after a sequence of transformations.

Common Core State Standards

8.G.A.1 Verify experimentally the properties of rotations, reflections, and translations:

8.G.A.1a Lines are taken to lines, and line segments to line segments of the same length.

8.G.A.1b Angles are taken to angles of the same measure.

8.G.A.2 Understand that a two-dimensional figure is congruent to another if the second can be obtained from the first by a sequence of rotations, reflections, and translations; given two congruent figures, describe a sequence that exhibits the congruence between them.

Notes

2.1 Connecting Congruent Polygons

When two polygons are congruent, you can match the vertices in a way that pairs sides and angles of the same size. Quadrilaterals *ABCD* and *PQRS* are congruent.

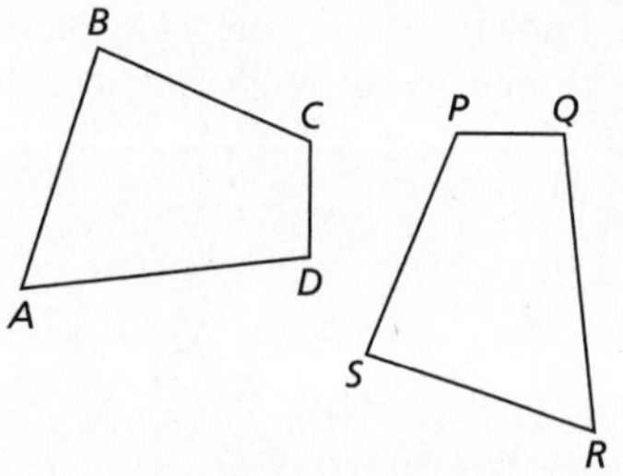

- What are the pairs of congruent sides and angles?
- How can you flip, turn, and/or slide one quadrilateral onto the other?

In this Problem, you will learn the standard language and symbols for describing congruent figures.

Problem 2.1

A Suppose you copied quadrilateral *ABCD* above, and moved the copy so that it fit exactly on quadrilateral *PQRS*. Copy and complete these statements to show which vertices correspond. The arrow means "corresponds to."

$A \rightarrow$ ■ $B \rightarrow$ ■ $C \rightarrow$ ■ $D \rightarrow$ ■

B The notation $\overline{AB}$ means "line segment *AB*." The symbol $\cong$ means "is congruent to." Copy and complete these statements to show which pairs of sides in the two quadrilaterals are congruent.

$\overline{AB} \cong$ ■ $\overline{BC} \cong$ ■ $\overline{CD} \cong$ ■ $\overline{DA} \cong$ ■

C The notation $\angle A$ means "angle *A*." Copy and complete these statements to show which angles are congruent.

$\angle A \cong$ ■ $\angle B \cong$ ■ $\angle C \cong$ ■ $\angle D \cong$ ■

D 1. Use a copy of quadrilateral *ABCD*. Investigate combinations of reflections, rotations, and translations that will move the copy exactly onto quadrilateral *PQRS*. Describe the exact transformations that will accomplish this. Is there more than one way?

2. How could you rename quadrilateral *PQRS* so that the name shows how its vertices correspond to those of quadrilateral *ABCD*?

ACE Homework starts on page 38.

STUDENT PAGE

Notes

2.2 Supporting the World
Congruent Triangles I

In Problem 2.1, you matched quadrilateral *ABCD* to quadrilateral *PQRS*. One sequence of transformations that accomplishes this is shown below. Since you can "move" quadrilateral *ABCD* onto quadrilateral *RSPQ*, you know these shapes are congruent.

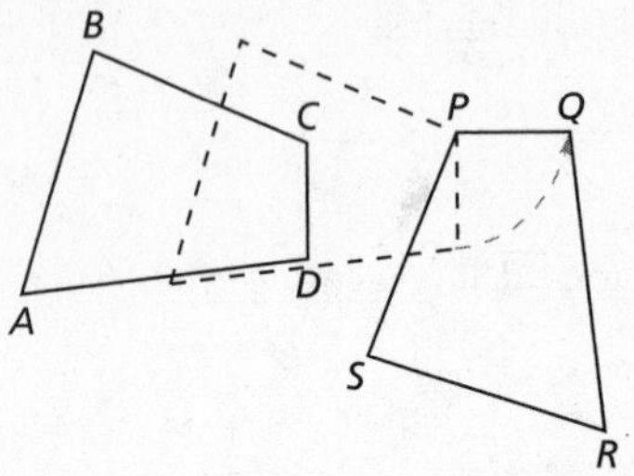

In this Problem, you are going to focus on congruent triangles. Triangles are a very special family of geometric figures. They are used in many construction projects to provide strength and stability for structures.

For example, this photograph of the George Washington Bridge, connecting New Jersey and New York City, shows congruent triangles in the bridge's towers.

Notes

Problem 2.2

For each pair of triangles:

- Inspect and measure parts of the figures to determine whether they are congruent.
- If the triangles are congruent, list the corresponding vertices.
- If the triangles are congruent, describe a sequence of transformations that would move one triangle onto the other.

A Are triangles *ABC* and *XYZ* congruent?

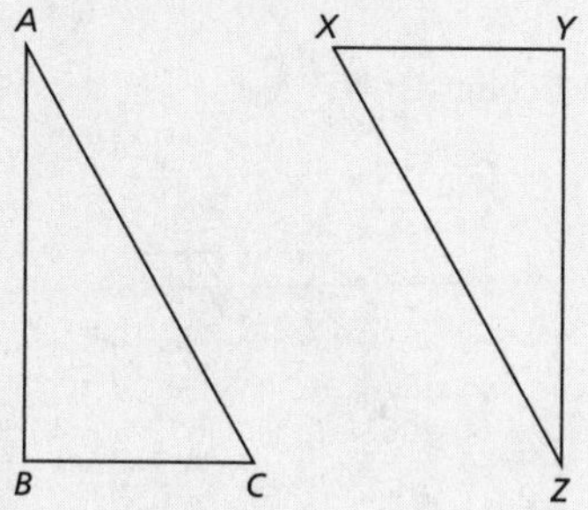

B Are triangles *DEF* and *STU* congruent?

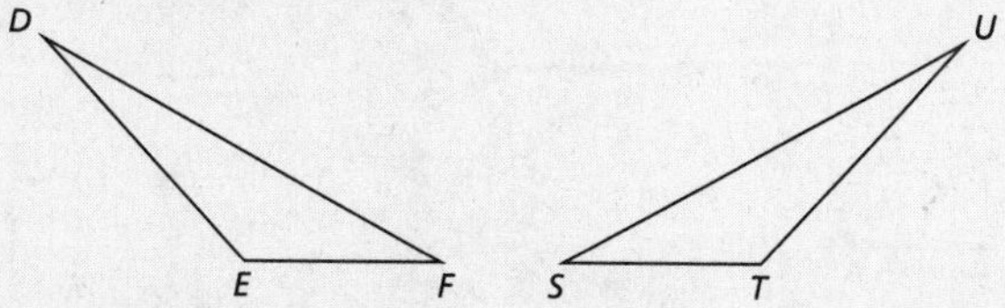

C Are triangles *GHI* and *VWX* congruent?

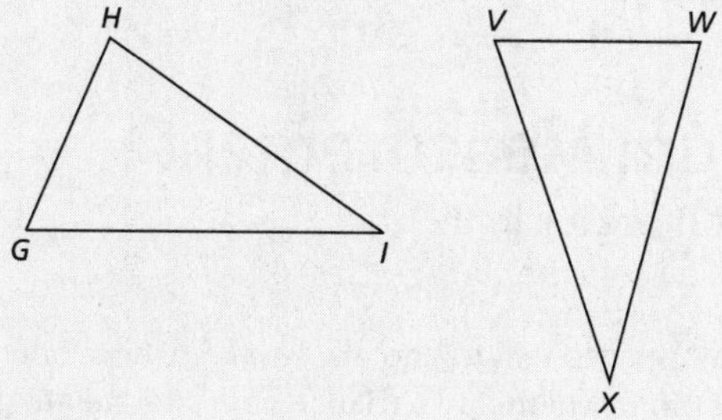

continued on the next page >

STUDENT PAGE

Notes

Problem 2.2 continued

D Are triangles *JKL* and *MNO* congruent?

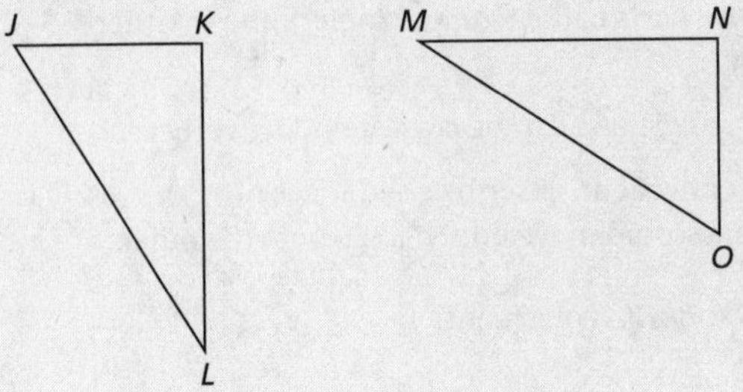

E Are triangles *STU* and *VWX* congruent?

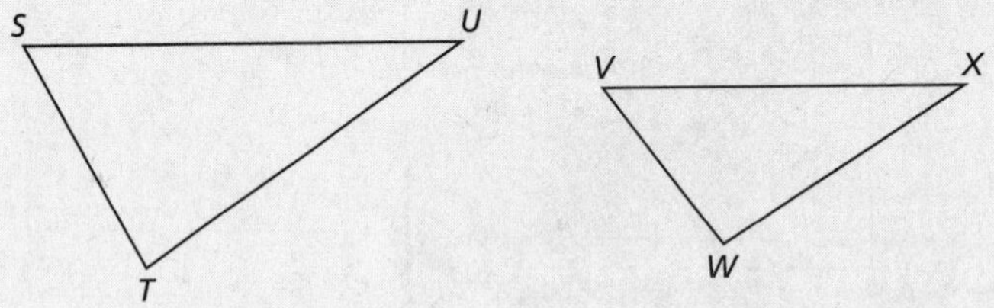

F Are triangles *ABC* and *PQR* congruent?

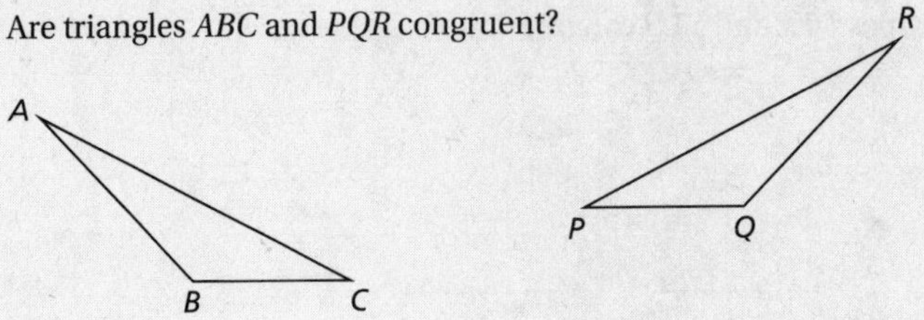

ACE Homework starts on page 38.

2.3 Minimum Measurement

Congruent Triangles II

In Problem 2.2, you might have noticed that it is not necessary to move one triangle onto the other to determine whether two triangles are congruent. If you know that the corresponding sides and angles are equal, you can conclude that the triangles are congruent.

Notes

For example, in triangles *ABC* and *RQP* below, $\angle A \cong \angle R$, $\angle B \cong \angle Q$, $\angle C \cong \angle P$, $\overline{AB} \cong \overline{RQ}$, $\overline{BC} \cong \overline{QP}$, and $\overline{CA} \cong \overline{PR}$. Since all *corresponding parts* are congruent, the two triangles are congruent. Triangles *ABC* and *RQP* show a common way of marking congruent sides and angles. The sides with the same number of tic marks are congruent. The angles with the name number of arcs are congruent.

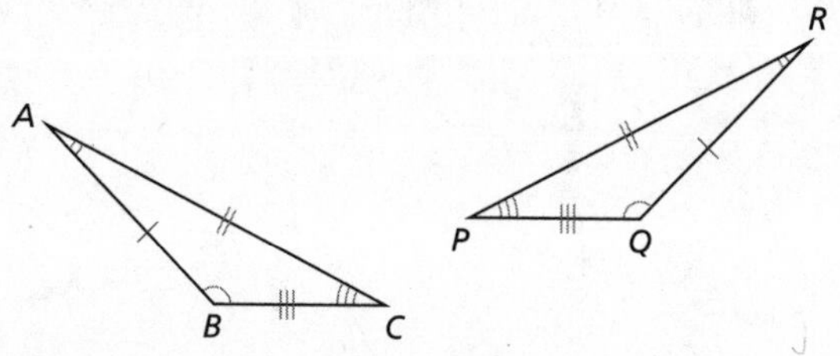

In this Problem, you will explore whether you need to know the measures of all the sides and angles of two triangles in order to determine congruence.

Can you conclude that two triangles are congruent if you know the measures of only one, two, or three pairs of corresponding parts? Explain.

Problem 2.3

Consider the conditions described in Questions A–C. For each case, give an argument to support your answer. If the conditions are not enough to determine two triangles are congruent, give a counterexample.

A Can you be sure that two triangles are congruent if you know only

1. one pair of congruent corresponding sides?
2. one pair of congruent corresponding angles?

B Can you be sure that two triangles are congruent if you know only

1. two pairs of congruent corresponding sides?
2. two pairs of congruent corresponding angles?
3. one pair of congruent corresponding sides and one pair of congruent corresponding angles?

continued on the next page >

Notes

Problem 2.3 continued

C Can you be sure that two triangles are congruent if you know

1. two pairs of congruent corresponding angles and one pair of congruent corresponding sides as shown? Use your understanding of transformations to justify your answer.

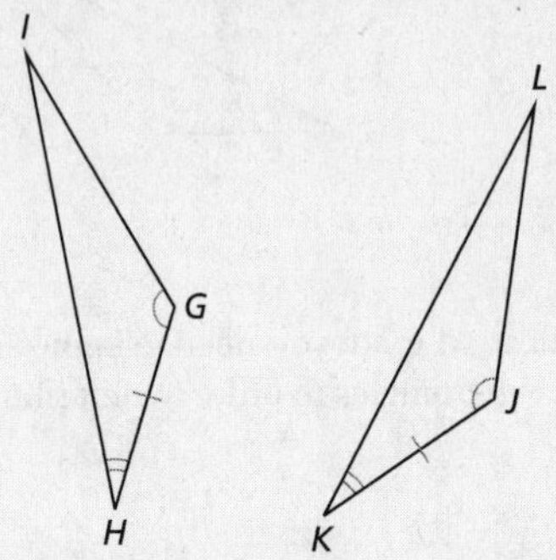

2. two pairs of congruent corresponding sides and one pair of congruent corresponding angles as shown? Use your understanding of transformations to justify your answer.

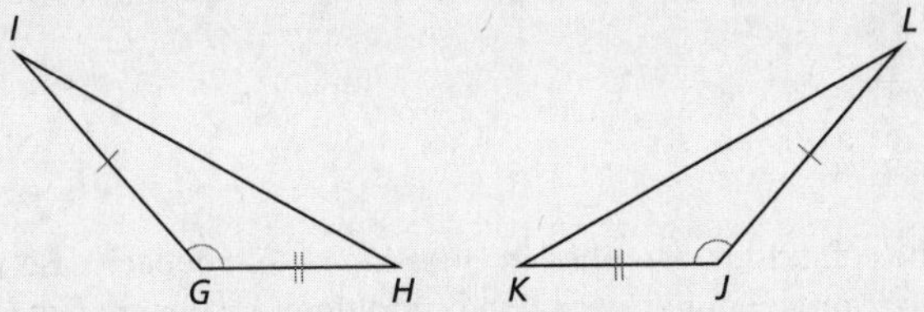

D Amy and Becky have different ideas about how to decide whether the conditions in Question C, part (2) are enough to show triangles are congruent.

1. Amy flips triangle *GHI* as shown. She says you can translate the triangle so that $H \rightarrow K$ and $G \rightarrow J$. So all the measures in triangle *GHI* match measures in triangle *JKL*. Do you agree with Amy's reasoning? Explain.

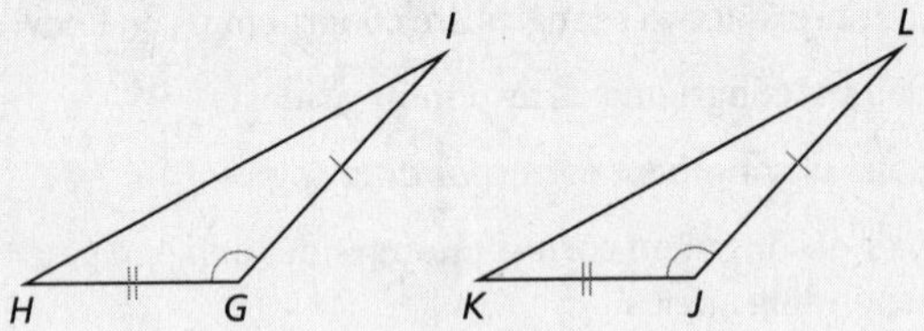

Notes

Problem 2.3 continued

2. Becky thinks Amy should also explain why the translation matches *all* the sides and angles. She says that if you translate triangle *GHI* so that $G \rightarrow J$, there will be two parallelograms in the figure. These parallelograms show her which corresponding angles and sides are congruent. What parallelograms does she see? How do these parallelograms help identify congruent corresponding sides and angles?

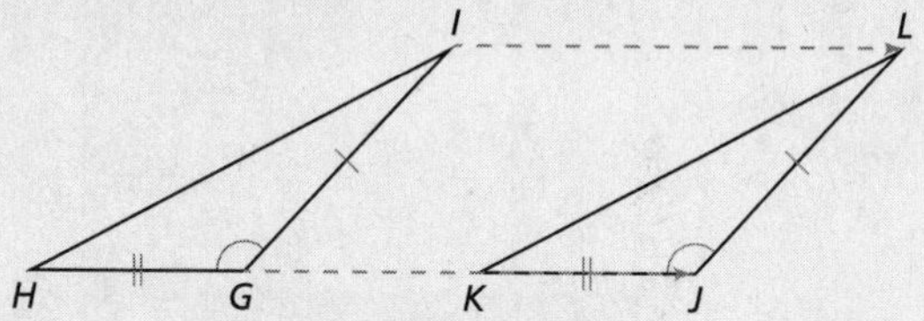

E 1. Can you be sure that two triangles are congruent if you know three pairs of congruent corresponding angles? Explain.

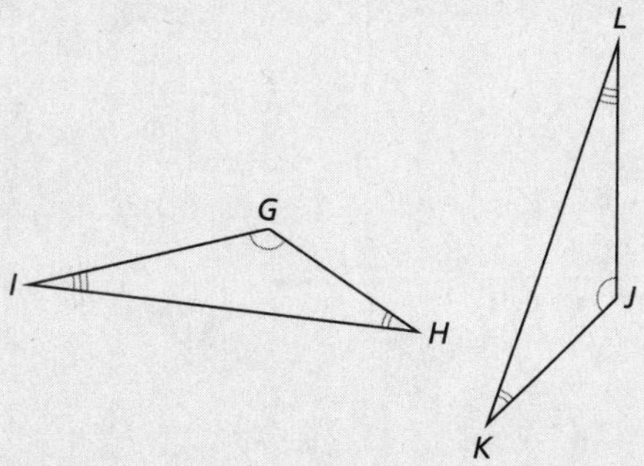

2. Are there any other combinations of three congruent corresponding parts that will guarantee two triangles are congruent? Make sketches to justify your answer.

3. Suppose two triangles appear to be *not* congruent. What is the minimum number of measures you should check to show they are not congruent?

ACE Homework starts on page 38.

STUDENT PAGE

Notes

ACE Applications | Connections | Extensions

Applications

In Exercises 1–4, the shapes in each pair are congruent. Match each vertex of the first shape to its corresponding vertex in the second shape.

1.

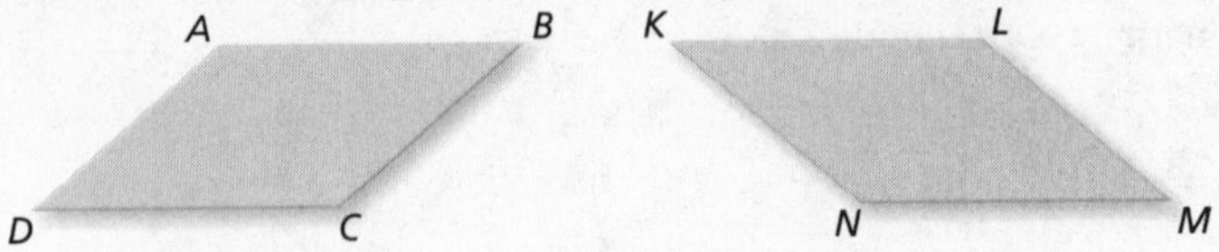

2.

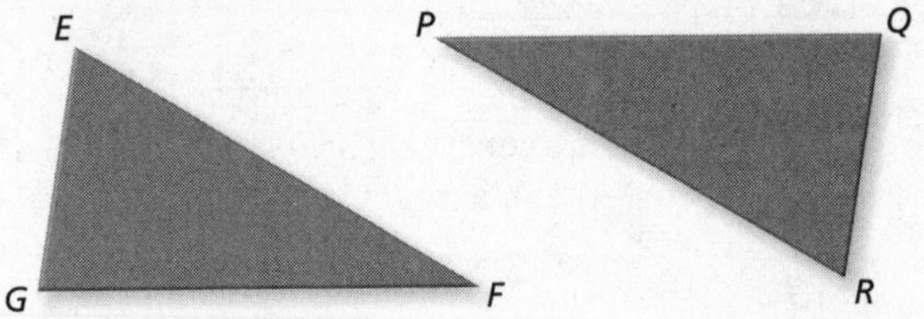

3.

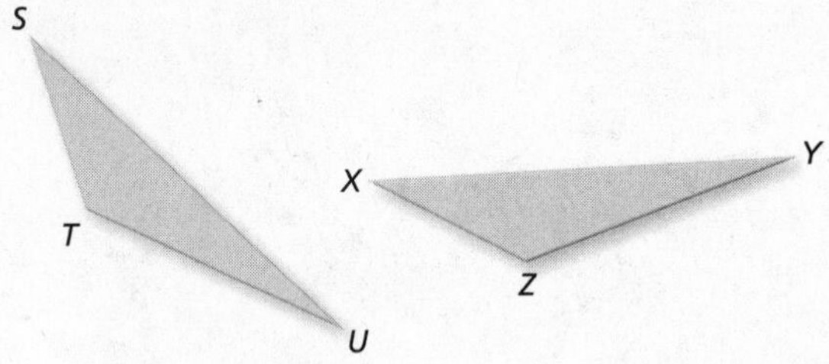

4.

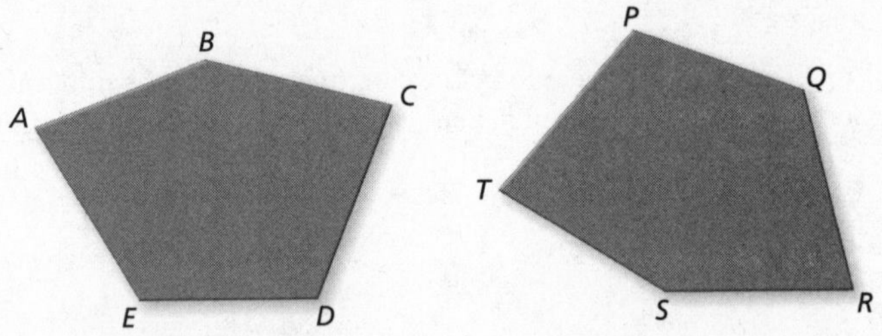

Notes

5. The figure below shows rectangle $JKLM$ and its diagonals $\overline{JL}$ and $\overline{KM}$. List all pairs of congruent triangles in the figure, labeling each in a way that shows the corresponding vertices.

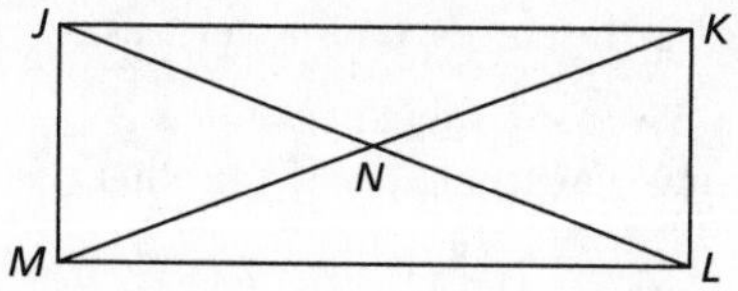

6. Select three different pairs of congruent triangles you identified in Exercise 5. Describe the flip, turn, and/or slide that would "move" one exactly onto the other.

For Exercises 7–12, decide whether you can tell that triangles in each pair are congruent based *only* on the given information.

7.

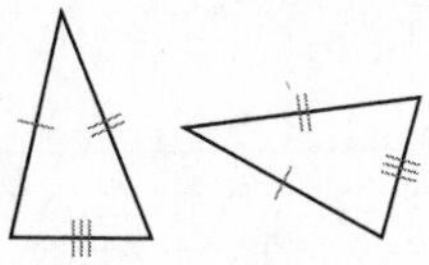

8.

9.

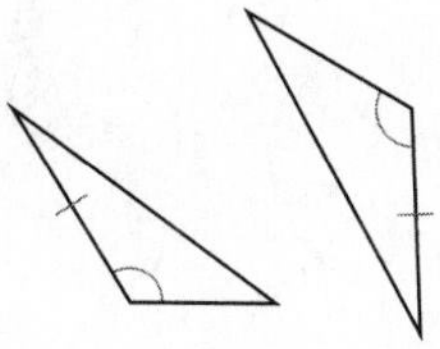

10.

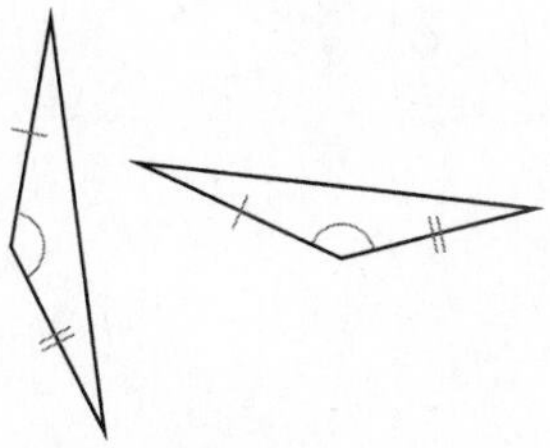

11.

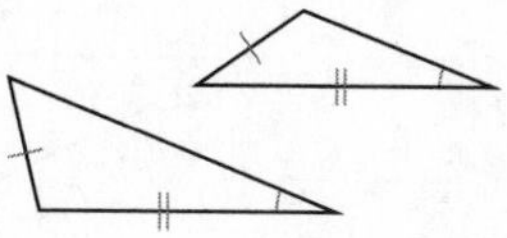

12.

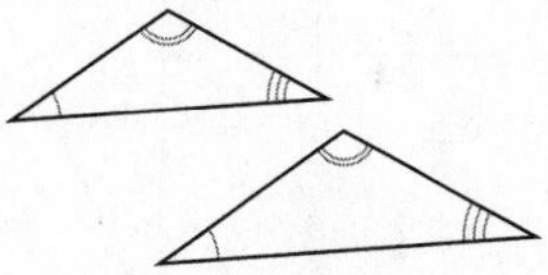

STUDENT PAGE

Notes

For Exercises 13–18, do the following for each pair of triangles.

- Inspect and measure parts of the figures to determine whether they are congruent.
- If the triangles are congruent, list the corresponding vertices.
- If the triangles are congruent, describe a sequence of transformations that would move one triangle onto the other.

13.

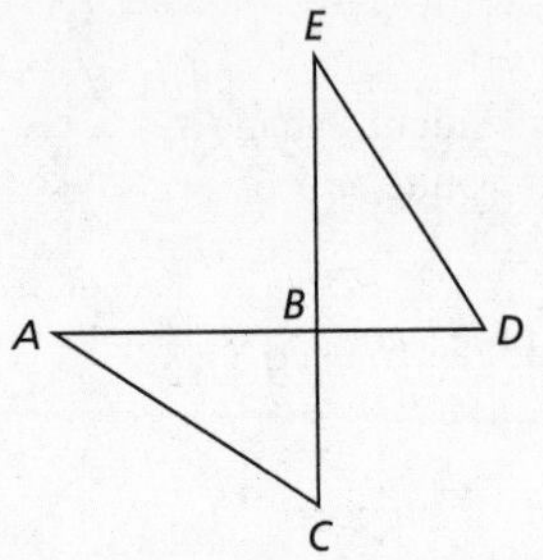

14.

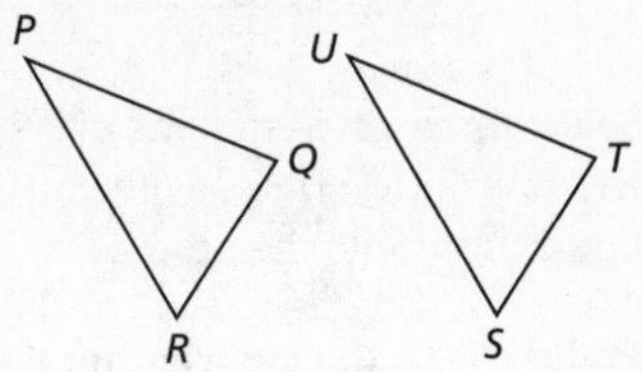

15.

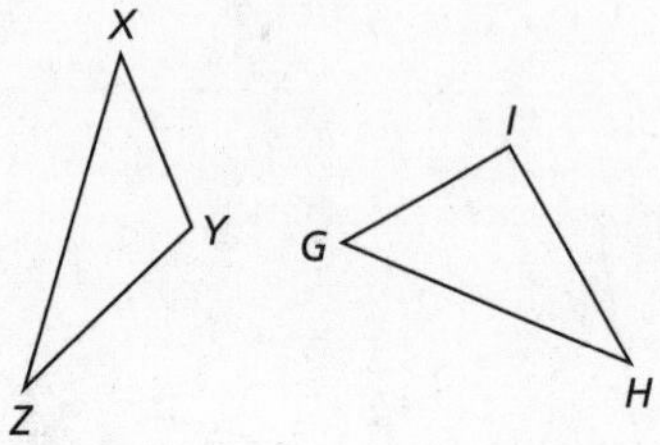

16.

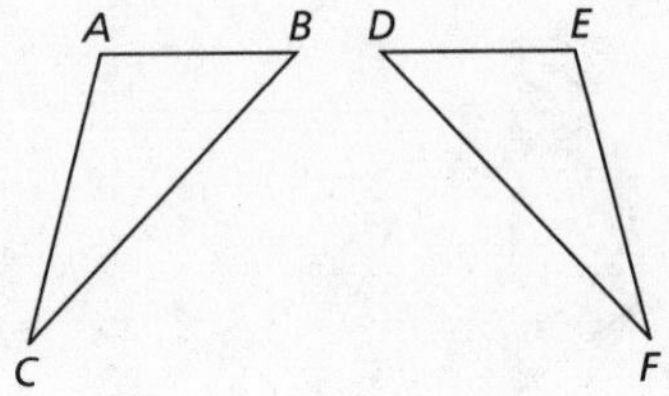

17.

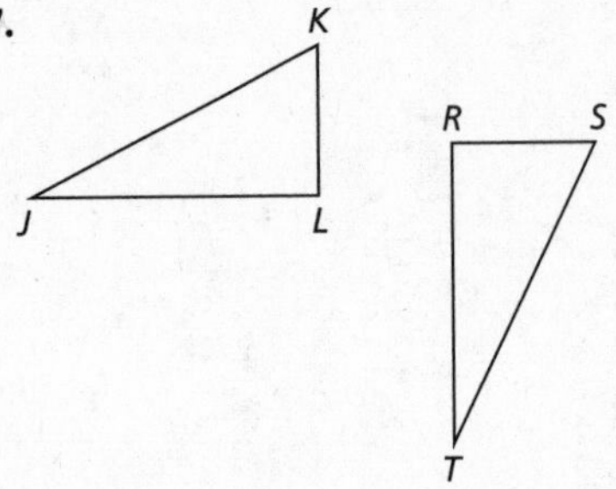

18.

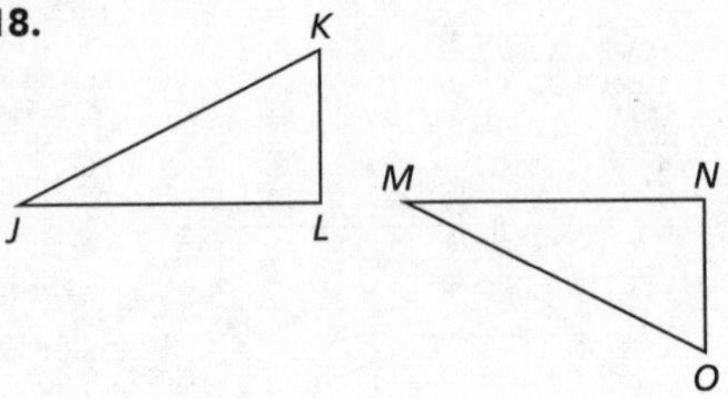

Notes

In Exercises 19–22, you are given a triangle *ABC* and information about another triangle, *DEF*. Tell whether triangle *DEF* is *definitely congruent* to triangle *ABC*, *possibly congruent* to triangle *ABC*, or *definitely not congruent* to triangle *ABC*. Explain your reasoning in each case.

19.

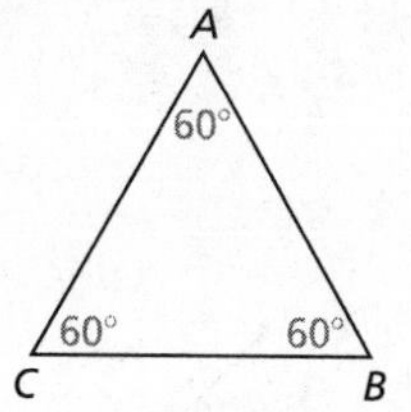

Angle *D*: 60°

Angle *E*: 60°

Angle *F*: 60°

20.

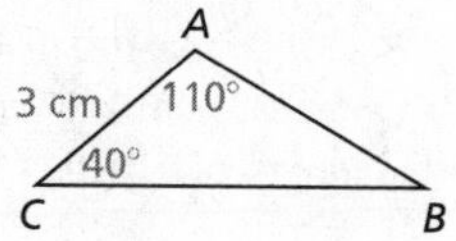

Angle *D*: 110°

Angle *E*: 40°

Side *DF*: 3 cm

21.

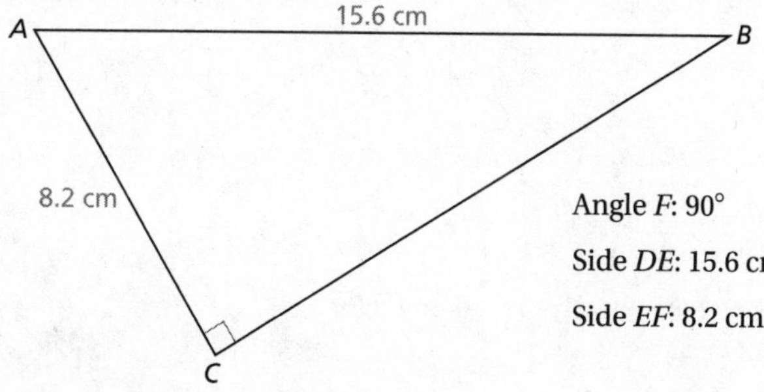

Angle *F*: 90°

Side *DE*: 15.6 cm

Side *EF*: 8.2 cm

22.

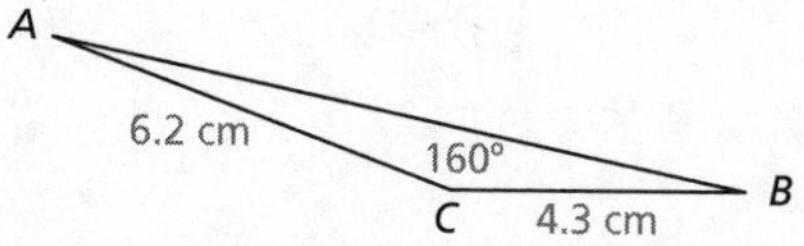

Angle F: 160°

Side *DF*: 4.3 cm

Side *EF*: 6.2 cm

Notes

Exercises 23–26 give different information for drawing the triangle below. Tell whether you would be certain to a draw a congruent copy of the triangle if you followed each set of directions.

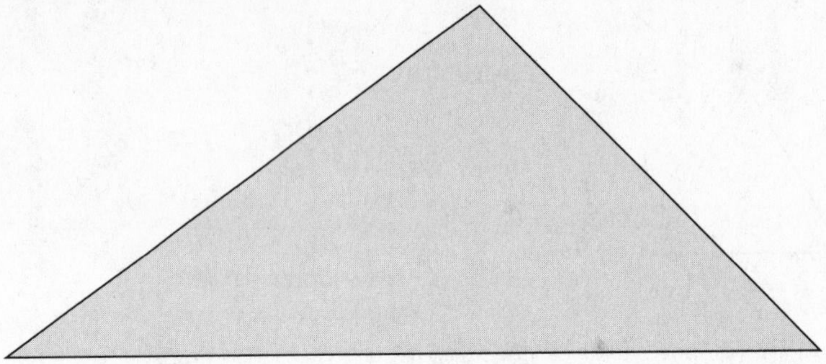

23. Draw $\angle A$ with a measure of 35°, $\angle B$ with a measure of 45°, and $\angle C$ with a measure of 100°.

24. Draw $\angle B$ with a measure of 45°, $\angle C$ with a measure of 100°, and $\overline{AB}$ with a length of 5 inches.

25. Draw $\angle B$ with a measure of 45°, $\overline{AB}$ with a length of 5 inches, and $\angle A$ with a measure of 35°.

26. Draw $\angle B$ with a measure of 45°, $\overline{AB}$ with a length of 5 inches, and $\overline{BC}$ with a length of 2.9 inches.

Connections

27. The kaleidoscope design at the right is composed of three congruent parts.

a. What is the shape of the basic design element for the symmetric pattern?

b. At what angle would you need to rotate the basic design element to complete the design?

Notes

28. Assume that the wallpaper design at the right extends without end in all directions.

a. Under what slide transformations would the design appear to be "unmoved" to a person who blinked while the transformation happened?

b. What basic design element could you use to produce the whole wallpaper design using only slide transformations?

c. What basic design element could you use to produce the whole wallpaper design using any transformation?

29. Are the circles shown below congruent? Explain your reasoning.

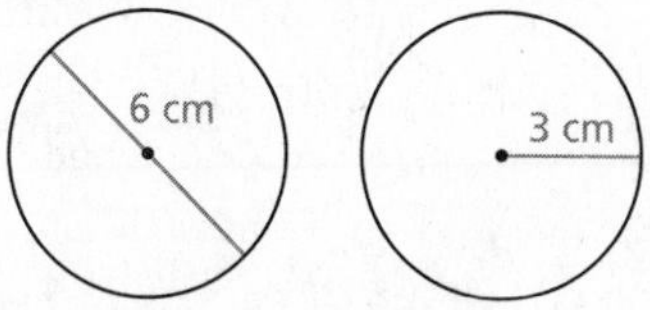

30. Use the rectangle and parallelogram at the right.

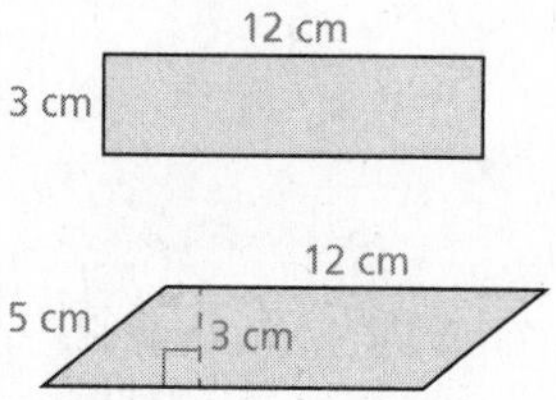

a. Find the perimeter and area of each figure.

b. Use your answers from part (a) and other examples, as needed, to justify your answers.

i. If two shapes have the same perimeter, must the shapes be congruent?

ii. If two shapes have the same area, must the shapes be congruent?

iii. If two shapes have the same perimeter, must they have the same area?

iv. If two shapes have the same area, must they have the same perimeter?

Notes

31. Suppose a friend asks you to draw a quadrilateral $ABCD$ with $AB = 4$ centimeters, $\angle B = 120°$, and $BC = 3$ centimeters.

a. Do you have enough information to draw the exact quadrilateral your friend has in mind?

b. Suppose your friend also tells you that the quadrilateral is a parallelogram. Will you be able to draw the exact shape with this additional information?

c. What is the least amount of information about side lengths and angle measures you would need to draw a quadrilateral $EFGH$ that is an exact copy of another quadrilateral $ABCD$?

32. Alejandro wants to build a footbridge directly across a pond from point A to point B. He needs to find the length of $\overline{AB}$. He places stakes at points A, B, and C to form a right triangle as shown in the diagram below.

a. Where should Alejandro place the stakes for points D and E to form a congruent triangle he can then measure?

b. What measurement will tell him the length of $\overline{AB}$?

Notes

33. Use triangle *ABC* below.

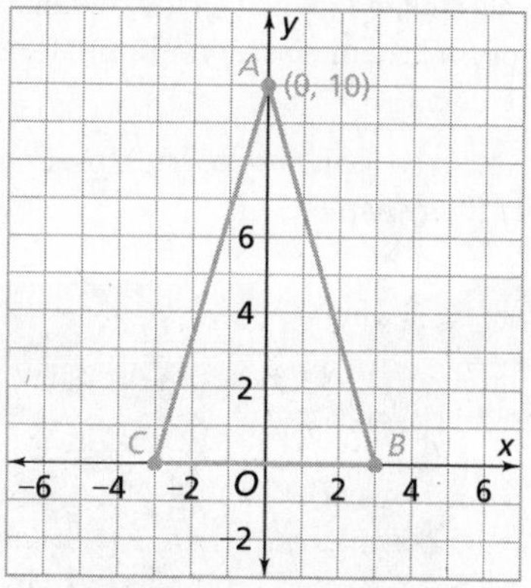

a. Explain how you know that $\triangle AOC \cong \triangle AOB$.

b. List the congruent corresponding sides and angles of the two figures.

34. Use trapezoid *PQRS* below.

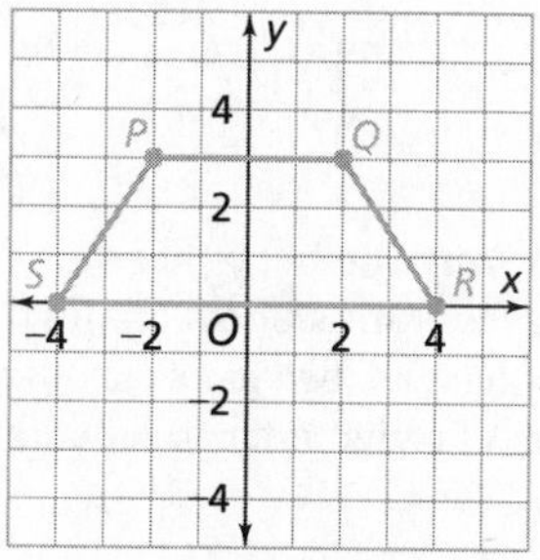

a. Explain how you know that $\overline{PS} \cong \overline{QR}$.

b. Explain how you know that $\angle P \cong \angle Q$ and $\angle S \cong \angle R$.

STUDENT PAGE

Notes

35. You know that triangles are rigid figures, but quadrilaterals are not.

a. How is the rigidity of triangles related to the fact that when two triangles have three pairs of congruent corresponding sides, the triangles are congruent?

b. How does this principle explain why braces are often used to help rectangular structures hold their shape?

Extensions

36. A teacher asks her students to explain whether or not the triangles shown below are congruent. One student argues that the triangles are congruent because there are two pairs of congruent corresponding sides and one pair of congruent corresponding angles. Do you agree or disagree? Explain.

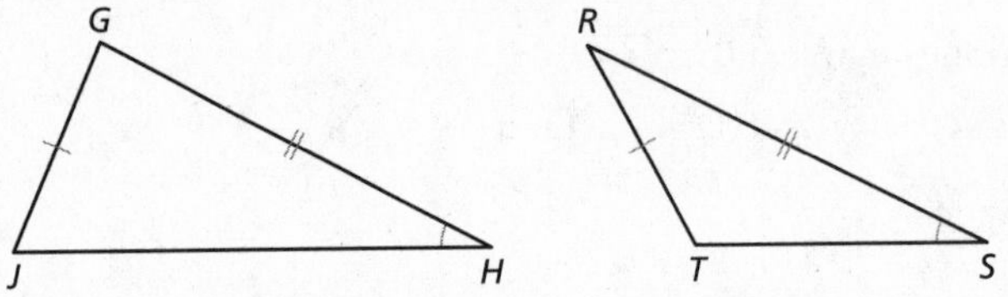

37. If two rectangles have the same area and the same perimeter, must they be congruent? Explore a variety of cases to develop a conjecture about this question.

Notes

38. In $\triangle FGH$ below, $\overline{FM}$ and $\overline{GN}$ are on lines of symmetry.

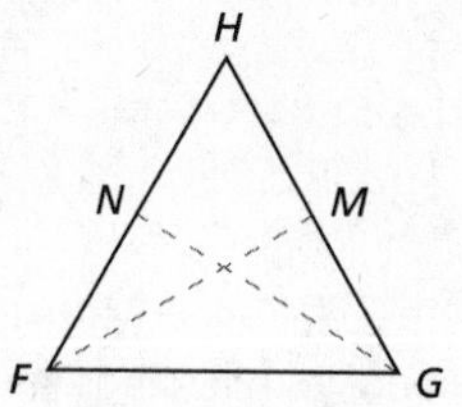

What does this symmetry tell you about

a. the angle measures in $\triangle FGH$?

b. the side lengths in $\triangle FGH$?

39. Pentagon *PQRST* has rotational symmetry about point *C* with an angle of rotation of 72°.

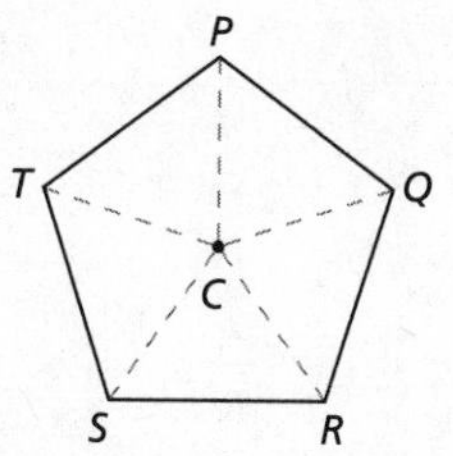

What does this symmetry tell you about

a. the angle measures of pentagon *PQRST*?

b. the side lengths of pentagon *PQRST*?

c. the segments from point *C* to each of the vertices?

40. In the figure below, $\overline{AB} \cong \overline{DE}$ and $\angle BAD \cong \angle EDA$. Use this information to show that $\triangle ABC \cong \triangle DEC$.

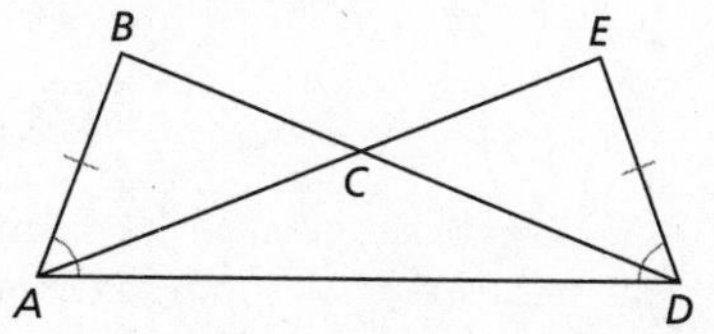

Notes

Mathematical Reflections 2

In this Investigation, you used geometric transformations to study congruence of figures. The following questions will help you summarize what you have learned.

Think about these questions. Discuss your ideas with other students and your teacher. Then write a summary of your findings in your notebook.

1. **How** can you find a sequence of flips, turns, and slides to "move" one figure exactly onto another to show that they are congruent?
2. **What** information about the sides and angles of two triangles will guarantee you can "move" one triangle onto the other?
3. **How** could you convince someone that two given triangles are *not* congruent?

Notes

Common Core Mathematical Practices

As you worked on the Problems in this Investigation, you used prior knowledge to make sense of them. You also applied Mathematical Practices to solve the Problems. Think back over your work, the ways you thought about the Problems, and how you used Mathematical Practices.

Shawna described her thoughts in the following way:

In Problem 2.2, we had to describe a sequence of transformations that would move one triangle onto another. It was challenging to break down the moves and describe exactly what was happening. We used tracing paper to show how two triangles match.

Once we knew the sequence of "moves" to make, we had to be very exact with the details. For flips, we provided the line of reflection. For turns, we provided the center and angle of rotation. For slides, we provided the direction and distance.

Common Core Standards for Mathematical Practice
MP6 Attend to precision.

- What other Mathematical Practices can you identify in Shawna's reasoning?
- Describe a Mathematical Practice that you and your classmates used to solve a different Problem in this Investigation.

STUDENT PAGE

Notes

Investigation 3

PLANNING

Transforming Coordinates

Investigation Overview

Investigation Description

This Investigation has five Problems. The first three Problems develop coordinate rules for line reflections, translations, and rotations. The fourth Problem develops the important special property of translations and half-turns that every line is mapped onto a parallel line. The fifth Problem applies that special result to review and prove important results about angles formed when parallel lines are cut by a transversal and about the angle sum of the interior or exterior angles of any triangle.

Investigation Vocabulary

There are no new glossary terms introduced in this Investigation.

Mathematics Background

- Reasoning From Symmetry and Congruence
- Coordinate Rules for Symmetry Transformations
- Combining Transformations

Planning Chart

Content	ACE	Pacing	Materials	Resources
Problem 3.1	1–3, 8, 16, 26	1 day	**Labsheet 3.1** Reflection **Labsheet 3ACE:** Exercises 1–3 (accessibility) **Labsheet 3ACE:** Exercise 8 (accessibility) **Labsheet 3ACE:** Exercise 16 (accessibility) **Labsheet 3ACE** Exercise 26 • Quarter-Inch Grid Paper graph paper	**Teaching Aid 3.1** Reflection in the *y*- and *x*-axis • Transformations
Problem 3.2	4, 5, 9, 17–20	1 day	**Labsheet 3.2** Translation **Labsheet 3ACE:** Exercises 4 and 5 (accessibility) **Labsheet 3ACE** Exercise 9 **Labsheet 3ACE:** Exercise 17 (accessibility) **Labsheet 3ACE:** Exercises 18 and 19 (accessibility) **Labsheet 3ACE** Exercise 20 • Quarter-Inch Grid Paper graph paper	Transformations

Content	ACE	Pacing	Materials	Resources
Problem 3.3	6, 7, 21, 22, 27	1 day	**Labsheet 3.3** Rotations of 90° and 180° **Labsheet 3ACE:** Exercises 6 and 7 (accessibility) **Labsheet 3ACE** Exercise 27 • Quarter-Inch Grid Paper graph paper	• Teaching Aid 3.3: Rotations of 90° and 180° • Transformations
Problem 3.4	10, 23, 28–30	1 day	**Labsheet 3.4** Special Property of Translations and 180° Rotations **Labsheet 3ACE** Exercise 28 • Quarter-Inch Grid Paper graph paper	**Teaching Aid 3.4** Special Property of Translations and 180° Rotations • Transformations
Problem 3.5	11–15, 24, 25, 31	1 day	**Labsheet 3.5** 180° Rotation Around Midpoints tracing paper, rulers, angle rulers, protractors (optional)	• Transformations
Mathematical Reflections		½ day		
Assessment: Check Up 2		½ day		• Check Up 2

Goals and Standards

Goals

Transformations Describe types of transformations that relate points by the motions of reflections, rotations, and translations, and methods for identifying and creating symmetric plane figures

- Recognize properties of reflection, rotation, and translation transformations
- Explore techniques for using rigid motion transformations to create symmetric designs
- Use coordinate rules for basic rigid motion transformations

Congruence and Similarity Understand congruence and similarity and explore necessary and sufficient conditions for establishing congruent and similar shapes

- Recognize that two figures are congruent if one is derived from the other one by a sequence of reflection, rotation, and/or translation transformations
- Recognize that two figures are similar if one can be obtained from the other by a sequence of reflections, rotations, translations, and/or dilations
- Use transformations to describe a sequence that exhibits the congruence between figures
- Use transformations to explore minimum measurement conditions for establishing congruence of triangles
- Use transformations to explore minimum measurement conditions for establishing similarity of triangles
- Relate properties of angles formed by parallel lines and transversals, and the angle sum in any triangle, to properties of transformations
- Use properties of congruent and similar triangles to solve problems about shapes and measurements

Mathematical Reflections

Look for evidence of student understanding of the goals for this Investigation in their responses to the questions in *Mathematical Reflections*. The goals addressed by each question are indicated below.

1. What are the general forms of coordinate rules for these transformations?
   - **a.** reflection in the y-axis
   - **b.** reflection in the x-axis
   - **c.** counterclockwise rotation of 90° about the origin
   - **d.** counterclockwise rotation of 180° about the origin
   - **e.** translations that "moves" points a units horizontally and b units vertically

Goal

- Use coordinate rules for basic rigid motion transformations

2. What is the effect of translations and half-turns on lines?

Goal

- Use coordinate rules for basic rigid motion transformations

3. How has your knowledge of transformations changed or extended what you already knew about the angles formed by two parallel lines and a transversal?

Goal

- Relate properties of angles formed by parallel lines and transversals, and the angle sum in any triangle, to properties of transformations

4. How has your knowledge of transformations changed or extended what you already knew about the sum of the angle measures of a triangle?

Goal

- Relate properties of angles formed by parallel lines and transversals, and the angle sum in any triangle, to properties of transformations

Standards

Common Core Content Standards

8.G.A.1 Verify experimentally the properties of rotations, reflections, and translations. *Problems 4 and 5*

8.G.A.1b Angles are taken to angles of the same measure. *Problem 5*

8.G.A.1c Parallel lines are taken to parallel lines. *Problems 4 and 5*

8.G.A.2 Understand that a two-dimensional figure is congruent to another if the second can be obtained from the first by a sequence of rotations, reflections, and translations; given two congruent figures, describe a sequence that exhibits the congruence between them. *Problem 5*

8.G.A.3 Describe the effect of dilations, translations, rotations, and reflections on two-dimensional figures using coordinates. *Problems 1, 2, 3, and 4*

8.G.A.5 Use informal arguments to establish facts about the angle sum and exterior angle of triangles, about the angles created when parallel lines are cut by a transversal, and the angle-angle criterion for similarity of triangles. *Problem 5*

Facilitating the Mathematical Practices

Students in *Connected Mathematics* classrooms display evidence of multiple Common Core Standards for Mathematical Practice every day. Here are just a few examples of when you might observe students demonstrating the Standards for Mathematical Practice during this Investigation.

Practice 1: Make sense of problems and persevere in solving them.
Students are engaged every day in solving problems and, over time, learn to persevere in solving them. To be effective, the problems embody critical concepts and skills and have the potential to engage students in making sense of mathematics. Students build understanding by reflecting, connecting, and communicating. These student-centered problem situations engage students in articulating the "knowns" in a problem situation and determining a logical solution pathway. The student-student and student-teacher dialogues help students not only to make sense of the problems, but also to persevere in finding appropriate strategies to solve them. The suggested questions in the Teacher Guides provide the metacognitive scaffolding to help students monitor and refine their problem-solving strategies.

Practice 3: Construct viable arguments and critique the reasoning of others.
In Problem 4, students use transformations to write conclusions after observing that translations and half-turns "move" lines to parallel lines. In Problem 5, they use transformations to prove that there are pairs of congruent angles in parallel lines cut by a transversal. They also use transformations to prove that the sum of the interior angles in a triangle is 180° and that the sum of the exterior angles of a triangle is 360°

Practice 7: Look for and make use of structure.
In Problems 1–3, students look for patterns in key coordinate points after applying a transformation or a sequence of transformations. After detecting the pattern, they write coordinate rules to describe the change of all coordinates under that transformation.

Practice 8: Look for and express regularity in repeated reasoning.
In Problem 3, students use repeated reasoning to understand the coordinate rules associated with 90° and 180° rotations around the center (0, 0). They also use this Practice in Problem 5. In that Problem, they rotate triangles 180° around side midpoints to observe the resulting image and figure. From the parallelogram, they can prove that the sum of the interior angles of a triangle is 180° using their results about parallel lines cut by a transversal.

Students identify and record their personal experiences with the Standards for Mathematical Practice during the Mathematical Reflections at the end of the Investigation.

PROBLEM

3.1 Flipping on a Grid

Coordinate Rules for Reflections

Problem Overview

Focus Question How can you describe how points "move" under a reflection with coordinate rules in the form $(x, y) \rightarrow (■, ■)$ when the reflection line is (1) the x-axis? (2) the y-axis? (3) the line $y = x$?

Problem Description

You might consider launching the Investigation and this Problem by asking students what they know about how animated films are made. You can make the point that when this work is done with computer software, every point, called a pixel, on the computer screen has a location and a pair of coordinates that specifies that location horizontally and vertically. Moving a figure is accomplished by using the rules for transformations. They can be more complicated than the flips, turns, and slides they have studied so far, but they involve the same ideas. In this Investigation, the Problems develop a basic understanding of transformations represented as operations on the coordinates of points.

Problem Implementation

Group students in pairs.

Materials

- **Labsheet 3.1:** Reflection
- **Labsheet 3ACE:** Exercise 26
- **Labsheet 3ACE:** Exercises 1–3 (accessibility)
- **Labsheet 3ACE:** Exercise 8 (accessibility)
- **Labsheet 3ACE:** Exercise 16 (accessibility)
- **Labsheet 3ACE:** Exercise 26
- **Quarter-Inch Grid Paper**
- **Teaching Aid 3.1:** Reflection in the y- and x-axis

graph paper

Using Technology

If the students have access to a computer, they may find it helpful to use **Transformations** to answer the Questions of this Problem. This activity may also help to reduce the amount of class time reserved for drawing designs. **Note:** The default setting of this activity includes a grid and axes.

Vocabulary

There are no new glossary terms introduced in this Problem.

Mathematics Background

- Reasoning From Symmetry and Congruence
- Coordinate Rules for Symmetry Transformations
- Combining Transformations

At a Glance and Lesson Plan

- At a Glance: Problem 3.1 Butterflies, Pinwheels, and Wallpaper
- Lesson Plan: Problem 3.1 Butterflies, Pinwheels, and Wallpaper

Launch

Launch Video

This animation shows Tori and Jayden playing the game Space Junk and puzzling over how images move. Using slow motion of the game, students see that the images move through a series of translations in the coordinate grid, from one point to the next. Visit Teacher Place at mathdashboard.com/cmp3 to see the complete video.

You can show students this animation before discussing the introduction to the Problem. Students can watch it instead of reading the introduction in the Student Edition.

Connecting to Prior Knowledge

To focus students on the questions of this particular Problem, have them study the flag pictured in the text and identify coordinates of the key points that could be used to give directions for drawing the figure. Some students might need a reminder that the points of interest are at grid intersection points.

Suggested Questions

- What are the coordinates of points *A*, *B*, *C*, *D*, and *E*? (*A*: (0, 0); *B*: (2, 4); *C*: (5, 4); *D*: (6, 6); *E*: (3, 6))
- How might you make a design with reflectional symmetry using this basic element? (We could reflect this flag over either the *y*- or the *x*-axis.)
- Are there any other lines of symmetry we might choose? (We can choose any line as the reflection line. The original and image in any reflection line makes a symmetric design.)
- How could you make a design with rotational symmetry using the flag as a basic element?(I could rotate the flag about the origin. I would have to make one copy if the angle of rotation is 180° and more copies if the angle of rotation is less than 180°.)
- Can you choose any other point as the center of the rotation? (I can choose any point as the center, but it will be more challenging to track the rotations and images if I choose a point not on the figure.)

Presenting the Challenge

The overarching goal of the Investigation is to find a rule for transforming coordinate pairs (and thus the flag figure) for each kind of transformation and then to be able to do that for a sequence of transformations. In Problem 3.1, we will focus on line reflections.

Explore

Providing for Individual Needs

Labsheet 3.1: Reflection is provided to help students organize their work. Some students will need to plot points and then fill out the table. Some will see immediately how the coordinates of the image relate to the original, particularly for reflection in the axes. Questions A, part (2); B, part (2); and C are less obvious, even for the most able students.

As you monitor progress, you will want to ask students questions that help them generalize and make sense of the patterns they see.

Suggested Questions

- In Question A, how did you know where to locate the images of each point on the original flag? (Some students will count grid squares and visually locate the image points. Some will say they knew that since *B* is two units to the right of the *y*-axis, *B′* must be two units to the left of the *y*-axis. Encourage students to use the latter method by asking them more questions.)

- How do you know how far *C* is from the *y*-axis (reflection line) without counting? (The *x*-coordinate tells you how far you are from the *y*-axis.)
- If we had point *W* at (13, 14) , where would you look for *W*′? (*W*′ would be 13 units to the left of the *y*-axis.)
- A reflection like this reflects the whole plane over the line of symmetry and not just the key points we choose to track. So, where is the image of the point in the center of the flag? The point $(x, 10)$? The point $(-10, y)$? The *x*-axis? The *y*-axis? (Center: $(4, 5) \rightarrow (-4, 5)$; $(x, 10) \rightarrow (-x, 10)$; *x*-axis → −*x*-axis (though specific points on the axis have "moved"); *y*-axis → *y*-axis, because all points on the *y*-axis are identical to their images in this reflection.)
- Describe what happens to the coordinates of a point when it is reflected over the *y*-axis. (The *y*-coordinate stays the same, and the *x*-coordinate is the opposite of the original point.)
- Under this reflection, is every point in a different location from its image? (The only points that do not "move" under this reflection are points for which the *x*-coordinates are 0, that is, points on the *y*-axis.)

Question C asks students to use the reflection line $y = x$.

- How can you find the image of *B* with coordinates (2, 4) in the line $y = x$? (Most students will draw the line and "measure" the distance from *B* to the line and then locate *B*′, probably using grid marks as units of measure. Students may need to be reminded that this distance should be a perpendicular distance.)
- Do you see a pattern in the relationship between the original point and its image? (The *x*- and *y*-coordinates have traded places.)
- Which points do not "move"? Why is this? (*A* and *D*. They are on the line $y = x$.)
- Remember that a reflection really "moves" all the points in the plane, not just the key points we choose to track. What would be the reflection of (5, 0) in the line $y = x$? (0, 6)? (−1, 0)? The *x*-axis? The *y*-axis? ($(5, 0) \rightarrow (0, 5)$; $(0, 6) \rightarrow (6, 0)$; $(-1, 0) \rightarrow (0, -1)$; *x*-axis → *y*-axis; *y*-axis → *x*-axis.))

Going Further

Draw any horizontal or vertical line on the grid. Reflect *ABCDE* over this line. Write the coordinate rule $(x, y) \rightarrow (■, ■)$ for the reflection in your chosen line.

Planning for the Summary

What evidence will you use in the summary to clarify and deepen understanding of the Focus Question?

What will you do if you do not have evidence?

Summarize

Orchestrating the Discussion

If time becomes an issue, you might begin the Summarize after all students have completed work on only Questions A and B.

You will know if any students are having trouble finding the images of the flag under various reflections. If some students did not get to work on Question C, then you can bring them into the discussion by using **Teaching Aid 3.1: Reflection in the *y*- and *x*-axis.** This shows the graphs for the answers for Questions A and B.

Suggested Questions

- Do the flag images from Questions A and B with the original figure produce a design with reflectional symmetry? (No. We would have to add another flag in the 3rd quadrant.)
- Does this show a design with rotational symmetry? (No. The flags are not oriented correctly for rotational symmetry.)
- Give the coordinates for a point and its image under a reflection in the *y*-axis. (Record a student suggestion.)
- Name another point, not on the flag, and its image under this reflection. (Record the point and image as suggested by a student.)
- What coordinate rule lets you name a point and its reflection in the *y*-axis? ($(x, y) \rightarrow (-x, y)$)
- Does this rule work for any point, say $(-3, 5)$? (Yes. $(-3, -5) \rightarrow (3, 5)$.)

Repeat with reflection in the *x*-axis.

You might choose a student or group to demonstrate how reflection in the line $y = x$ works. Ask the same questions:

- Show us a point and its reflection in the line $y = x$. What are the coordinates for the point and the image? (Record a student suggestion.)
- Show us another point, not on the flag, and its reflection in $y = x$. What coordinate rule describes the reflection of a point (x, y) in the line $y = x$? ($(x, y) \rightarrow (y, x)$.)

Reflecting on Student Learning

Use the following questions to assess student understanding at the end of the lesson.

- What evidence do I have that students understand the Focus Question?
  - Where did my students get stuck?
  - What strategies did they use?
  - What breakthroughs did my students have today?
- How will I use this to plan for tomorrow? For the next time I teach this lesson?
- Where will I have the opportunity to reinforce these ideas as I continue through this Unit? The next Unit?

ACE Assignment Guide

- **Applications**: 1–3, 8
- **Connections:** 16
- **Extensions:** 26
- **Labsheet 3ACE:** Exercises 1–3 (accessibility)
- **Labsheet 3ACE:** Exercise 8 (accessibility)
- **Labsheet 3ACE:** Exercise 16 (accessibility)
- **Labsheet 3ACE:** Exercise 26

You can give the accessibility labsheets to students to help them organize their answers. This will allow them to remain focused on the mathematics of the Exercises and save time.

PROBLEM

3.2 Sliding on a Grid

Coordinate Rules for Translations

Problem Overview

Focus Question What kind of coordinate rule $(x, y) \rightarrow (\blacksquare, \blacksquare)$ tells how to "move" any point to its image under a translation?

Problem Description

This Problem parallels Problem 3.1; however, it focuses on the coordinate definition and operation of a translation. The goal is to develop student understanding of the general principle that any translation takes all points (x, y) to points $(x + a, y + b)$ for some fixed parameters a and b.

Problem Implementation

Group students in pairs.

Materials

- **Labsheet 3.2:** Translation
- **Labsheet 3ACE:** Exercise 9
- **Labsheet 3ACE:** Exercise 20
- **Labsheet 3ACE:** Exercises 4 and 5 (accessibility)
- **Labsheet 3ACE:** Exercise 17 (accessibility)
- **Labsheet 3ACE:** Exercise 18 (accessibility)
- **Quarter-Inch Grid Paper**

graph paper (optional)

Using Technology

If the students have access to a computer, they may find it helpful to use **Transformations** to answer the Questions of this Problem. This activity may also help to reduce the amount of class time reserved for drawing designs. **Note:** The default setting of this activity includes a grid and axes.

Vocabulary

There are no new glossary terms introduced in this Problem.

Mathematics Background

- Reasoning From Symmetry and Congruence
- Coordinate Rules for Symmetry Transformations
- Combining Transformations

At a Glance and Lesson Plan

- At a Glance: Problem 3.2 Butterflies, Pinwheels, and Wallpaper
- Lesson Plan: Problem 3.2 Butterflies, Pinwheels, and Wallpaper

Launch

Connecting to Prior Knowledge

You can probably launch this Problem by asking what students recall about the Mug Wumps in Problem 2.1 from *Stretching and Shrinking*.

Suggested Questions

- Why did we compare the results of the Wump drawing with different coordinate rules? (We were trying to figure out which coordinate rules made similar figures and which distorted the figure and made imposters.)
- What did you find out? (Students might recall that they found out that adding to or subtracting from the coordinates did not change the figure. Multiplying x and y by the same factor made similar figures. If they do not recall this, they will rediscover the stretching and shrinking effect of multiplying both coordinates in Problem 4.1.)

Presenting the Challenge

Tell students that they are going to find coordinate rules for translations. Now that your students know how translations work, i.e., that a translation preserves the shape of a figure and changes its position, they can explore how these characteristics appear in coordinate models.

You can give **Labsheet 3.2: Translation** to students to help them organize their answers. This can allow them to remain focused on the mathematics of the Exercises and save time.

Explore

Providing for Individual Needs

The key points on the different images of Mugs are as follows:

Point	*A*	*B*	*C*	*D*	*E*	*F*
Coordinates of Mug 1	(–5, –7)	(–1, –7)	(–2, –4)	(–2, –3)	(–4, –3)	(–4, –4)
Coordinates of Mug 2	(3, –5)	(7, –5)	(6, –2)	(6, –1)	(4, –1)	(4, –2)
Coordinates of Mug 3	(1, 3)	(5, 3)	(4, 6)	(4, 7)	(2, 7)	(2, 6)
Coordinates of Mug 4	(–8, 1)	(–4, 1)	(–5, 4)	(–5, 5)	(–7, 5)	(–7, 4)

Distribute **Labsheet 3.2: Translation Rules** to students as they collect and organize the data from the four Mugs. Students might need some help figuring out how to inspect this data to find the requested patterns for each translation. If they seem lost in the data, you might ask the following:

Suggested Questions

- Focus on the motion of points on Mug 1 to corresponding points on Mug 2. How are the corresponding *x*-coordinates related for each point? (The *x*-values for Mug 2 are eight more than the *x*-values for Mug 1.)
- How are the corresponding *y*-coordinates related for each point? (The *y*-values for Mug 2 are two more than the *y*-values for Mug 1.)
- How can you use these patterns to write a coordinate rule $(x, y) \rightarrow (■, ■)$? ($(x, y) \rightarrow (x + 8, y + 2)$)

For Question D, help students relate these examples of translations to the general characteristics of a translation.

- How can you show that *AF* is parallel to *A′ F′*? (Slope of *AF* is $\frac{-4-(-7)}{-4-(-5)} = \frac{3}{1} = 3$. Slope of *A′ F′* is also $\frac{3}{1} = 3$, for any of Mug 2, 3, or 4.)
- How does the translation rule that produced *A′ F′* guarantee it will be parallel to *AF*? (The rule for Mug 2 was $(x, y) \rightarrow (x + 8, y + 2)$, or in terms of "moving," the rule is "right 8, up 2." To find the slope of a line between two points, you find the difference of the *y*-values and the difference of the *x*-values. Then you make a ratio of the two differences. If you add 2 to each *y*-coordinate to get the image, then the difference of *y*-values is the same as before. If you add 8 to each *x*-coordinate, then the difference of *x*-values is the same as before.)
- What else is always true about translations? Can we show how the coordinate rules for translations relate to this? (We said that the distance and slope of the movement would be the same for each point. The coordinate rule for Mug 2, for example, is $(x, y) \rightarrow (x + 8, y + 2)$. The distance of the translation is the length of the hypotenuse of a triangle with leg lengths of 2 and 8 units. The slope of the translation is $\frac{2}{8} = \frac{1}{4}$.)

Planning for the Summary

What evidence will you use in the summary to clarify and deepen understanding of the Focus Question?

What will you do if you do not have evidence?

Summarize

Orchestrating the Discussion

You will probably want to check the rules students come up with in Questions A, B, and C and then pose the general Questions D and E.

Suggested Questions

Ask about Question E first:

- If a translation of a figure on a coordinate grid moves the figure *a* units horizontally and *b* units vertically, what rule will show how the coordinates of each point on the figure will change? ($(x, y) \rightarrow (x + a, y + b)$ since a and *b* will be either positive or negative depending on the direction of the "move.")

If you have had a conversation with students about Question D during the Explore, then you can call on them to explain how a particular coordinate rule, for Mug 2 for example, relates to the ideas about translations. Under translations, segments "move" to parallel segments, and the distance and direction of the translation is the same for every point. Help students extend this to the general case. Students in an algebra class should be able to generalize from the slopes and distances in examples.

- If the general rule for a translation is $(x, y) \rightarrow (x + a, y + b)$, how does this rule guarantee that for any two points (x, y) and (w, z), the distance of the translation is the same? The direction of the translation is the same? (Each point "moves" right or left a distance *a* and up or down a distance *b*. The slant distance is the length of the hypotenuse: $\sqrt{a^2 + b^2}$. And the slope of the translation is $\frac{b}{a}$.)
- How does this rule guarantee that sides "move" to parallel sides? (The side joining (x, y) and (w, z) has slope $\frac{y - z}{x - w}$. After a translation, the images are $(x + a, y + b)$ and $(w + a, z + b)$. The slope between the image points is $\frac{(y + b) - (z + b)}{(x + a) - (w + a)}$, which is again, $\frac{y - z}{x - w}$.)

Reflecting on Student Learning

Use the following questions to assess student understanding at the end of the lesson.

- What evidence do I have that students understand the Focus Question?
  - Where did my students get stuck?
  - What strategies did they use?
  - What breakthroughs did my students have today?
- How will I use this to plan for tomorrow? For the next time I teach this lesson?
- Where will I have the opportunity to reinforce these ideas as I continue through this Unit? The next Unit?

ACE Assignment Guide

- **Applications:** 4, 5, 9
- **Connections:** 17–20
- **Labsheet 3ACE:** Exercises 4 and 5 (accessibility)
- **Labsheet 3ACE:** Exercise 9
- **Labsheet 3ACE:** Exercise 17 (accessibility)
- **Labsheet 3ACE:** Exercises 18 and 19 (accessibility)
- **Labsheet 3ACE:** Exercise 20

You can give the accessibility labsheets to students to help them organize their answers. This will allow them to remain focused on the mathematics of the Exercises and save time.

PROBLEM 3.3

Spinning on a Grid

Coordinate Rules for Rotations

Problem Overview

Focus Question What are the coordinate rules that describe "motion" of points on a grid under turns of 90° and 180°?

Problem Description

Expressing the coordinate rules of rotations generally requires trigonometric functions; however, the special cases of 90° and 180° rotations can be expressed without advanced mathematics. The goal of this Problem is to have students discover the coordinate rules for those two special rotations.

Problem Implementation

Group students in pairs.

Materials

- **Labsheet 3.3:** Rotations of 90° and 180°
- **Labsheet 3ACE:** Exercise 27
- **Labsheet 3ACE:** Exercises 6 and 7 (accessibility)
- **Labsheet 3.3:** Rotations of 90° and 180°
- **Quarter-Inch Grid Paper**
- **Teaching Aid 3.3:** Rotations of 90° and 180°

graph paper

rulers

protractors or angle rulers

tracing paper (optional)

Using Technology

If the students have access to a computer, they may find it helpful to use **Transformations** to answer the Questions of this Problem. This activity may also help to reduce the amount of class time reserved for drawing designs. **Note:** The default setting of this activity includes a grid and axes.

The National Council of Teachers of Mathematics operates a Web site called Calculation Nation® that offers visitors the opportunity to play mathematical games against other players online or against the computer. Have students play the game *Flip-n-Slide*, where they can practice thinking with flips, turns, and slides on a coordinate grid. Have them come up with some strategies for scoring points in this game.

Vocabulary

There are no new glossary terms introduced in this Problem.

Mathematics Background

- Reasoning From Symmetry and Congruence
- Coordinate Rules for Symmetry Transformations
- Combining Transformations

At a Glance and Lesson Plan

- At a Glance: Problem 3.3 Butterflies, Pinwheels, and Wallpaper
- Lesson Plan: Problem 3.3 Butterflies, Pinwheels, and Wallpaper

Launch

Connecting to Prior Knowledge

You might launch this Problem by showing the image in the grid.

Suggested Questions

- In which quadrant is the image after a quarter-turn counterclockwise? (second quadrant)
- How can you be sure you have made a rotation angle, say BAB', that is 90°, and that $BA = B'A$? (Students may say that they should use an angle ruler and a ruler. But some will offer that you can use the gridlines as a guide. If this happens, you can follow up by asking how that can be, because BA does not lie along a gridline. Students may mention slopes of perpendicular lines. These are all helpful and related ideas. You do not need to push too far on this. You can return to this in the Explore and the Summarize.)
- This reminds me of trying to draw a tilted square in *Looking for Pythagoras*. How did we draw perpendicular lines then? (Students will recall how they used the grid to find the slope of one side of the square and, from that, determined the slope of an adjacent side.)

- In which quadrant is the image after a half-turn counterclockwise? (third quadrant)
- How can you be sure you have made a rotation angle, say BAB', that is 180°?
- Students will likely say that they know that the result should be 180° because BAB' is a straight line.

Presenting the Challenge

Pose the Problem of finding coordinate rules that could accomplish these "motions" in a computer graphics program.

Explore

Providing for Individual Needs

Since this is the third in a sequence of similar problems, students will know what the goals are. In this Problem, in which they study rotations, the coordinates of image points for quarter-turns will not be immediately obvious. **Labsheet 3.3: Rotations of 90° and 180°** will help students organize their work.

As you circulate, check to see that students are coming up with the right locations. Ask about the rotation images they sketch.

Suggested Questions

- In Question A, what is the image of B? $(-4, 2)$
- How did you find B'? (If students are using rulers and protractors, you can push them to think about the slope of BA and $B'A'$.)
- From the center A, we count 2 to the right and 4 up to locate B. Does that help us think about the location of B'? (4 to the left and 2 up. This is probably a technique students used in *Looking for Pythagoras*.)
- The slope of AB is $\frac{4}{2} = 2$. What is the slope of AB'? ($\frac{-2}{4} = \frac{-1}{2}$)

If students' images are incorrect, you can suggest that they check them using rulers and protractors, or you can continue to ask about slopes.

- It looks like C' (for example) is not in the right place. Remember that spinning C around A means there is a radius AC that spins around and becomes AC'. AC and AC' should be the same length and form a 90° angle. Are they the same length? Do they form a 90° angle? (Students can check using protractors, or you can ask them about the slope of AC and repeat the same discussion as for finding B'.)

In Question *B*, a turn of 180° should be simpler to accomplish, but students might not be consistent. For example, they might make *BAB′* a straight angle but not do the same for *CAC′*, because *CA* is not joined.

- The angle of rotation is 180°. Is *BAB′* 180°? Is *CAC′* 180°? How about *DAD′*? (Yes; they are all 180° since they are all straight angles.)

Planning for the Summary

What evidence will you use in the summary to clarify and deepen understanding of the Focus Question?

What will you do if you do not have evidence?

Summarize

Orchestrating the Discussion

The Summarize for this Problem can be initiated by two questions:

Suggested Questions

- **What coordinate rules show how points "move" under quarter- and half-turns?**
- **How do you know that the rules you arrived at are correct?**

For the second question, students might offer a variety of explanations. Some will rely on measuring. This is acceptable, because it shows an understanding of *how* to rotate points to make images. More helpful for the current goal are the slopes of the radii implied by the rotation around *A*. If you observed students using slopes, have them share their work. **Teaching Aid 3.3: Rotations of 90° and 180°** is provided to facilitate the discussion.

- How do slopes help you locate the image of *B*? Of *D*? (Their answers might involve a pattern of counting grid squares, similar to the technique for tilted squares in *Looking for Pythagoras*. Or, students might say that perpendicular lines have slopes that are negative reciprocals of each other.)
- Do we have a design with rotational symmetry after doing these two rotations? (No. We need the original and three images; we only have two.)

Help your students connect the rules they find from the patterns in the tables to the general characteristics of rotations.

- Remember that a rotation does not just "move" the points we are interested in. A rotation "moves" the whole plane around the center point and carries the flag along in it. Choose a point not on the flag, say (5, 0). What would be the image after a rotation of 90° counterclockwise? What would be the image of (10, 0)? (0, 5)? (0, 10)? (5, 5)? ((5, 0) → (0, 5); (10, 0) → (0, 10); the *x*-axis → *y*-axis; (0, 5) → (−5, 0); (0, 10) → (−10, 0); the *y*-axis → *x*-axis; (5, 6) → (−6, 5))

- We all found that the rule for a 90-degree rotation counterclockwise around A is $(x, y) \rightarrow (-y, x)$. How does this relate to the observations you made that a rotation of a point X around a center A makes an image X' that is the same distance from A and the angle XAX' is the angle of rotation? (Since the center is (0, 0), the distance $XA = \sqrt{(x^2 + y^2)}$. The distance $X'A$ is the same. The slope of $XA = \frac{y}{x}$. The slope of $X'A = \frac{-x}{y}$. These slopes are opposites and reciprocals.)
- Suppose the center is not (0, 0). Would the same rule work? (No.)
- We all found that the rule for a 180-degree rotation around A is $(x, y) \rightarrow (-x, -y)$. How does this relate to the observations you made about how rotations work? (If $X = (x, y)$, then distance $XA = \sqrt{(x^2 + y^2)}$ and slope $XA = \frac{y}{x}$. If $X' = (-x, -y)$, then distance $AX' = \sqrt{(x^2 + y^2)}$ and slope $AX' = \frac{y}{x}$. So, X is the same distance from A as X', and X, A, and X' are collinear, i.e., they make a straight angle.)

Reflecting on Student Learning

Use the following questions to assess student understanding at the end of the lesson.

- What evidence do I have that students understand the Focus Question?
  - Where did my students get stuck?
  - What strategies did they use?
  - What breakthroughs did my students have today?
- How will I use this to plan for tomorrow? For the next time I teach this lesson?
- Where will I have the opportunity to reinforce these ideas as I continue through this Unit? The next Unit?

ACE Assignment Guide

- **Applications:** 6, 7
- **Connections:** 21, 22
- **Extensions:** 27
- **Labsheet 3ACE:** Exercises 6 and 7 (accessibility)
- **Labsheet 3ACE:** Exercise 27

You can give the accessibility labsheet to students to help them organize their answers. This will allow them to remain focused on the mathematics of the Exercises and save time.

PROBLEM

3.4

A Special Property of Translations and Half-Turns

Problem Overview

Focus Question How are lines and their images under translations and half-turns related to each other?

Problem Description

The fact that both translations and half-turns, or 180° rotations, always "move" lines onto parallel lines is a very useful property. This result does not occur for other rotations and occurs only for line reflections when lines are parallel to the line of reflection. The goal of this Problem is to highlight the special effect of translations and half-turns by having students study a diagram that shows images of a pentagon under those two transformations.

Problem Implementation

Group students in pairs.

Materials

- **Labsheet 3.4:** Special Property of Translations and 180° Rotations (one per pair)
- **Labsheet 3ACE:** Exercise 28
- **Quarter-Inch Grid Paper**
- **Teaching Aid 3.4:** Special Property of Translations and 180° Rotations

graph paper

Using Technology

If the students have access to a computer, they may find it helpful to use **Transformations** to answer the Questions of this Problem. This activity may also help to reduce the amount of class time reserved for drawing designs. **Note:** The default setting of this activity includes a grid and axes.

Vocabulary

There are no new glossary terms introduced in this Problem.

Mathematics Background

- Reasoning From Symmetry and Congruence
- Coordinate Rules for Symmetry Transformations
- Combining Transformations

At a Glance and Lesson Plan

- At a Glance: Problem 3.4 Butterflies, Pinwheels, and Wallpaper
- Lesson Plan: Problem 3.4 Butterflies, Pinwheels, and Wallpaper

Launch

Launch Video

This animation shows forming a design from translations and 180° rotations only. The parallel line segments, a characteristic of these transformations, are highlighted. Visit Teacher Place at mathdashboard.com/cmp3 to see the complete video.

You can show students this animation before the Launch. Students can watch it instead of reading the introduction to the Problem in the Student Edition.

Connecting to Prior Knowledge

You might choose to launch the Problem by asking students to study the diagram.

Suggested Questions

- Do the pentagons all look congruent? How could you check this? How would you name them to show this correspondence? (Measure sides and angles of *ABCDE*, *FGHIJ*, and *KLMNO*.)
- What sequence of transformations will "move" *ABCDE* onto *FGHIJ*? Could you write a coordinate rule for this? (A translation of 7 to the left and 1 down; as a coordinate rule, $(x, y) \rightarrow (x - 7, y - 1)$.)
- What sequence of transformations will "move" *FGHIJ* onto *KLMNO*? Is there another way to do this? (A 180° rotation about $(-3.5, -0.5)$ will do it.)
- What sequence of transformations will move *ABCDE* onto *KLMNO*? Is there another way to do this? (A half-turn around (0, 0), or a slide to *FGHIJ* and then a rotation.)

Presenting the Challenge

We are convinced that these pentagons are congruent.

Suggested Questions

- What does it mean for the pentagons to be congruent? (Corresponding sides and angles are congruent or have the same measure.)

Ask the question in the text and let students find the answer from the Problem.

- What special relationships are there among the sides of the pentagons? (Students can conjecture about parallel sides, but you should make no comment.)
- How can you use coordinates to prove your conjectures?

Explore

Providing for Individual Needs

In Question A, students may continue to want to check lengths with rulers and slopes with protractors. Push them to consider how the coordinates of points might help to justify statements, rather than using the measurements.

Suggested Questions

- What are the coordinates of points A and B? How can you use these to find length AB? Slope of AB? ((-1, 5) and (1, 1). Distance AB can be found by applying the Pythagorean Theorem to a right triangle with AB as the hypotenuse: $\sqrt{(2^2 + 4^2)} = \sqrt{20}$. Slope of $AB = \frac{-4}{2} = -2$.)
- How can you use the coordinates of F and G to show that FG is parallel to AB and the same length? (Students can repeat the calculations, or they might point out that the calculations refer to a right triangle with the same side lengths in both cases.)

In Question B, students may focus on the equal lengths of the segments, since that is what is expected after any rigid transformation, including rotation. When they last examined the effects of a rotation, parallelism was not an issue.

- I see you have used the coordinates of the endpoints to confirm $AB = KL$. What else is true about these sides? (They are parallel.)
- How can you prove they are parallel? (Show that their slopes are equal.)

This is the time to push some students to consider why a half-rotation moves a segment to a parallel segment, or you may delay this general discussion until the Summarize.

- We found that the coordinate rule for a half-turn about the origin is $(x, y) \rightarrow (-x, -y)$. Suppose you have a segment joining two general points (x, y) and (w, z). What are the images of these two points under a half-turn around (0, 0)? What is the slope of the segment joining these two points? What is the slope of the image of the segment? (The slope of the segment joining (x, y) and (w, z) is $\frac{y - z}{x - w}$. The slope of the segment joining the image points $(-x, -y)$ and $(-w, -z)$ is $\frac{-y - (-z)}{-x - (-w)} = \frac{-1}{-1} \cdot \frac{y - z}{x - w} = \frac{y - z}{x - w}$.)

Since Question C is really the summary of the Problem discoveries, you can start a summary discussion when most students have had a chance to at least think about the questions given there.

Question D can be viewed as an "extra for experts." **Labsheet 3.4: Special Property of Translations and 180° Rotations** is available for this. All students do not need to complete it prior to beginning the Summarize.

Planning for the Summary

What evidence will you use in the summary to clarify and deepen understanding of the Focus Question?

What will you do if you do not have evidence?

Summarize

Orchestrating the Discussion

The Summarize can focus on the Question C in the Problem. You might say that everyone has agreed that both translations and half-turns "move" segments to parallel and congruent segments, or that they "move" lines to parallel lines.

Suggested Questions

- What evidence do you have that your statements are true in these examples? (Students can demonstrate that lengths and slopes are equal using the coordinates of endpoints.)
- Does showing that this statement is true for the sides of these pentagons constitute a proof that this will be true for all segments (or lines)? (Students should be able to think about their work with examples and counterexamples and realize that they need to work with something more general.)

- Suppose you have a segment joining two general points (x, y) and (w, z). What are the images of these two points under a half-turn around (0, 0)? What is the slope of the segment joining these two points? What is the slope of the image of the segment? ($(x, y) \rightarrow (-x, -y)$ and $(w, z) \rightarrow (-w, -z)$. The slope of the segment joining (x, y) and (w, z) is $\frac{y-z}{x-w}$. The slope of the segment joining the image points $(-x, -y)$ and $(-w, -z)$ is $\frac{-y-(-z)}{-x-(-w)} = \frac{-1}{-1} \cdot \frac{y-z}{x-w} = \frac{y-z}{x-w}$.)

For Question D, you might use the provided **Labsheet 3.4: Special Property of Translations and 180° Rotations** or **Teaching Aid 3.4: Special Property of Translations and 180° Rotations** and ask:

- I can see how to translate line *n* onto line *m*. But how would I achieve this by rotating line *n*? What would be the center of rotation? (If we want to rotate segment *AB* onto segment *A'B'*, then the center shown on **Labsheet 3.4: Special Property of Translations** and 180° Rotations will work.)
- Suppose I wanted to move segment *AB* onto segment *A''B''*. How would I do that? (Join *AA''* and *BB''* to find the center of rotation.)
- So I can "move" segment *AB* anywhere onto line *m* using a half-turn. What do all the centers have in common? (They are on the line parallel to *m* and *n* and equidistant from *m* and *n*.)

Reflecting on Student Learning

Use the following questions to assess student understanding at the end of the lesson.

- What evidence do I have that students understand the Focus Question?
  - Where did my students get stuck?
  - What strategies did they use?
  - What breakthroughs did my students have today?
- How will I use this to plan for tomorrow? For the next time I teach this lesson?
- Where will I have the opportunity to reinforce these ideas as I continue through this Unit? The next Unit?

ACE Assignment Guide

- **Applications:** 10
- **Connections:** 23
- **Extensions:** 28 –30
- **Labsheet 3ACE:** Exercises 28

PROBLEM
3.5

Parallel Lines, Transversals, and Angle Sums

Problem Overview

Focus Question When two parallel lines are cut by a transversal, what can be said about the angles formed? What is always true about the angle measures in a triangle? How do you know that your answers are correct?

Problem Description

The goal of this Problem is to review and extend your students' understanding of two very useful geometric properties—that parallel lines cut by a transversal form various pairs of congruent angles, and that the angle sum of any triangle is 180°. These results were developed in Grade 7 in *Shapes and Designs*. Since the Common Core State Standards for Mathematics list these properties in the Grade 8 objectives, we include them here again, with a proof based on transformations.

Problem Implementation

Group students in pairs.

Materials

- **Labsheet 3.5:** 180° Rotation Around Midpoints (one per pair)

tracing paper

rulers

angle rulers

protractors (optional)

- **Check Up 2**

Using Technology

If the students have access to a computer, they may find it helpful to use **Transformations** to answer the Questions of this Problem. This activity may also help to reduce the amount of class time reserved for drawing designs. **Note:** The default setting of this activity includes a grid and axes but there is the option to remove them.

Vocabulary

There are no new glossary terms introduced in this Problem.

Mathematics Background

- Reasoning From Symmetry and Congruence
- Coordinate Rules for Symmetry Transformations

At a Glance and Lesson Plan

- At a Glance: Problem 3.5 Butterflies, Pinwheels, and Wallpaper
- Lesson Plan: Problem 3.5 Butterflies, Pinwheels, and Wallpaper

Launch

Connecting to Prior Knowledge

The two results are related but somewhat different in character. You might want to treat this as a two-day Problem.

You might choose to launch the two Problems by presenting only the two drawings in the introduction and asking students what they know about the measures of angles in each figure. When they have reviewed their prior knowledge as a whole class, you might ask how they know that these results are true.

Suggested Questions

- How did you show that when a transversal cuts two parallel lines, it makes 2 groups of 4 congruent angles? What Unit were you studying? (Students may well not recall the development of these ideas, just the results. But you can remind them that they started with some ideas about a parallelogram, one of the shapes they were studying, and thought of this as two pairs of parallel lines cutting each other. From that, they reasoned about the angles made when only one transversal cuts two parallel lines.)
- How did you show that the angle sum of a triangle is 180°? (Again, students may not recall the process, only the result. One way they showed this was to rip the corners off paper triangles and reassemble the corners adjacent to each other to show that they always form a straight angle.)

- What are the interior angles of a triangle? The exterior angles? (Students may need to be reminded that by exterior angle, we mean the angle formed by extending a side. Each polygon has one exterior angle at each of its vertices as shown below.)

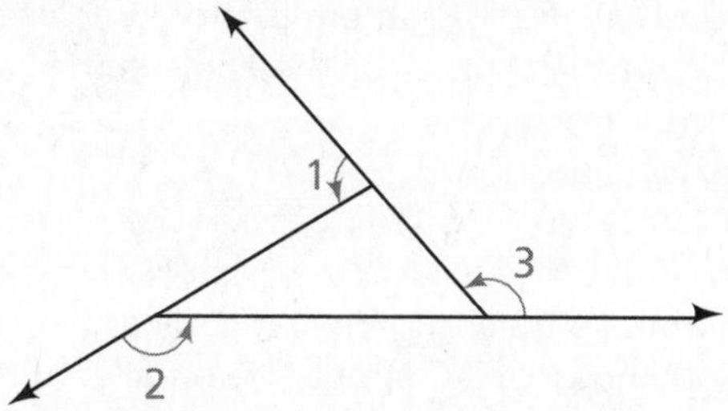

Presenting the Challenge

Tell students that they can now prove these results using their knowledge about translations and half-turn rotations. Their task is to provide justifications for their arguments.

Explore

Providing for Individual Needs

Since proofs, like those outlined in this Problem, are not familiar material to students at this level, you might find that students need help figuring out just what they are supposed to do. You might give them some time to consider Question A and then have an intermediate whole-class discussion to talk through the proof. Then, they should be able to move ahead to Question B, which asks them to use the proof from Question A as a template to prove similar results about angles formed by transversals.

Suggested Questions

For Question A, if necessary:

- Why are angles 1 and 3 congruent? (Because vertical angles are congruent, i.e., they are supplementary to the same angle. Angles 5 and 7 are congruent for the same reason.)
- Are you sure that if you translate angle 5, it will "move" exactly onto angle 1? (You might have to push students to use their knowledge of the characteristics of a translation. If we slide angle 5 along the transversal until the vertex of angle 5 coincides with the vertex of angle 1, then we have also "moved" the side that coincides with line *n*, and we know that this side has to end up parallel to the original. This means that it "moves" onto line *m*.)

- Explain why this shows that angles 1, 3, 5, and 7 are all congruent. Would it help if you started with an example? (If we say that angle 1 is 58°, then so is angle 5 by translation. So is angle 3, because it is vertically opposite angle 1, and so is angle 7, because it is vertically opposite angle 5.)

Questions C and D ask students to use results from Problem 3.4 to complete the outline of a transformation proof for the major results that the angle sum in any triangle is 180°, and the angle sum of the exterior angles is 360°. Use **Labsheet 3.5: 180° Rotation Around Midpoints** for Question C.

- How are you rotating the triangle about M_1? What do we know about the result of a half-turn? (Students might use tracing paper to copy and rotate the triangle. We know the resulting image of *AC* should be parallel to *AC*, etc.)
- Which segments are parallel to *AC*? (The images of *AC* under these rotations will be *BC′* and *BA′*.)

If students do not see that angles 1, 2, and 3 are now arranged around point *B*, making a straight line, ask them to mark all the angles they know are equal because of the rotations.

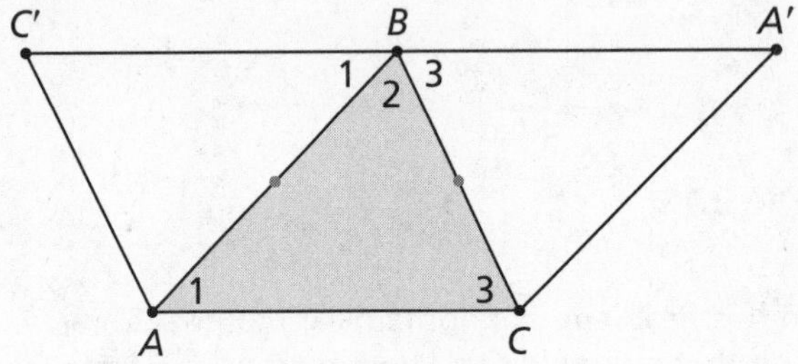

For Question D:

- What transformations created Erin's drawing? (Several sequences are possible. Rotating the original triangle around the midpoints of the two sides can make Erin's drawing. This is helpful because it gives us parallel sides and a straight angle.)
- I see Erin has marked the exterior angles on this triangle. They each seem to be made of two other angles. How does that help us? (The sum of the two angles is equal to the difference between 180° and the interior angle at that vertex.)

Then Question E guides students through the traditional proof of that result.

Planning for the Summary

What evidence will you use in the summary to clarify and deepen understanding of the Focus Question?

What will you do if you do not have evidence?

Summarize

Orchestrating the Discussion

If you summarize Question A before assigning Question B and do a separate summary for Questions C, D, and E, then the following questions are organized for those two summaries.

Suggested Questions

For Question A, display the drawing and ask students how they know that the given pairs of angles are congruent.

- Who can explain why all four angles are equal? (Push for reasons for every statement of equality.)
- Is this result true for only this example or is it true for all cases where a transversal cuts two parallel lines? (It is true for all cases. There is nothing in the argument that is specific to angle sizes.)
- What other transformation, if any, would match an angle at one vertex with an angle at the other vertex? Explain. (A half-turn about a point on the transversal halfway between the vertices will "move" angle 5 to angle 3.)

For Question C, D, and E you might display the work of three groups (more if you see any interesting variations) and ask them to explain their reasoning. Be sure to focus on why they know they have only one line through B parallel to AC in Question C.

- How can you be sure that the result of these rotations is a straight line through B? (The two segments are each parallel to AC, because they are the images of AC under a half-turn, and they share endpoint B, so they are in the same straight line.)
- Does this argument work for all triangles? (It will always be possible to choose midpoints of sides and perform half-turns, creating a line parallel to the base. There was nothing specific about the triangle chosen.)

Reflecting on Student Learning

Use the following questions to assess student understanding at the end of the lesson.

- What evidence do I have that students understand the Focus Question?
  - Where did my students get stuck?
  - What strategies did they use?
  - What breakthroughs did my students have today?
- How will I use this to plan for tomorrow? For the next time I teach this lesson?
- Where will I have the opportunity to reinforce these ideas as I continue through this Unit? The next Unit?

ACE Assignment Guide

- **Applications:** 11–15
- **Connections:** 24, 25
- **Extensions:** 31

Mathematical Reflections

Possible Answers to Mathematical Reflections

1. The general forms of coordinate rules for flips, turns, and slides are
   a. Reflection in the y-axis: $(x, y) \rightarrow (-x, y)$
   b. Reflection in the x-axis: $(x, y) \rightarrow (x, -y)$
   c. Counterclockwise rotation of 90° about the origin (0, 0) : $(x, y) \rightarrow (-y, x)$
   d. Rotation of 180° about the origin: $(x, y) \rightarrow (-x, -y)$
   e. Translations that "move" points a units horizontally and b units vertically: $(x, y) \rightarrow (x \pm a, y \pm b)$.
2. The special effect of translations and half-turns is that they "move" lines onto parallel lines.
3. We already knew that the eight angles formed when two parallel lines are cut by a transversal fall into two sets that are congruent to each other. The technical names for the pairs that are congruent are alternate interior angles, alternate exterior angles, and corresponding angles on the same side of the transversal. It is easiest to indicate which pairs are congruent with a quick sketch that looks like this:

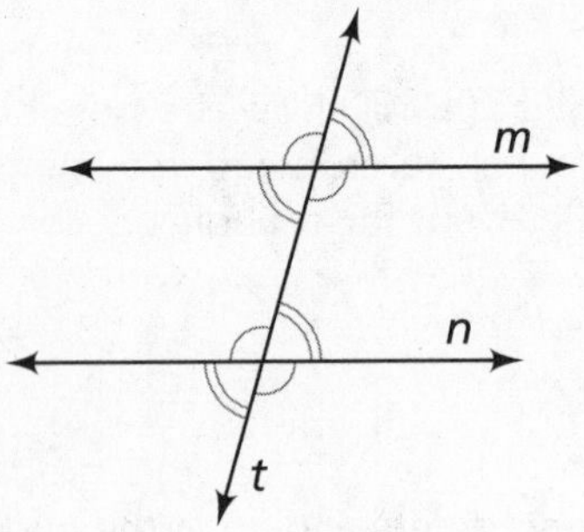

When we learned about this in *Shapes and Designs*, we reasoned from a parallelogram and noticed that any parallelogram had two pairs of congruent angles and that opposite angles are congruent. We also knew that the angle sum of any quadrilateral is 360°, so consecutive angles in a parallelogram must add to 180°. From there, we drew two pairs of parallel lines, which formed a parallelogram, and we could deduce all the congruent angles.

In this Unit, we used transformations. You can think of translating an angle at one vertex on the above figure to the corresponding angle at the other vertex. That gets four pairs of matching angles. Also, we know that vertical angles are congruent, so really there are two groups of four congruent angles. We started from a different place but ended up with the same information.

4. We already knew that the sum of measures of angles in any triangle is equal to a straight angle, or 180°. When we learned this in *Shapes and Designs*, we did it by tearing corners off of a triangle and reassembling the corners to show that the sum is always 180°.

This time, we started with the idea that a half-turn takes a line to a parallel line. So, when we rotated a triangle about the midpoint of a side, we created a line through one vertex that was parallel to the opposite side of the triangle. The images of the angles of the triangle made a straight angle, or 180°. We ended up with the same information, but this time it seems more like a proof because it did not depend on tearing up specific triangles.

Possible Answers to Mathematical Practices Reflections

Students may have demonstrated all of the eight Common Core Standards for Mathematical Practice during this Investigation. During the class discussion, have students provide additional Practices that the Problem cited involved and identify the use of other Mathematical Practices in the Investigation.

One student observation is provided in the Student Edition. Here is another sample student response.

> *We looked for coordinate rules for transformations. When you make a table showing several points and their images, you see a pattern that helps you find a general rule.*
>
> **MP8: Look for and express regularity in repeated reasoning.**

Investigation 3

Transforming Coordinates

The computer programs that manage video displays for television shows and video games all use coordinate graphing systems. The axes and grid lines are hidden from view, but are essential to setting the color of the pixels that you see.

Rules for geometric transformations guide the movement of characters on the screen. In this Investigation, you will develop your understanding of coordinate rules for transformations and skill in using that knowledge to solve geometry problems.

3.1 Flipping on a Grid

Coordinate Rules for Reflections

When you draw a geometric figure on a grid, each point has a pair of coordinates. Most graphics programs have methods for moving figures from one position to another. The programs move key points (like vertices of polygons) first and then automatically fill in line segments to connect the key points. Recall that you followed this process to draw the Wump family in *Stretching and Shrinking*.

Common Core State Standards

8.G.A.2 Understand that a two-dimensional figure is congruent to another if the second can be obtained from the first by a sequence of rotations, reflections, and translations; given two congruent figures, describe a sequence that exhibits the congruence between them.

8.G.A.3 Describe the effect of dilations, translations, rotations, and reflections on two-dimensional figures using coordinates.

8.G.A.5 Use informal arguments to establish facts about the angle sum and exterior angle of triangles, about the angles created when parallel lines are cut by a transversal, and the angle-angle criterion for similarity of triangles.

Also 8.G.A.1, 8.G.A.1b, 8.G.A.1c

Notes

The diagram below shows a flag located in the first quadrant. Notice the labels on key points.

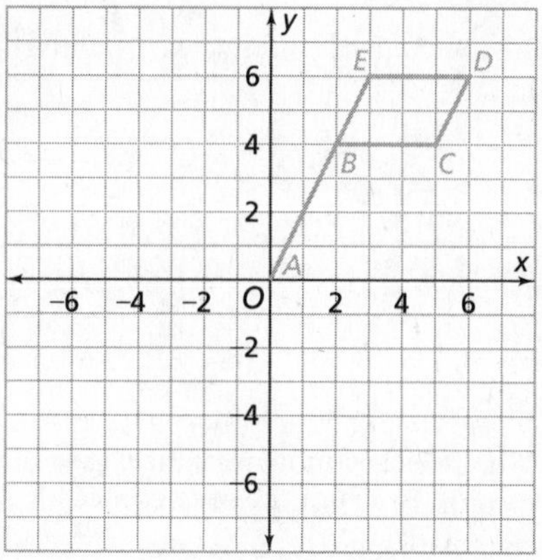

- How can you find the coordinates of the images of those key points under flips, turns, slides, and other sequences of transformations?

In this Problem, you will find rules to relate coordinates of key points on the flag to coordinates of their images after line reflections.

Problem 3.1

A Copy and complete the table showing the coordinates of points *A*–*E* and their images under a reflection in the *y*-axis.

Point	*A*	*B*	*C*	*D*	*E*
Original Coordinates	(0, 0)	(2, 4)	■	■	■
Coordinates After a Reflection	■	■	■	■	■

1. Write a rule relating coordinates of key points and their images after a reflection in the *y*-axis: $(x, y) \rightarrow (■, ■)$.
2. Would your rule give the correct coordinates if the flag started in the second, third, or fourth quadrant? Justify your answer with sketches and samples of coordinates that match.
3. **a.** Do any points remain unchanged under this reflection? Explain.

   b. Do the flag and its image make a symmetric design?

continued on the next page >

STUDENT PAGE

Notes

Problem 3.1 continued

B Copy and complete the table showing the coordinates of points *A*–*E* and their images under a reflection in the *x*-axis.

Point	*A*	*B*	*C*	*D*	*E*
Original Coordinates	(0, 0)	(2, 4)	■	■	■
Coordinates After a Reflection	■	■	■	■	■

1. Write a rule relating coordinates of key points and their images after a reflection in the *x*-axis: $(x, y) \rightarrow$ (■, ■).
2. Would your rule give the correct coordinates if the flag started in the second, third, or fourth quadrant? Justify your answer with sketches and samples of coordinates that match.
3. **a.** Do any points remain unchanged under this reflection? Explain.

   b. Do the flag and its image make a symmetric design?

C Copy and complete the table showing coordinates of points *A*–*E* and their images under a reflection in the line $y = x$.

Point	*A*	*B*	*C*	*D*	*E*
Original Coordinates	(0, 0)	(2, 4)	■	■	■
Coordinates After a Reflection	■	■	■	■	■

1. Write a rule relating coordinates of key points and their images after a reflection in the line $y = x$: $(x, y) \rightarrow$ (■, ■).
2. Would your rule give the correct coordinates if the flag started in the second, third, or fourth quadrant? Justify your answer with sketches and samples of coordinates that match.

ACE Homework starts on page 61.

Notes

3.2 Sliding on a Grid

Coordinate Rules for Translations

The diagram at the right shows four figures that look like Mug Wump with a hat. You can slide or translate Mug 1 to get the other three Mugs.

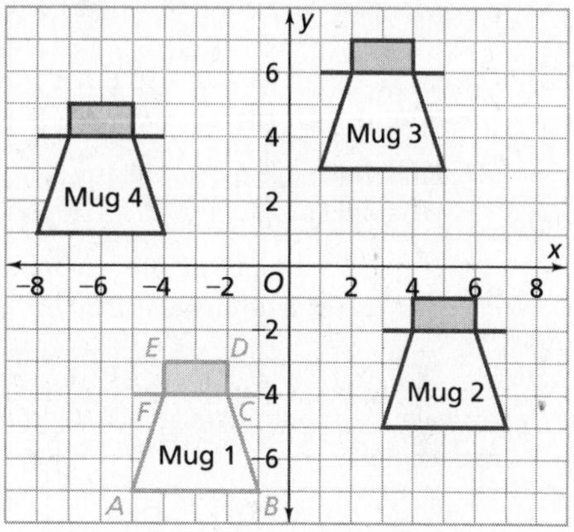

What coordinate rules for translations would "move" Mug 1 to the positions of the other Mugs?

Problem 3.2

Make a table of the coordinates of key points for Mug 1 and his images under the translations. Look for patterns.

Point	A	B	C	D	E	F
Coordinates of Mug 1	(−5, −7)	(−1, −7)	■	■	■	■
Coordinates of Mug 2	(3, −5)	■	■	■	■	■
Coordinates of Mug 3	■	■	■	■	■	■
Coordinates of Mug 4	■	■	■	■	■	■

A Write a rule showing how coordinates of key points on Mug 1 relate to their images after a translation to Mug 2: $(x, y) \rightarrow (■, ■)$.

B Write a rule showing how coordinates of key points on Mug 2 relate to their images after a translation to Mug 3: $(x, y) \rightarrow (■, ■)$.

continued on the next page >

STUDENT PAGE

Notes

Problem 3.2 continued

C Write a rule showing how coordinates of key points on Mug 3 relate to their images after a translation to Mug 4: $(x, y) \rightarrow (\blacksquare, \blacksquare)$.

D In Investigation 1, you learned that a translation of a segment, such as $\overline{AF}$, "moved" the segment to a *parallel* image segment.

1. Find the image of $\overline{AF}$ on Mug 2, Mug 3, or Mug 4. Show that the image is parallel to $\overline{AF}$.
2. How does the coordinate rule for any translation guarantee that a segment and its image will be parallel?

E Suppose a translation moves a figure a units horizontally and b units vertically on a coordinate grid. What rule describes the coordinates of each image point?

ACE Homework starts on page 61.

3.3 Spinning on a Grid
Coordinate Rules for Rotations

Look again at the flag in the first quadrant.

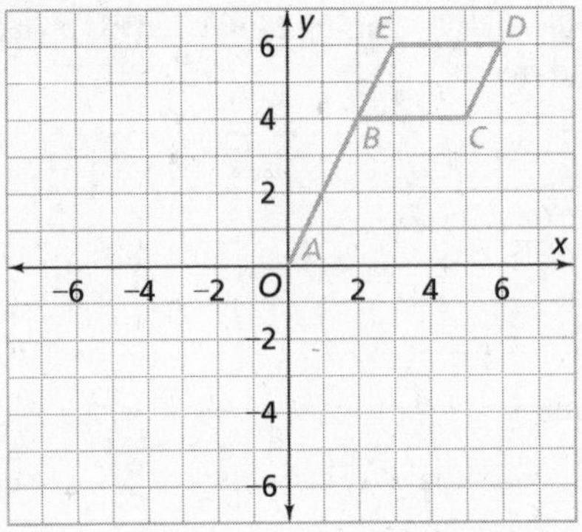

What coordinate rules for rotations would rotate the flag 90° or 180° counterclockwise about point A?

Notes

In this Problem, you will find rules relating coordinates of key points on the flag to coordinates of their images after quarter- and half-turn rotations.

Problem 3.3

A Rotate points A–E 90° counterclockwise about the origin. Copy and complete the table showing the coordinates of points A'–E', which are the images of points A–E.

Point	*A*	*B*	*C*	*D*	*E*
Original Coordinates	(0, 0)	(2, 4)	■	■	■
Coordinates After a 90° Rotation	■	■	■	■	■

1. Write a rule for the pattern relating the coordinates of key points to the coordinates of their images after a rotation of 90°: $(x, y) \rightarrow$ (■, ■).
2. Would your rule give the correct coordinates if the flag started in the second, third, or fourth quadrant? Justify your answer with sketches and examples of coordinates that match.
3. **a.** Do any points remain unchanged under this rotation? Explain.

   b. Do the flag and its image make a symmetric design?

B Rotate points A–E another 90° counterclockwise about the origin so that they rotate a total of 180°. Copy and complete the table showing the coordinates of points A''–E'', which are the images of points A'–E'.

Point	*A*	*B*	*C*	*D*	*E*
Original Coordinates	(0, 0)	(2, 4)	■	■	■
Coordinates After a 180° Rotation	■	■	■	■	■

1. Write a rule for the pattern relating the coordinates of key points to the coordinates of their images after a rotation of 180°: $(x, y) \rightarrow$ (■, ■).
2. Would your rule give the correct coordinates if the flag started in the second, third, or fourth quadrant? Justify your answer with sketches and examples of coordinates that match.

ACE Homework starts on page 61.

STUDENT PAGE

Notes

3.4 A Special Property of Translations and Half-Turns

When studying mathematical or scientific questions, asking yourself "What will happen if . . . ?" is helpful. In geometry, that means asking how properties of a figure will or will not change when you apply a transformation to it.

Your study of flips, turns, and slides showed that those transformations do not change the size or shape of a figure. Line segments "move" to line segments that are the same length. Angles "move" to angles of the same measure. In addition to these basic properties of transformations, translations and half-turn rotations have a special effect on lines.

The diagram below shows the effect of "moving" pentagon *ABCDE* in two ways. The first is a translation to pentagon *FGHIJ*. The second is a half-turn or 180° rotation about the origin to pentagon *KLMNO*.

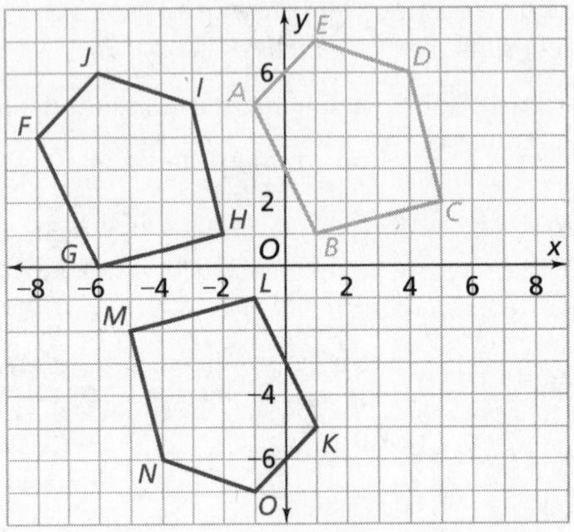

- What is the special relationship among the corresponding sides of the three figures?
- How can you use the coordinates of the vertices to prove your conjecture?

Notes

In the Problem, you will discover and prove the special relationship among corresponding sides of pentagon *ABCDE* and its images after a translation and after a 180° rotation.

Problem 3.4

A Look at $\overline{AB}$ and its image after a translation, $\overline{FG}$.

1. In Investigation 1, you observed that a segment and its image after a translation appear to be congruent and parallel. Use the coordinates of the endpoints and slopes of lines to prove that your observation is correct.
2. Are other pairs of segments in pentagons *ABCDE* and *FGHIJ* related in the same way?

B Look at $\overline{AB}$ and its image after a half-turn, $\overline{KL}$.

1. How do the two segments appear to be related?
2. Use the coordinates of the endpoints to test your conjecture.
3. Are other pairs of segments in pentagons *ABCDE* and *KLMNO* related in the same way?

C Complete the following sentences to describe the pattern you found:

1. A translation "moves" every line *m* to a line *n* so that . . .
2. A half-turn "moves" every line *m* to a line *n* so that . . .

D If lines *m* and *n* are parallel, will it always be possible to find a translation or half-turn that "moves" one line onto the other? If so, what point should you choose for the center of the rotation? Explain.

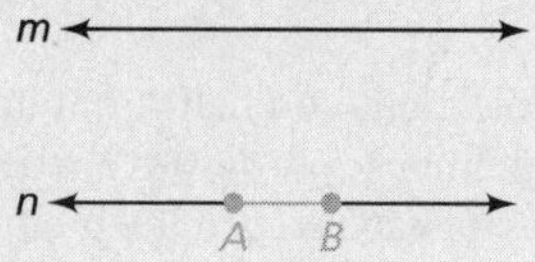

ACE Homework starts on page 61.

Notes

3.5 Parallel Lines, Transversals, and Angle Sums

In *Shapes and Designs*, you learned two very important and related properties of geometric figures.

If a transversal cuts two parallel lines, many pairs of angles formed are congruent.

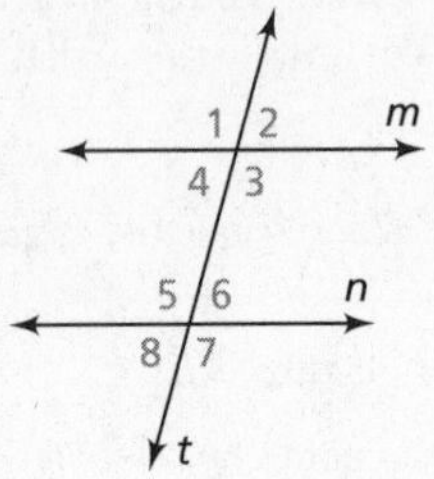

Angles 1, 3, 5, and 7 are congruent.
Angles 2, 4, 6, and 8 are congruent.

In any triangle, the sum of the measures of the interior angles is equal to a straight angle, or 180°.

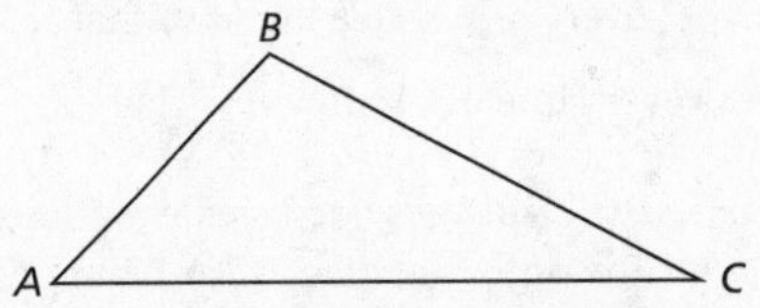

The sum of the measures of angles *A*, *B*, and *C* is 180°.

What you have learned about translations and half-turn rotations will help you explain why those two geometric properties are true. In this Problem, you will provide reasons for each step in the proofs of these two important properties.

Notes

Problem 3.5

For Questions A and B, use the diagram of the parallel lines and transversal on the previous page.

A Complete the following sentences to explain why angles 1, 3, 5, and 7 are congruent.

1. Angles 1 and 3 are congruent because . . .
2. Angles 5 and 7 are congruent because . . .
3. What transformation "moves" angle 5 exactly onto angle 1? Explain.
4. Are angles 1, 3, 5, and 7 all congruent? Explain.

B Construct an argument of your own to show that angles 2, 4, 6, and 8 are congruent.

C Use the transformations described below to explain why the sum of the measures of the interior angles of triangle ABC is 180°.

1. Rotate triangle ABC 180° about point M_1, the midpoint of $\overline{AB}$. Mark any congruent corresponding angles and sides, and any parallel segments. Justify your claims.

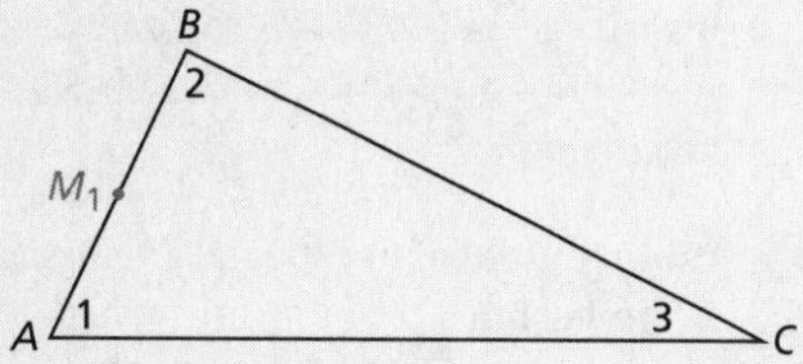

2. Rotate triangle ABC 180° about point M_2, the midpoint of $\overline{BC}$. Mark any congruent corresponding angles and sides, and any parallel segments. Justify your claims.

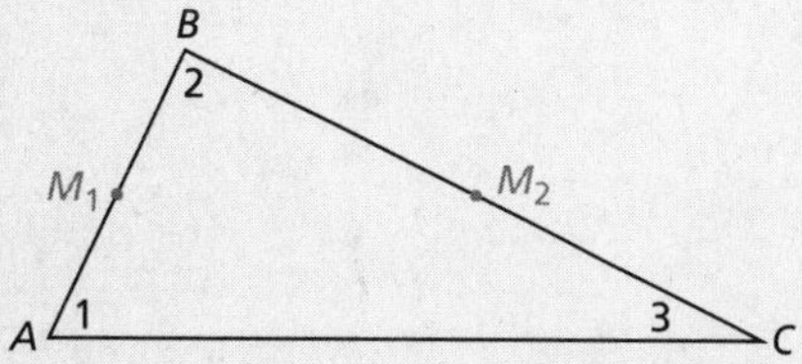

3. How can you be sure that you have one straight line through point B, and not two nonparallel segments? Explain.
4. How do triangle ABC and its images under 180° rotations about points M_1 and M_2 show that the sum of the measures of angles 1, 2, and 3 is 180°?
5. Do you think this argument would work for any triangle? Explain.

continued on the next page >

STUDENT PAGE

Notes

Problem 3.5 continued

D Erin extended her drawing for Question C by continuing to rotate the images of triangle *ABC* around the midpoint of every side. The result is shown below.

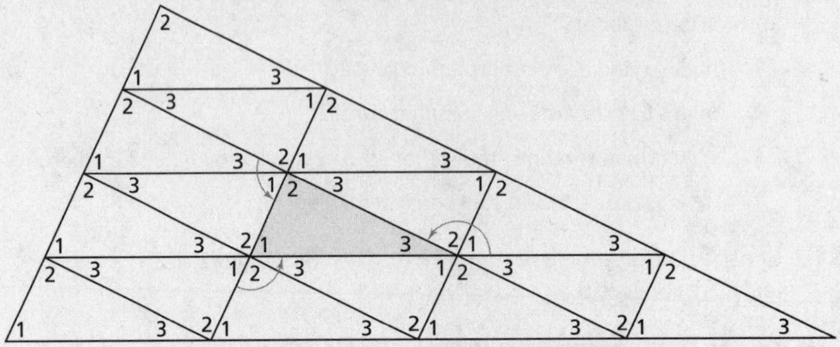

Erin says that if you know that the sum of the measures of the interior angles of a triangle is 180°, then you can show that the sum of the measures of the exterior angles of a triangle is 360°. How does her diagram support her conclusion?

E Another proof of the special angle-sum property of triangles uses a property of parallel lines cut by a transversal: If a transversal cuts two parallel lines, then alternate interior angles are congruent. In the diagram below, the line through point *B* is parallel to $\overline{AC}$.

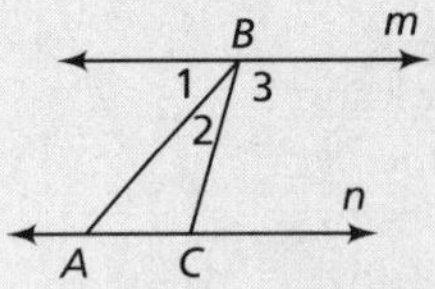

1. Which two angles are congruent because they are alternate interior angles formed by two parallel lines and a transversal?
2. How can you use this information about congruent angles to show that the sum of the measures of $\angle BAC$, $\angle ACB$, and $\angle ABC$ is 180°?

ACE Homework starts on page 61.

Notes

Applications

For Exercises 1–7, make a copy of the figure below. Then, find the image of the figure after each transformation.

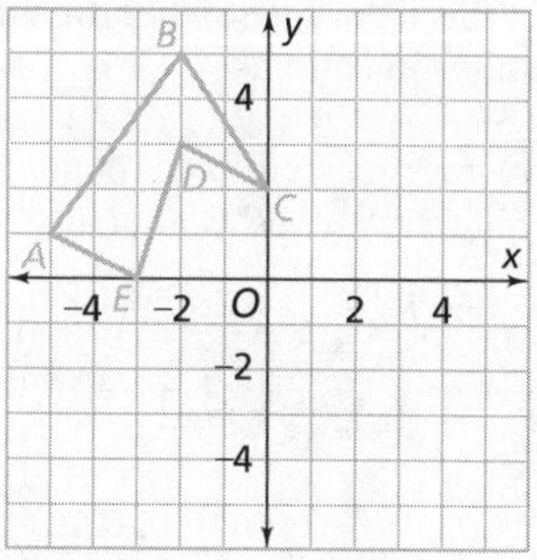

1. Copy and complete the table showing the coordinates of points A–E and their images after a reflection in the y-axis.

Point	A	B	C	D	E
Original Coordinates	(−5, 1)	(−2, 5)	■	■	■
Coordinates After a y-axis Reflection	■	■	■	■	■

   a. Draw the image.

   b. Write a rule relating coordinates of key points and their images after a reflection in the y-axis: $(x, y) \rightarrow$ (■, ■).

2. Add a row to your table from Exercise 1 to show the coordinates of points A–E and their images after a reflection in the x-axis.

   a. Draw the image.

   b. Write a rule relating coordinates of key points and their images after a reflection in the x-axis: $(x, y) \rightarrow$ (■, ■).

STUDENT PAGE

Notes

3. Add another row to your table from Exercise 1 to show the coordinates of points *A*–*E* and their images after a reflection in the *x*-axis, followed by a reflection in the *y*-axis.

 a. Draw the final image.

 b. Write a rule relating coordinates of key points and their images after both reflections: $(x, y) \rightarrow (■, ■)$.

 c. What single transformation in this Investigation has the same effect as the sequence of two line reflections?

4. Copy and complete the table showing the coordinates of points *A*–*E* and their images after a translation that "moves" point *B* to point (3, 4).

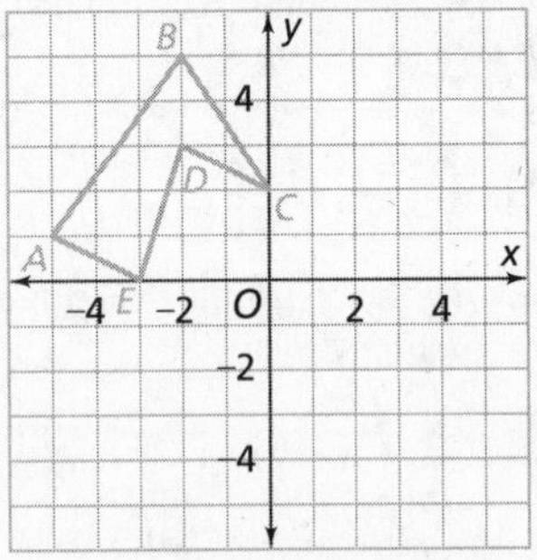

Point	A	B	C	D	E
Original Coordinates	(–5, 1)	(–2, 5)	■	■	■
Coordinates After Translating *B* to (3, 4)	■	■	■	■	■

 a. Draw the image.

 b. Write a rule relating coordinates of key points and their images after the translation: $(x, y) \rightarrow (■, ■)$.

Notes

5. Add a row to your table from Exercise 4 to show the coordinates of points A–E and their images after the first translation, followed by a translation that "moves" point B' to $(-1, 0)$.

   a. Draw the image.

   b. Write a rule relating coordinates of key points and their images after the second translation: $(x, y) \rightarrow (■, ■)$.

   c. Write a rule relating coordinates of key points and their images after the sequence of the two translations: $(x, y) \rightarrow (■, ■)$.

   d. What single transformation is equivalent to the sequence of the two translations?

6. Copy and complete the table showing the coordinates of points A–E and their images after a counterclockwise rotation of 90° about the origin.

Point	*A*	*B*	*C*	*D*	*E*
Original Coordinates	(–5, 1)	(–2, 5)	■	■	■
Coordinates After a 90° Rotation	■	■	■	■	■

   a. Draw the image.

   b. Write a rule relating coordinates of key points and their images after a rotation of 90°: $(x, y) \rightarrow (■, ■)$.

7. Add a row to your table from Exercise 6 to show the coordinates of points A–E and their images after two counterclockwise rotations of 90° about the origin.

   a. Draw the final image.

   b. Write a rule relating coordinates of key points and their images after both rotations: $(x, y) \rightarrow (■, ■)$.

   c. What single transformation is equivalent to the sequence of the two rotations?

STUDENT PAGE

Notes

8. a. Use triangle ABC shown in the diagram.

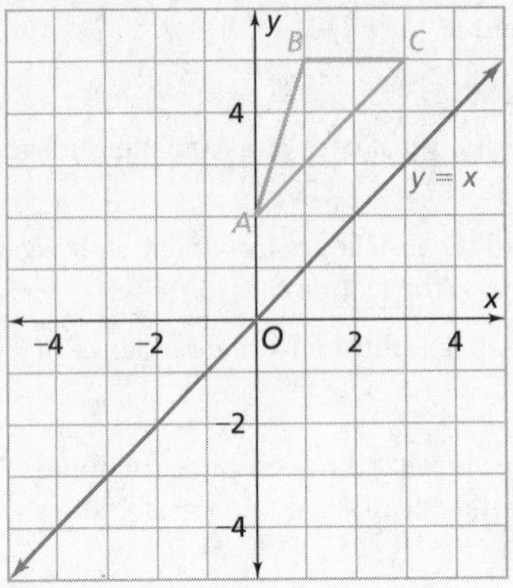

Copy and complete the table showing the coordinates of points A–C and their images after a reflection in the line $y = x$.

Point	A	B	C
Original Coordinates	■	■	■
Coordinates After a Reflection in $y = x$	■	■	■

b. Draw the image and label the vertices A', B', and C'.

c. Add a row to your table to show the coordinates of points A–C and their images after a reflection of triangle $A'B'C'$ in the x-axis.

d. Draw the image and label the vertices A'', B'', and C''.

e. Draw the image of triangle ABC after the same two reflections, but in the reverse order. That is, reflect triangle ABC in the x-axis and then reflect its image, triangle $A'B'C'$, in the line $y = x$. What does the result suggest about the commutativity of a sequence of line reflections?

Notes

9. **a.** Use triangle ABC from Exercise 8. Draw triangle ABC on a coordinate grid.

   i. Translate ABC according to the rule $(x, y) \rightarrow (x + 2, y - 3)$. Label its image $A'B'C'$.

   ii. Translate ABC according to the rule $(x, y) \rightarrow (x - 4, y - 6)$. Label its image $A''B''C''$.

   b. Use the coordinates of the vertices of triangle ABC and its two images to compare the slopes of each pair of line segments.

   i. $\overline{AB}$ and $\overline{A'B'}$; $\overline{AC}$ and $\overline{A'C'}$; $\overline{CB}$ and $\overline{C'B'}$

   ii. $\overline{AB}$ and $\overline{A''B''}$; $\overline{AC}$ and $\overline{A''C''}$; $\overline{CB}$ and $\overline{C''B''}$

   c. What do your results from parts (a) and (b) say about the effect of translations on the slopes of lines? About the relationship between a line and its image under a translation?

10. **a.** Use triangle ABC from Exercise 8. Draw triangle ABC on a coordinate grid and its image after a 180° rotation about the origin. Label the image $A'B'C'$.

    b. Use the coordinates of the vertices of triangle ABC and its image to compare the slopes of each pair of line segments.

    i. $\overline{AB}$ and $\overline{A'B'}$ **ii.** $\overline{AC}$ and $\overline{A'C'}$ **iii.** $\overline{CB}$ and $\overline{C'B'}$

    c. What do your results from parts (a) and (b) say about the effect of half-turns or 180° rotations on the slopes of lines? About the relationship between a line and its image under a 180° rotation?

11. In the diagram below, lines L_1 and L_2 are parallel. What are the measures of angles *a*–*g*?

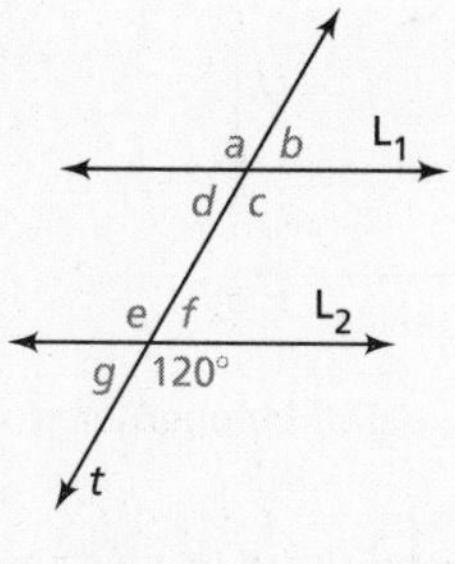

STUDENT PAGE

Notes

12. What are the measures of angles *a* and *b* in the triangle at the right?

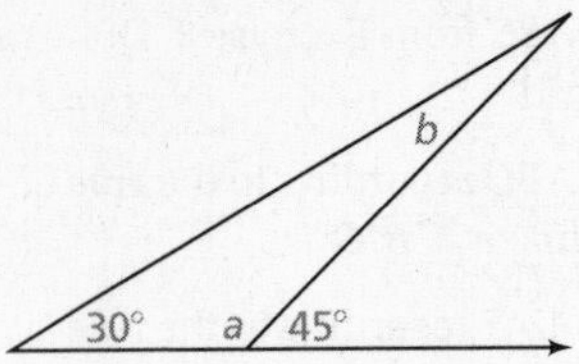

13. What is the value of *x* in the diagram at the right?

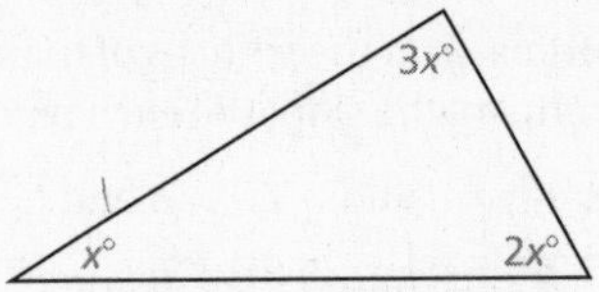

14. The diagram at the right shows parallelogram *ABCD* with one diagonal *DB*. Assuming only that opposite sides of any parallelogram are parallel:

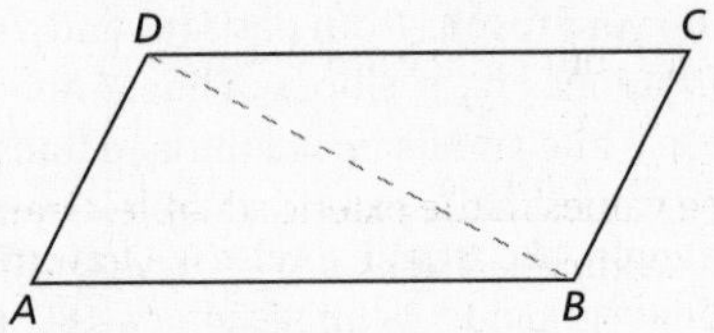

a. Which angles are congruent? How do you know?

b. How can you be sure that triangle *ABD* is congruent to triangle *ADB*? What are the corresponding vertices, sides, and angles?

c. How does the congruence of triangles *ABD* and *ADB* imply that the opposite angles of the parallelogram are congruent?

d. How does the congruence of triangles *ABD* and *ADB* guarantee that, in a parallelogram, opposite sides are the same length?

15. The diagram below shows a rectangle with two diagonals.

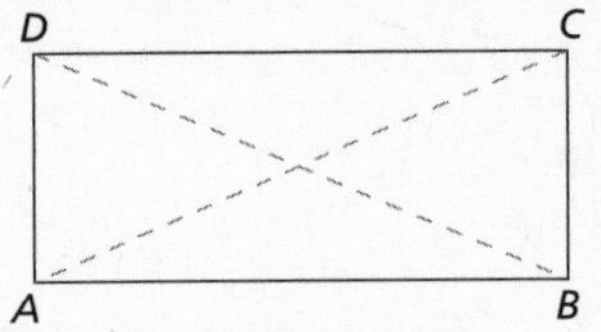

a. How can you be sure that triangle *ABC* is congruent to triangle *BAD*?

b. Why does this congruence guarantee that, in a rectangle, the diagonals are the same length?

Notes

Connections

16. Copy and complete the table of values for the function $y = -x^2$.
Remember: $-(-3)^2 = -9$.

x	−3	−2	−1	0	1	2	3
y	■	■	■	■	■	■	■

a. Use the table of values to graph the function $y = -x^2$.

b. Describe the symmetries of the graph of the function $y = -x^2$.

17. Add a row to your table from Exercise 16 to show values of the function $y = -x^2 + 4$.

a. Use the values in the extended table. Graph $y = -x^2 + 4$ on the same coordinate grid as $y = -x^2$ from Exercise 16.

b. Write a coordinate rule that "moves"

i. the graph of $y = -x^2$ to the position of the graph of $y = -x^2 + 4$.

ii. the graph of $y = -x^2 + 4$ to the position of the graph of $y = -x^2$.

18. Complete the table of values for the function $y = |x|$.
Remember: $|-4| = |4| = 4$.

x	−4	−3	−2	−1	0	1	2	3	4
y	■	■	■	■	■	■	■	■	■

a. Use the table of values to graph the function $y = |x|$.

b. Describe the symmetries of the graph of the function $y = |x|$.

19. Add a row to your table from Exercise 18 to show values of the function $y = |x| - 3$.

a. Use the values in the extended table. Graph $y = |x| - 3$ on the same coordinate grid as $y = |x|$ from Exercise 18.

b. Write a coordinate rule that "moves"

i. the graph of $y = |x|$ to the position of the graph of $y = |x| - 3$.

ii. the graph of $y = |x| - 3$ to the position of the graph of $y = |x|$.

Notes

20. Points A and B are on the x-axis.

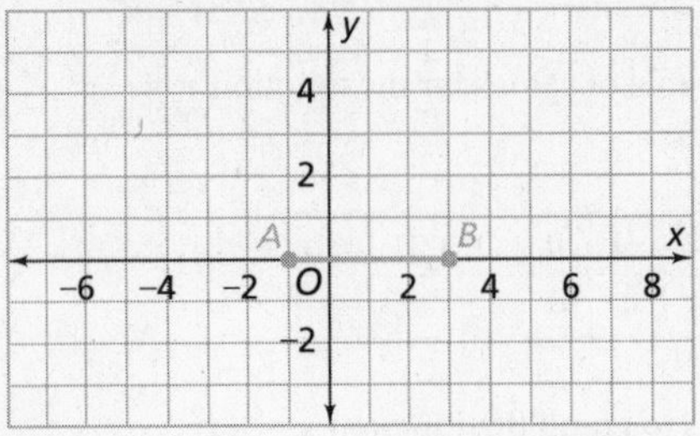

a. Compare the x-coordinates of points A and B.

b. Translate points A and B five units to right. Compare the x-coordinates of the image points.

c. Translate points A and B five units to left. Compare the x-coordinates of the image points.

d. Rotate points A and B 180° about the origin. Compare the x-coordinates of the image points.

e. Write a general rule about the effect of adding or subtracting a constant c from two integers, a and b. Complete the following sentence: If $a < b$, then when you add a constant c to a and b....

f. Write a general rule about the effect of multiplying integers a and b by -1. Complete the following sentence: If $a < b$, then when you multiply each by -1....

Notes

For Exercises 21 and 22, describe the symmetries of each design.

21. 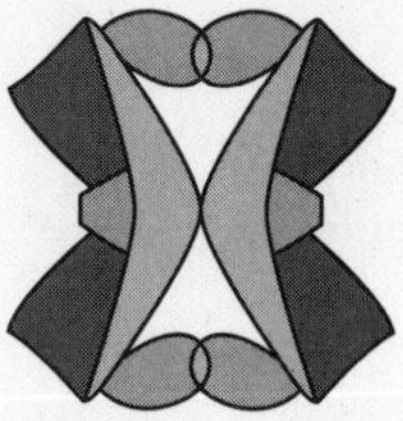

22. 

23. Multiple Choice Squares, rectangles, and rhombuses are all types of parallelograms. Which of these statements is true for all parallelograms?

A. The diagonals are congruent.

B. Each diagonal divides the other in two congruent segments.

C. The diagonals divide a parallelogram into four congruent triangles.

D. The diagonals bisect the angles at each vertex.

24. What is the area of triangle *ABC*?

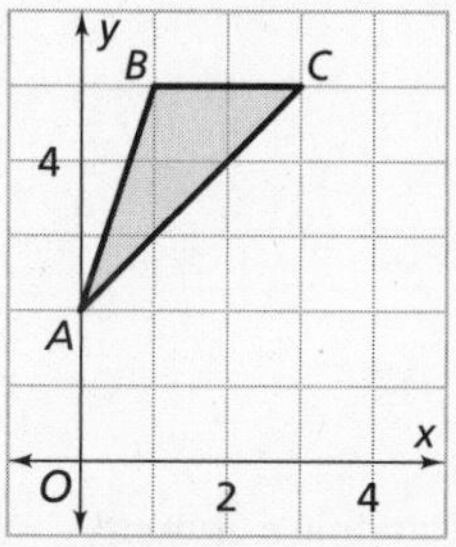

25. What are the side lengths and the perimeter of triangle *ABC* from Exercise 24?

STUDENT PAGE

Notes

Extensions

For Exercises 26–28, draw the figure on grid paper. Then, use symmetry transformations to draw a design that meets the given condition(s). Describe the transformations you used and the order in which you applied them.

26. a design that has at least two lines of symmetry

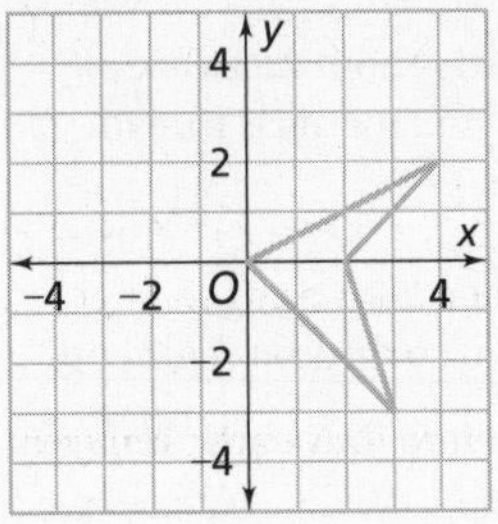

27. a design that has rotational symmetry

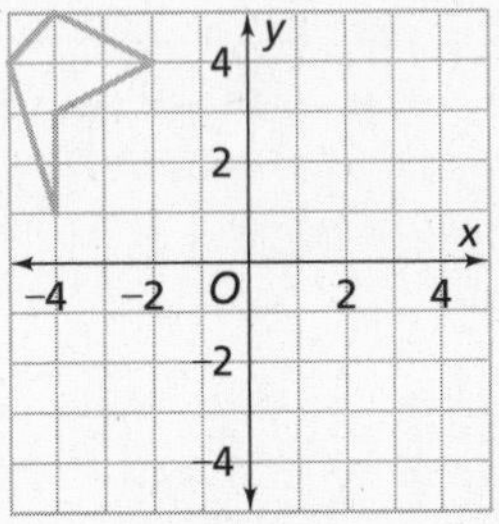

28. a design that has both reflectional and rotational symmetry

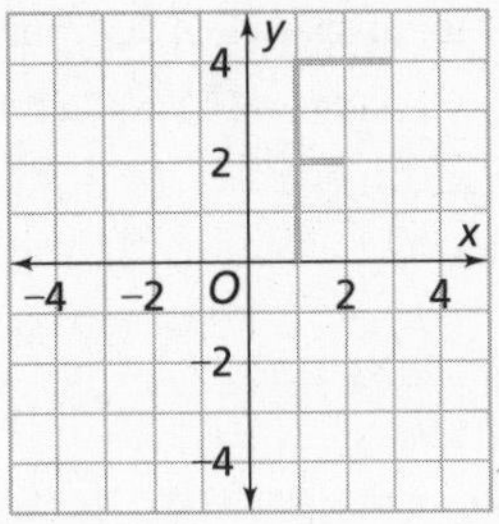

Notes

29. Multiple Choice Which of these statements is *not* true about the figure below if lines m and ℓ are parallel?

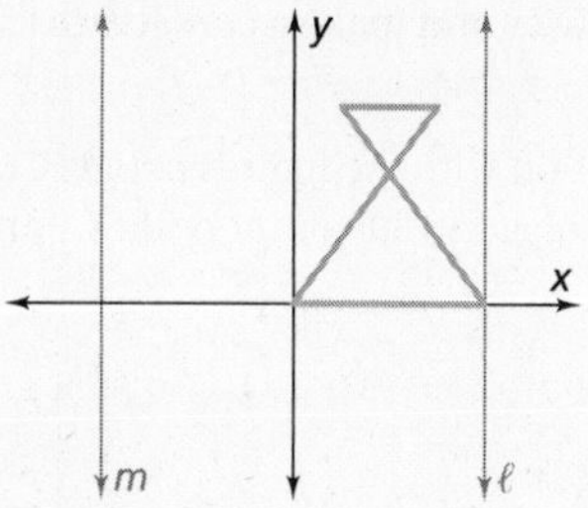

F. Reflecting the figure in the y-axis, and then reflecting the image in the x-axis, gives the same final image as rotating the figure 180° about the origin.

G. Reflecting the figure in line ℓ, and then reflecting the image in the y-axis, gives the same final image as reflecting the figure in line m.

H. Reflecting the figure in the y-axis and then rotating the image 180° about the origin gives the same final image as reflecting the figure in the x-axis.

J. Rotating the figure 90° counterclockwise about the origin and then rotating the image another 90° counterclockwise gives the same image as rotating the original image 180° about the origin.

STUDENT PAGE

Notes

30. Investigate what happens when you rotate a figure 180° about a point and then rotate the image 180° about a different point. Is the combination of the two rotations equivalent to a single transformation? Test several cases and make a conjecture about the result.

You might start your investigation with the figures below. Copy them onto grid paper. Rotate each polygon 180° about point C_1 and then 180° about point C_2.

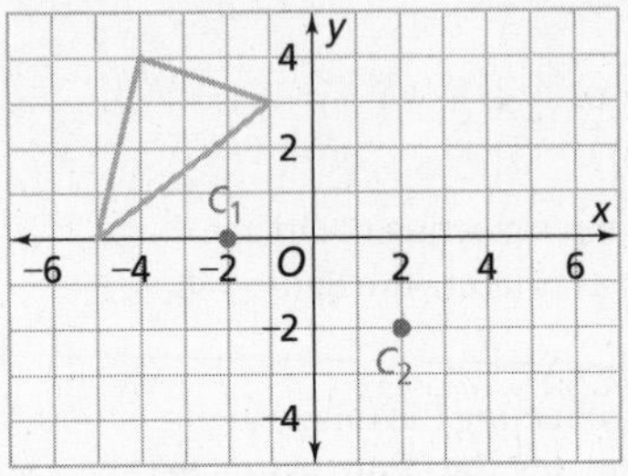

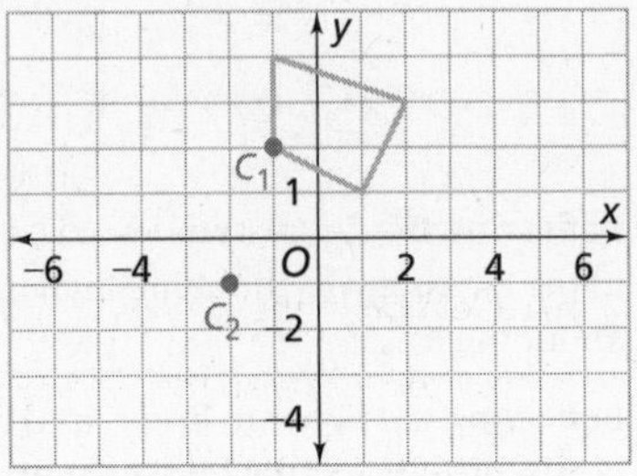

31. Plot points $P(-2, 4)$ and $Q(2, 1)$ on a coordinate grid.

a. Find the coordinates of the points P' and Q' that are the images of points P and Q after a reflection in the x-axis. Then, use the Pythagorean Theorem to prove that $PQ = P'Q'$.

b. Find coordinates of the points P'' and Q'' that are the images of points P and Q after a counterclockwise rotation of 180° about the origin. Then, prove that $PQ = P''Q''$.

c. Find coordinates of the points P''' and Q''' that are the images of points P and Q after a translation with the rule $(x, y) \rightarrow (x + 3, y - 5)$. Then, prove that $PQ = P'''Q'''$.

Notes

Mathematical Reflections 3

In this Investigation, you used coordinate methods to study flips, turns, and slides. You also studied properties of parallel lines and properties of angles in triangles. The following questions will help you summarize what you have learned.

Think about these questions. Discuss your ideas with other students and your teacher. Then write a summary of your findings in your notebook.

1. **What** are the general forms of the coordinate rules for these transformations?
   - **a.** reflection in the *y*-axis
   - **b.** reflection in the *x*-axis
   - **c.** counterclockwise rotation of 90° about the origin
   - **d.** counterclockwise rotation of 180° about the origin
   - **e.** translation that "moves" points *a* units horizontally and *b* units vertically
2. **What** is the effect of translations and half-turns on lines?
3. **How** has your knowledge of transformations changed or extended what you already knew about the angles formed by two parallel lines and a transversal?
4. **How** has your knowledge of transformations changed or extended what you already knew about the sum of the angle measures of a triangle?

STUDENT PAGE

Notes

Common Core Mathematical Practices

As you worked on the Problems in this Investigation, you used prior knowledge to make sense of them. You also applied Mathematical Practices to solve the Problems. Think back over your work, the ways you thought about the Problems, and how you used Mathematical Practices.

Tori described her thoughts in the following way:

In Problem 3.5, I really liked how understanding transformations helped me prove that the sum of the measures of the interior angles of a triangle is 180°, and the sum of the measures of the exterior angles is 360°. I remember showing this in *Shapes and Designs* by measuring angles.

Using transformations to show these results are always true, not just for the examples I drew and measured, was very satisfying. I like this way of reasoning better because it is visual, but does not depend on specific measurements.

Common Core Standards for Mathematical Practice

MP3 Construct viable arguments and critique the reasoning of others.

- What other Mathematical Practices can you identify in Tori's reasoning?
- Describe a Mathematical Practice that you and your classmates used to solve a different Problem in this Investigation.

Notes

Dilations and Similar Figures

Investigation Overview

Investigation Description

This Investigation has four Problems. The first Problem reviews student understanding of dilations and their properties that have been developed earlier in *Stretching and Shrinking* from Grade 7. The second Problem parallels the earlier work showing how constructing combinations of dilations and flips/turns/slides can be used to prove the similarity of figures. The third Problem develops the key similarity result for triangles—that any two triangles with two pairs of congruent corresponding angles must be similar. The fourth Problem applies notions of similarity to problems about finding lengths of inaccessible objects.

Investigation Vocabulary

- dilation
- similarity transformation

Mathematics Background

- Similarity
- Dilations
- Similar Figures
- Applications of Similarity

Planning Chart

Content	ACE	Pacing	Materials	Resources
Problem 4.1	1–10, 23–25	1½ days	**Labsheet 4.1** Dilation **Labsheet 4ACE** Exercises 1–6 **Labsheet 4ACE** Exercises 7–10 **Labsheet 4ACE** Exercise 25 rulers, angle rulers, protractors (optional)	• Transformations
Problem 4.2	11–15, 26, 27	1 day	**Labsheet 4.2** Similarity **Labsheet 4ACE** Exercises 11–15 rulers, angle rulers, protractors (optional)	• Transformations
Problem 4.3	16–20, 28, 29	1 day	**Labsheet 4.3** Similar Triangles and Slope of a Line **Labsheet 4ACE** Exercise 28 rulers, angle rulers, protractors (optional)	• Transformations
Problem 4.4	21, 22, 30, 31	1 day	mirrors, meter sticks	
Mathematical Reflections		½ day		
Looking Back		1 day		
Assessment: Unit Project		Optional		
Assessment: Self-Assessment		Take home		• Self-Assessment • Notebook Checklist
Assessment: Unit Test		1 day		• Unit Test

Goals and Standards

Goals

Congruence and Similarity Understand congruence and similarity and explore necessary and sufficient conditions for establishing congruent and similar shapes

- Recognize that two figures are congruent if one is derived from the other one by a sequence of reflection, rotation, and/or translation transformations
- Recognize that two figures are similar if one can be obtained from the other by a sequence of reflections, rotations, translations, and/or dilations
- Use transformations to describe a sequence that exhibits the congruence between figures
- Use transformations to explore minimum measurement conditions for establishing congruence of triangles
- Use transformations to explore minimum measurement conditions for establishing similarity of triangles
- Relate properties of angles formed by parallel lines and transversals, and the angle sum in any triangle, to properties of transformations
- Use properties of congruent and similar triangles to solve problems about shapes and measurements

Mathematical Reflections

Look for evidence of student understanding of the goals for this Investigation in their responses to the questions in *Mathematical Reflections*. The goals addressed by each question are indicated below.

1. How would you explain what it means for two geometric shapes to be similar in

a. everyday words that most people could understand?

b. technical terms of mathematics?

Goal

- Recognize that two figures are similar if one can be obtained from the other by a sequence of reflections, rotations, translations, and/or dilations

2. a. Suppose you dilate a polygon to form a figure of a different size. How will the side lengths, angle measures, perimeters, areas, and slopes of the sides of the two figures be alike? How will they be different?

b. How has your knowledge of dilations changed or extended what you already knew about similarity?

Goal

- Recognize that two figures are similar if one can be obtained from the other by a sequence of reflections, rotations, translations, and/or dilations

3. What is the least amount of information you need in order to be sure that two triangles are similar?

   Goal

   - Use transformations to explore minimum measurement conditions for establishing similarity of triangles

4. How do you use similarity to find the side lengths of similar figures?

   Goal

   - Use properties of congruent and similar triangles to solve problems about shapes and measurements

Standards

Common Core Content Standards

8.EE.B.6 Use similar triangles to explain why the slope m is the same between any two distinct points on a non-vertical line in the coordinate plane; derive the equation $y = mx$ for a line through the origin and the equation $y = mx + b$ for a line intercepting the vertical axis at b. *Problem 1 and 3*

8.G.A.3 Describe the effect of dilations, translations, rotations, and reflections on two-dimensional figures using coordinates. *Problem 1 and 3*

8.G.A.4 Understand that a two-dimensional figure is similar to another if the second can be obtained from the first by a sequence of rotations, reflections, translations, and dilations; given two similar two-dimensional figures, describe a sequence that exhibits the similarity between them. *Problems 1, 2, 3, and 4*

8.G.A.5 Use informal arguments to establish facts about the angle sum and exterior angle of triangles, about the angles created when parallel lines are cut by a transversal, and the angle-angle criterion for similarity of triangles. *Problem 3*

Facilitating the Mathematical Practices

Students in *Connected Mathematics* classrooms display evidence of multiple Common Core Standards for Mathematical Practice every day. Here are just a few examples of when you might observe students demonstrating the Standards for Mathematical Practice during this Investigation.

Practice 1: Make sense of problems and persevere in solving them.

Students are engaged every day in solving problems and, over time, learn to persevere in solving them. To be effective, the problems embody critical concepts and skills and have the potential to engage students in making sense of mathematics. Students build understanding by reflecting, connecting, and communicating. These student-centered problem situations engage students in articulating the "knowns" in a problem situation and determining a logical solution pathway. The student-student and student-teacher dialogues help students not only to make sense of the problems, but also to persevere in finding appropriate strategies to solve them. The suggested questions in the Teacher Guides provide the metacognitive scaffolding to help students monitor and refine their problem-solving strategies.

Practice 2: Reason abstractly and quantitatively.

In the Problems of this Investigation, students use rigid and nonrigid transformations to discover that, for triangles, they only need to know that two corresponding angles are congruent to determine similarity. This minimum requirement is practical for determining vertical heights and distances that are unreachable assuming that the angle the vertical object makes with the ground is 90°.

Practice 3: Construct viable arguments and critique the reasoning of others.

In Problem 3, students evaluate the arguments of other students about whether or not two triangles are similar. To do this, they nest the smaller triangle in the larger triangle using one corresponding angle and observe that the third sides that do not form the angle are parallel. Then, students use the results from Problem 3.5 about parallel lines cut by a transversal to deduce the equality of corresponding angles in the triangles. They also use the sum of the interior angles of a triangle. They reason that two angle measures are enough to determine similarity, since the third angle can be found by subtracting the sum of the two known angles from 180°.

Practice 4: Model with mathematics.

In Problem 4, students use the scale factor between two similar triangles to determine vertical heights that they are unable to measure. They use a mirror with the fact that angles of reflection are congruent and relate the corresponding parts of similar triangles in their diagram of the situation. With the angle of reflection and the assumption that the object they cannot measure forms a 90° angle with the ground, they know that two triangles are similar. The smaller triangle is used in this exploration as a model of the larger triangle. For example, they use height from the ground to their eyes when they are able to see the reflection of the top of the object that they want to measure in the mirror. They also use the distances from the mirror to the object and to their position given a pair of corresponding sides to use to calculate the scale factor. With the scale factor, they can use multiplication to estimate the height that they are unable to measure.

Practice 5: Use appropriate tools strategically.

In Problems 1–3, students use their rulers and angle rulers or protractors to verify measurements of corresponding parts of triangles. They learn that they only need to measure two corresponding angles and verify congruence to determine similarity. If they decide to use measurements of sides, they learn that they need to verify that the scale factor is constant for all pairs of corresponding sides. In Problem 4, students use a mirror and meter stick to find the appropriate position to take measurements to estimate the height of an object they cannot reach using properties of similarity.

Students identify and record their personal experiences with the Standards for Mathematical Practice during the Mathematical Reflections at the end of the Investigation.

PROBLEM

4.1 Focus on Dilations

Problem Overview

Focus Question What coordinate rules model dilations? How do dilations change or preserve the properties of the original figure?

Problem Description

This Problem reviews what students have learned about similarity in a previous Unit, *Stretching and Shrinking*. What they learned is that similar figures have the same shape but possibly different size. By using coordinate rules, students can check some of their prior observations about distances and slopes. This is the fourth type of transformation students will learn about, and they will contrast dilation with the other transformations.

Problem Implementation

Group students in pairs.

Materials

- **Labsheet 4.1:** Dilation (one per pair)
- **Labsheet 4ACE:** Exercises 1–6
- **Labsheet 4ACE:** Exercises 7–10
- **Labsheet 4ACE:** Exercise 25

rulers
angle rulers
protractors (optional)

Using Technology

If the students have access to a computer, they may find it helpful to use **Transformations** to answer the Questions of this Problem. This activity may also help to reduce the amount of class time reserved for drawing designs.
Note: The default setting of this activity includes a grid and axes.

Vocabulary

- dilation
- similarity transformation

Mathematics Background

- Similarity
- Dilations

At a Glance and Lesson Plan

- At a Glance: Problem 4.1 Butterflies, Pinwheels, and Wallpaper
- Lesson Plan: Problem 4.1 Butterflies, Pinwheels, and Wallpaper

Launch

Launch Video

This animation depicts Tori and Jayden playing the Wump game. In this game, the characters use their understanding of similarity to select similar figures, which are members of the Wump family from *Stretching and Shrinking*. Visit Teacher Place at mathdashboard.com/cmp3 to see the complete video.

You can show students this animation to launch the Problem. Students can watch it instead of reading the introduction in the Student Edition.

Connecting to Prior Knowledge

You might consider launching the Investigation and this Problem by asking students what they remember about the Wump family—who were the legitimate members of the family and what kinds of characters were imposters. You could have them study the set of four drawings in the Student Edition to identify the imposters, the nonsimilar shapes, and explain why they are imposters. You can then review the meaning of *similar figures* and the stretching or dilating transformation. These ideas were investigated in *Stretching and Shrinking*.

Presenting the Challenge

Segue into the challenge of Problem 4.1 by asking about the dilation pictured in the introduction.

Suggested Questions

- What is meant by a dilation? (Let students express this in their own words, but be sure to draw their attention to the way that *dilation* is used mathematically—as both stretching and shrinking. Remind students that this figure looks a lot like the rubber-band method for enlarging figures, from *Stretching and Shrinking*.)

- How is this kind of transformation different from reflections, rotations, and translations? (The other transformations are called rigid transformations because both size and shape are preserved. A dilation preserves shape but not size, unless the scale factor is 1.)
- Which triangles seem to be similar? (Students are likely to concentrate on triangles *ABC* and *XYZ*, since they are highlighted. Be sure students notice the order of vertices for naming the triangles. Push students to look for other similar triangles. There are other important triangles in the figure, and these other pairs of triangles actually model the action of the dilation. The triangle pairs are *PAB* and *PXY*, and *PCB* and *PZY*. These pairs of triangles show the center of the dilation, *P*, and the corresponding distances from the center, for example, *PA* and *PX*. Triangles *ABC* and *XYZ* show the finished result of the dilation; triangle *XYZ* is the image of triangle *ABC*.)
- What is meant by a dilation with a scale factor of $\frac{3}{2}$? (Students are likely to concentrate on a comparison of the sides of triangles *ABC* and *XYZ*; this is a comparison between lengths of sides on the original and lengths of sides on the image, for example, $XY = \frac{3}{2}AB$, etc. Push them to look for more comparisons. The distance from *X* to $P = \frac{3}{2}$ (distance from *A* to *P*). This is the underlying reason that the lengths of sides of triangle *XYZ* are $\frac{3}{2}$ times the lengths of corresponding sides of triangle *ABC*.)
- Can you see a dilation of $\frac{2}{3}$ in this figure? What is being compared? (This compares sides of triangles *ABC* to triangle *XYZ*, for example, $AB = \frac{2}{3}XY$, etc. Also, $AP = \frac{2}{3}XP$.)

Now ask students to look at the figure in Question A. Help them connect the challenge of the Problem to the idea of a dilation as pictured in the introduction. Ask:

- How does the idea of a dilation connect to this figure drawn on a coordinate grid? (The center will be the origin. The distance from the origin to points on the image will be a multiple of the distance from the origin to points on the original figure.)

Tell students they are going to look for coordinate rules for dilations. Much of what students investigate in this Problem will be a review and extension of what they learned in *Stretching and Shrinking*.

Explore

Providing for Individual Needs

By this point, students should be fairly familiar with the scaling effects of dilations, based on their prior experience in the *Stretching and Shrinking* Unit. However, in order to answer Question A, parts (1)–(6) correctly, they will need to locate the image points from the starting figure accurately. Check on this work early to see that students are on the right track.

Suggested Questions

- How do you know that points P', Q', R', and S' are 3 times as far from the origin (0, 0) as P, Q, R, and S, the points from which they "moved"? (Students may have used a ruler to measure OP, for example, or they may already be implicitly using a coordinate rule. They may not draw OP and OP', for example, to make the distances visible, but they will be asked to do this in Question B.)
- How are you able to compare side lengths for the figure and its image? (Some side lengths lie along gridlines. For SR and $S'R'$, students will have to use the Pythagorean Theorem if they want exact lengths.)
- How are you able to compare angle sizes? (Students may measure with protractors or find the slopes of the sides.)
- How can you check and compare the perimeters? Areas? (Students may reason that if each side of the image is 3 times the corresponding side of the original, then the perimeter of the image must be 3 times bigger than the original. For areas, they can see that the shapes are comprised of a square and a triangle. These areas are easily calculated from formulas. They may refer back to *Stretching and Shrinking* or *Filling and Wrapping*.)
- I see that you have checked slopes and found that the slopes of the sides of the image are the same as the slopes of the sides of the original. What does that mean about a pair of corresponding sides? (Push students to see that this means corresponding sides are parallel. The fact that dilations produce parallel lines will be useful going forward.)

For Question B, students make the distances from the origin explicit, and the underlying similar triangles become apparent.

- What similar triangles can you see? How do you know they are similar? (OPQ and $OP'Q'$. The distances OP and OP', and OQ and OQ', are related by a scale factor of 3. That is how the dilation works. PQ and $P'Q'$ are corresponding sides of the shapes explored in Question A.)

Students may not see that point $Z(2z, 4z)$ must lie on the line OP. Help them connect $(2z, 4z)$ to the coordinate rule for the dilation in Question A.

- The coordinate rule for the dilation in Question A was $(x, y) \rightarrow (3x, 3y)$. What rule would move $P(2, 4)$ to $Z(2z, 4z)$? What does this mean about O, P, and Z? ($P = (2, 4)$, so P would "move" to Z under a dilation with scale factor z, centered at the origin. This means that O, P, and Z are all on a straight line, i.e., collinear.)

Planning for the Summary

What evidence will you use in the summary to clarify and deepen understanding of the Focus Question?

What will you do if you do not have evidence?

Summarize

Orchestrating the Discussion

Questions D and E address the points that you want to make from this Problem, so use those questions in the Summarize. Connect back to students' work on specific dilation examples in Questions A–C by asking what evidence supports their generalizations about all dilations.

Suggested Questions

- What statements did you make for Question D? (Make a list of all the proposed statements and push for more information. Students will probably say that corresponding side lengths are related by a scale factor k and are parallel, that corresponding angles are congruent, and areas are related by a scale factor of k^2.)

Ask about Question E. Push for the coordinate rule that connects corresponding points: $(x, y) \rightarrow (kx, ky)$.

- How did you come up with statements for Question E? (By drawing figures with symmetry, like a square or isosceles triangle or parallelogram, the resulting image is the same shape, so it has the same kind of symmetry.)

Be sure to ask students whether the two specific cases they have studied give them confidence that their conjectures will be true for other shapes and other scale factors. Two specific cases are not enough to prove a conjecture. But because of their earlier experience with dilations, there is little reason to suspect that they have met examples here that do not illustrate a general pattern.

You might have another example ready to test using a different scale factor. For example, sketches like the ones shown below can be used. Apply scale factors of $\frac{3}{2}$ and $\frac{2}{3}$ to these figures using the origin for the center of dilation.

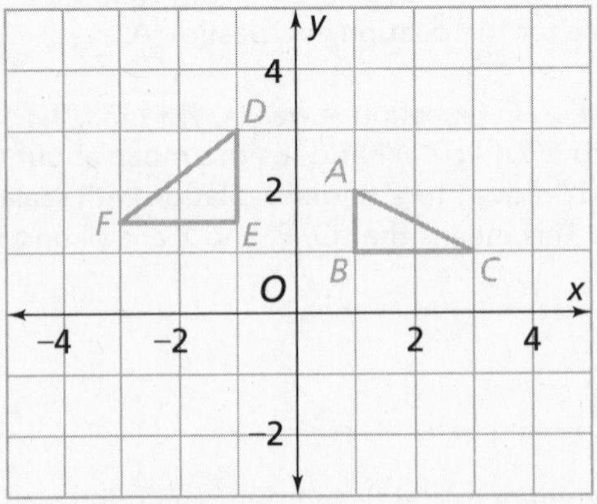

You may want to conclude by reminding students that the Investigations in this Unit started by exploring the symmetry of familiar objects and designs. Additionally, they learned about three transformations that create symmetric shapes. Tell them that symmetry is so pervasive that they can find articles on the subject in mathematics, physics, biology, chemistry, history, religion, architecture, art, crafts, music, and social interactions. Encourage your students to look for such articles online.

Reflecting on Student Learning

Use the following questions to assess student understanding at the end of the lesson.

- What evidence do I have that students understand the Focus Question?
  - Where did my students get stuck?
  - What strategies did they use?
  - What breakthroughs did my students have today?
- How will I use this to plan for tomorrow? For the next time I teach this lesson?
- Where will I have the opportunity to reinforce these ideas as I continue through this Unit? The next Unit?

ACE Assignment Guide

- **Applications:** 1–10
- **Connections:** 23–25
- **Labsheet 4ACE:** Exercises 1–6
- **Labsheet 4ACE:** Exercises 7–10
- **Labsheet 4ACE:** Exercise 25

PROBLEM
4.2 Return of Super Sleuth

Similarity Transformations

Problem Overview

Focus Question How can you use transformations to check whether two figures are similar or not?

Problem Description

The goal of this Problem is to begin developing student understanding and skill in working with the idea that similar figures can be transformed exactly onto each other by suitable combinations of flips, turns, and/or slides and one dilation.

Problem Implementation

Group students in pairs.

Materials

- **Labsheet 4.2:** Similarity
- **Labsheet 4ACE:** Exercises 11–15

rulers
angle rulers
protractors (optional)

Using Technology

If the students have access to a computer, they may find it helpful to use **Transformations** to answer the Questions of this Problem. This activity may also help to reduce the amount of class time reserved for drawing designs. **Note:** The default setting of this activity includes a grid and axes.

Vocabulary

There are no new glossary terms introduced in this Problem.

Mathematics Background

- Similarity
- Dilations
- Similar Figures

At a Glance and Lesson Plan

- At a Glance: Problem 4.2 Butterflies, Pinwheels, and Wallpaper
- Lesson Plan: Problem 4.2 Butterflies, Pinwheels, and Wallpaper

Launch

Connecting to Prior Knowledge

You might launch the Problem by reminding students how they checked two triangles for congruence:

Suggested Questions

- In Investigation 2, how did you show that two triangles were congruent? (If one triangle could be "moved" onto the other by a chain of rigid transformations, the triangles were congruent.)
- What were some of the discoveries that made some sequences easier to describe than others? (Since it is difficult to find a center of rotation that is not on a figure and to describe the angle of rotation exactly without referencing an existing angle, we often chose to do slides and reflections first to get one pair of points matched up. Then, the last transformation was a rotation that matched up all the other points.)

Presenting the Challenge

You can segue into the Problem by asking about the drawings of "Super Sleuth."

Suggested Questions

- Do these figures look similar? (Yes; they have the same shape but different sizes; one is larger than the other.)
- How can you check? (Find a sequence of transformations to "move" one onto the other.)
- What transformations do you think will "move" one onto the other? Does the order of the transformations matter? (There must be a reflection, a translation, and a dilation. It might be easiest to leave the dilation until last.)
- What might be a key point to locate? (the center of the dilation)

- How do you think we can show that these figures are similar? (One possibility is to translate the small figure until the coat tails coincide. Then, reflect over a vertical line passing through this shared point. That will make that pair of angles coincide. Then, dilate from that shared point until corresponding sides are the same length.)
- How can we figure out the scale factor? (Compare the lengths of corresponding sides.)

When you are sure that your students understand the challenge, set them loose on the Problem.

Explore

Providing for Individual Needs

This Problem gives students the challenge of judging "same shape" for figures using informal reasoning. They might be tempted to simply look at the given pairs of polygons and make a snap judgment that the figures are similar or not. It is important that they measure with a ruler and an angle ruler/protractor to check their intuition. **Labsheet 4.2: Similarity** can be used to facilitate this.

Suggested Questions

- How did you make the judgment that the figures were similar? (Students may measure corresponding sides and angles. Then they figure the scale factors. This is familiar from *Stretching and Shrinking*.)
- How did you decide that the figures were not similar? (I measured the sides and checked that the scale factor was the same for all pairs of corresponding sides, or checked internal ratios.)
- Could you have just used angle measures to check if two figures are similar? Explain. (No. It is tempting to think that congruent angles guarantee similarity, but as we see in Question B, this is not the case.)
- Once you establish that you think figures are similar, how do you decide which transformations to use? Does deciding on corresponding angles or sides help? (Identifying corresponding sides and angles is a good start. Then, use rigid motions to nest the smaller triangle in the larger with two corresponding sides and one vertex matching. Finally, use a dilation from the common vertex.)

Check that students are naming figures correctly so that intended correspondences are obvious.

Planning for the Summary

What evidence will you use in the summary to clarify and deepen understanding of the Focus Question?

What will you do if you do not have evidence?

Summarize

Orchestrating the Discussion

The Focus Question is actually given as Question D, so after checking to see that groups agree that the figures are similar in Questions A and C and not similar in Question B, ask how they made those decisions and what evidence they can offer to support their claims. Also, ask them to describe the sequence of transformations (flip, turn, slide, and final dilation) that will map one figure exactly onto the other. Have groups critique each other's ideas and push each other to be exact in their descriptions.

Suggested Questions

- Do you think that other sequences are possible? Explain. (It is certainly possible to dilate the smaller figure before flipping/turning/sliding it on top of the other. So if students don't suggest this sequence of transformations, you might ask them whether it would be acceptable.)
- If corresponding angles of a figure are congruent, are the figures guaranteed to be similar? Explain. (No; think of two rectangles, one with side lengths 2 and 3; and another with side lengths 1 and 5. All pairs of corresponding angles in the rectangle would be 90°, but the rectangles are not similar. If corresponding angles of two triangles are congruent in pairs, then the triangles must be similar.)
- If corresponding sides of a figure are scaled copies of each other, are the figures guaranteed to be similar? Explain. (No. Think of a rectangle made with side lengths 2 and 3 units, and a parallelogram made with side lengths 4 and 6 units without 90° angles. These are not scaled copies of each other.)

Reflecting on Student Learning

Use the following questions to assess student understanding at the end of the lesson.

- What evidence do I have that students understand the Focus Question?
  - Where did my students get stuck?
  - What strategies did they use?
  - What breakthroughs did my students have today?
- How will I use this to plan for tomorrow? For the next time I teach this lesson?
- Where will I have the opportunity to reinforce these ideas as I continue through this Unit? The next Unit?

ACE Assignment Guide

- **Applications:** 11–15
- **Connections:** 26, 27
- **Labsheet 4ACE:** Exercises 11–15

PROBLEM
4.3 Checking Similarity Without Transformations

Problem Overview

Focus Question What information about the sides and angles of two triangles will guarantee that they are similar?

Problem Description

In the same way that it is possible to confirm congruence of triangles without actually doing the "moves" of flips, turns, and/or slides, it is possible to check similarity of triangles without doing congruence and dilation transformations. This Problem has as its goal the development of one fundamental strategy for proving similarity of triangles—the Angle-Angle criterion. This is an explicit requirement of the Common Core State Standards for Mathematics in Grade 8.

Problem Implementation

Group students in pairs.

For Question E, distribute **Labsheet 4.3: Similar Triangles and Slope of a Line** to provide an example for students to sketch on during their search for similar triangles.

Materials

- **Labsheet 4.3:** Similar Triangles and Slope of a Line (one per pair)
- **Labsheet 4ACE:** Exercise 28

rulers
angle rulers
protractors (optional)

Using Technology

If the students have access to a computer, they may find it helpful to use **Transformations** to answer the Questions of this Problem. This activity may also help to reduce the amount of class time reserved for drawing designs. **Note:** The default setting of this activity includes a grid and axes.

Vocabulary

There are no new glossary terms introduced in this Problem.

Mathematics Background

- Similarity
- Similar Figures

At a Glance and Lesson Plan

- At a Glance: Problem 4.3 Butterflies, Pinwheels, and Wallpaper
- Lesson Plan: Problem 4.3 Butterflies, Pinwheels, and Wallpaper

Launch

Connecting to Prior Knowledge

You might choose to launch this Problem by asking students to remember how they were able to develop some ways of showing two triangles congruent without or before doing the flips, turns, or slides in Problem 2.3.

Suggested Questions

- What were some combinations of sides and/or angle measurements that would guarantee that two triangles are congruent? (All three sides congruent; two sides with an included angle congruent; two angles with an included side congruent; and two angles and an adjacent side congruent. **Note:** In High School Geometry, these are abbreviated SSS, SAS, ASA, AAS, respectively.)

Presenting the Challenge

Have students study the diagram and information about triangles *ABC* and *XYZ* in the text. Then they should make conjectures about the minimum amount of information they think they would need to conclude that two triangles are similar.

Suggested Questions

- Do you think it would be sufficient to know that one pair of corresponding angles are congruent? Explain. (No. Students should be able to come up with a counterexample. For example, they could present two right triangles that are not similar.)
- Suppose you knew the ratio of the longest sides in a pair of triangles was 1 : 2. Would that be enough to guarantee similarity? Explain. (No. Again, a counterexample can disprove this. For example, they could present two triangles with their longest sides in ratio 1 : 2, but other sides not in that ratio.)

- Suppose that two sides of one triangle were related by the same scale factor to two sides of a second triangle. Do you think you could conclude that the triangles were similar? Explain. (No. One counterexample to this would be a pair of isosceles triangles that have different vertex angles. **Note:** There are other counterexamples.)

At this point, you could transition to the Problem by suggesting that the task is to analyze the reasoning of other students and to see what makes sense.

Explore

Providing for Individual Needs

Students often find critiquing others' reasoning challenging. First, you have to understand how someone else thought about something. Then, you have to construct an articulate critique. You may have to support students more than usual as they work on the Questions in this Problem.

Suggested Questions

In Question A:

- Do you agree with the general idea that it is the angles that give a polygon its shape? Think about shapes you know a lot about, triangles and quadrilaterals. (In general, angles contribute to a polygon's shape. For example, if all the angles of a quadrilateral are 90°, then the quadrilateral is a rectangle or a square, but we would not know which one. If a quadrilateral has angles of 30°, 150°, 30°, and 150°, the shape might be a parallelogram or a trapezoid, depending on the order of the angles. So, angles do tell us a lot about a shape, but not everything.)
- Let's put specific numbers to Kevin and Ming's idea. Suppose the triangles have angles of 30°, 70°, and 80°. Will the triangles have the same shape? Can you think of a counterexample? (Students might try drawing triangles with these angles. They should find that all the triangles with those angles would be similar, though they may have to reflect or rotate them to see the correspondence.)
- Do you think that what you found with triangles having angles 30°, 70°, and 80° will be true for all triangles with corresponding congruent angles? (It will be true, but at this point students are still conjecturing and discussing the examples.)

For Question B, you might draw the two triangles separately, or have a student do this if it becomes apparent that this will help other students.

- For the triangles you drew in Question A, could you have "moved" the smaller triangle onto the larger so the triangles are "nested" as in the diagram in Question B? (Yes. It is important that students take time to think about how they would accomplish this in similar ways to Problem 4.2.)

- What are the two triangles in Question B? Would it help to see these triangles drawn separately? (*ABC* and *XYZ*. Some students will need to see the triangles drawn separately to visualize them "moving" so that they overlap. Starting with the nested triangles may obscure the congruent corresponding angles.)
- When you "move" triangle *ABC* onto *XYZ*, why does *C* end up on side *YZ* and *A* end up on side *YX*? (The angle at *Y* and *B* are the same size, so the sides of the angle will coincide.)
- Question B, part (3) talks about a dilation. What is the center of that dilation? How can you be sure that, if you dilate the small triangle, you will "move" side *AC* onto side *XZ*? (The center of dilation is point *B* (or *Y*). First, you can see that *AC* and *XZ* are parallel. Then recall that a dilation will "move" the original to a parallel image, if not onto the image. So, as side *BC* stretches to coincide with side *YZ*, side *BA* is simultaneously stretching to coincide with side *YX*.)
- How can we find the scale factor of the dilation? (Compare $ZY : CB$, $XY : AB$, or $XZ : AC$.)
- What other ratios are equal? (Scale factor: $\frac{ZY}{CB} = \frac{XZ}{AC} = \frac{XY}{AB}$. Also, internal ratios: $\frac{AC}{AB} = \frac{XZ}{XY}$; $\frac{AC}{BC} = \frac{XZ}{YZ}$; and $\frac{AB}{BC} = \frac{XY}{YZ}$.)

For Question C:

- Would it help to think of some examples? Say we know that two angles of one triangle are 40° and 60°, and two angles of another triangle are also 40° and 60°. Would the third angles also be equal? Can you think of a counterexample when the third angles would not be equal? (The third angles are both $180 - (40 + 60) = 80°$. This pattern will always work. If two angles are *a* and *b* degrees, then the third angle must be $180 - (a + b)$ degrees.)

For Question E, a requirement of the CCSSM:

- Where are your similar triangles? How do you know these are similar? (The triangles are shown below the line $y = ax + b$. There are three right triangles with their hypotenuses coincident with the line $y = ax + b$. They are similar because the angles at *P* and *Z* are equal due to the angle the line makes with the *x*-axis or any line parallel to the *x*-axis, the slope of the line, and because they each have a 90° angle.)
- What ratios would give the slopes of *PZ*? *PW*? Why are they equal? ($\frac{ZA}{AP}$ and $\frac{WB}{BP}$. These are internal ratios of corresponding sides of similar triangles.)

Note: In *Stretching and Shrinking*, students found that the ratios between corresponding sides within similar shapes are equal. For example, the ratio of the shortest side of a triangle to the longest side of the same triangle is the same for two similar triangles. This is a different ratio from the ratio comparing corresponding sides *between* triangles, a major focus in *Stretching and Shrinking*. If some students have not studied *Stretching and Shrinking*, then you will have to help them see that the proportion $\frac{ZA}{AP} = \frac{WB}{BP}$ is equivalent to $\frac{ZA}{WB} = \frac{AP}{BP}$ because both of these proportions are valid for similar triangles.

Going Further

There were several combinations of measurements that would ensure that triangles are congruent. In this Problem, you found one combination of measurements that would ensure that two triangles are similar. What other combinations do you think would guarantee that two triangles are similar? Students might try sketching pairs of triangles with various combinations of matched parts and looking for ways to "move" one triangle onto another. There are two other common criteria for similarity of triangles that are like the criteria for congruence of triangles. These are

- If corresponding sides of two triangles are related by the same scale factor, then the two triangles are similar.
- If triangles *ABC* and *XYZ* have $\angle ABC \cong \angle XYZ$ and $\frac{AB}{XY} = \frac{BC}{YZ}$, then the two triangles are similar.

Planning for the Summary

What evidence will you use in the summary to clarify and deepen understanding of the Focus Question?

What will you do if you do not have evidence?

Summarize

Orchestrating the Discussion

You can conduct a class summary after completing work on Questions A–C, since the key result of the Problem is the statement in Question D. Question E could be done as a large-group activity as part of the Summarize.

After discussing Question B, push students to explain why this reasoning would always work.

Suggested Questions

- Will this reasoning work for all triangles? Acute angled? Right angled? Obtuse angled? (Yes. The transformations needed for "nesting" one triangle inside another are always possible; we just need the angles to match. We will always have a pair of parallel sides, so dilating will always be a possibility.)

- How does this relate to the rep-tile triangles you made in *Stretching and Shrinking* ? (They always had a whole-number scale factor. At that time, we did not pay attention to the parallel sides that were created. See the diagram in Problem 3.5, Question D.)

Then share student statements for Question D, and either apply this new knowledge to solve Question E as a whole class or have students share their explanations for Question E.

Note: There are other common minimal criteria for determining that two triangles are similar. For example, if $\triangle ABC$ and $\triangle DEF$ have $\angle B \cong \angle E$ and $\frac{AB}{DE} = \frac{BC}{EF}$, then the triangles will be similar. Also, if $\frac{AB}{DE} = \frac{BC}{EF} = \frac{CA}{FD}$, then the triangles will be similar. The Common Core State Standards for Grade 8 do not require this complete delineation of similarity criteria, so we focus on what is expected, the angle-angle criterion.

Reflecting on Student Learning

Use the following questions to assess student understanding at the end of the lesson.

- What evidence do I have that students understand the Focus Question?
  - Where did my students get stuck?
  - What strategies did they use?
  - What breakthroughs did my students have today?
- How will I use this to plan for tomorrow? For the next time I teach this lesson?
- Where will I have the opportunity to reinforce these ideas as I continue through this Unit? The next Unit?

ACE Assignment Guide

- **Applications:** 16–20
- **Connections:** 28
- **Extensions:** 29
- **Labsheet 4ACE:** Exercise 28

PROBLEM

4.4 Using Similar Triangles

Problem Overview

Focus Question What facts about similar triangles allow you to find lengths in very large figures that you are unable to reach?

Problem Description

The goal of this Problem is to give students insight into the ways that similar triangles can be used to solve practical measurement problems using a scale model. We use only one example of the technique that has been demonstrated in other contexts in *Stretching and Shrinking*. Question C asks students to collect their own measurements. This will require some foresight on the part of the teacher. You will need to consider what sites would work well, what materials will be needed, and how much time it will take.

Problem Implementation

Group students in pairs.

Materials

mirrors

meter sticks

- **Self-Assessment**
- **Notebook Checklist**
- **Unit Test**

Vocabulary

There are no new glossary terms introduced in this Problem.

Mathematics Background

- Similarity
- Similar Figures
- Applications of Similarity

At a Glance and Lesson Plan

- At a Glance: Problem 4.4 Butterflies, Pinwheels, and Wallpaper
- Lesson Plan: Problem 4.4 Butterflies, Pinwheels, and Wallpaper

Launch

Launch Video

This animation depicts Jim and Su measuring the height of a basketball hoop. They use a mirror placed on the ground. Then they measure the distance on the ground from the mirror to the base of the light and the distance from the mirror to the position of the person who can see the top of the light in the mirror. Using that person's height and the fact that ratios of corresponding sides between similar figures are constant, they calculate the height of the basketball hoop. Visit Teacher Place at mathdashboard.com/cmp3 to see the complete video.

You can show students this animation before discussing the introduction to the Problem. Students can watch it instead of reading the introduction in the Student Edition.

Connecting to Prior Knowledge

Discuss briefly why the two triangles pictured in the introduction are similar.

Suggested Questions

- Where are the equal angles? (One pair of angles is noted to be congruent and share a vertex at the mirror. The other pair of equal angles is the pair of right angles formed by the vertical heights of the person and traffic light.)
- Now that you know the triangles are similar, what else do you know? (Corresponding sides are in the same ratio.)

Presenting the Challenge

You might confirm the concept of the equal angles at the mirror by placing a mirror on the floor of your classroom and having two students of very different heights stand where they can see each other's faces in the mirror. The key physical principle is that the angle of incidence equals the angle of reflection in the mirror. Once that idea is clear to students, they can apply what they have learned about similar triangles to solve the Problem.

Explore

Providing for Individual Needs

You might choose to do a summary of Questions A and B before students apply the same reasoning to their own experimental data in Question C.

The critical fact about similar triangles that allows calculation of unmeasured parts is that there is a common scale factor (or proportionality constant) relating pairs of corresponding parts. Encourage your students to mark all the known lengths on their sketches and name corresponding vertices of triangles so the discussion is clearer.

If students are finding it difficult to set up helpful proportions, you might ask about the scale factor.

Suggested Questions

- You know the triangles are similar. What is the scale factor from the smaller triangle to the larger? How do you find this? (450 : 100. It is the ratio of corresponding sides; the sides that lie along the ground.)
- What lengths are in the ratio 450 : 100? (the distances on the ground to the mirror)
- What other sides must also be related by the same scale factor? (Height of traffic light and height to person's eyes; also, the distances from person's eyes to the mirror and the traffic light to the mirror, but we are not trying to find either of these.)
- How can you write that as an equation? ($\frac{\text{height of traffic light}}{150} = \frac{450}{100}$)

Push students to see that the method will always work.

- Suppose we had a shorter person than Jim. Then the height to the person's eyes would not be the same. Would that wreck your calculations? (We would still have similar triangles, but the lengths, angles, and scale factor would be different.)

For Question C, you might assign two groups to find the measure of the same object. This will demonstrate that, while the specifics of the similar triangles may differ, the result will be the same, except for measurement error.

Planning for the Summary

What evidence will you use in the summary to clarify and deepen understanding of the Focus Question?

What will you do if you do not have evidence?

Summarize

Orchestrating the Discussion

Since this Problem is really only one application of the ideas developed throughout the Investigation, the Summarize that is needed probably should focus on the student reasoning to solve either Question A or B. Ask a group to explain their reasoning.

Suggested Questions

- How did you know the triangles were similar? (They had two pairs of equal angles.)
- What was the scale factor? Did you use this in your solution? (Students may or may not use the scale factor directly. In Question A, for example, students might write a proportion using corresponding sides, $\frac{\text{height of traffic light}}{150} = \frac{450}{100}$, and then solve by finding a common denominator. Or they might write $\frac{\text{height of traffic light}}{150} = 4.5$ and solve by multiplying both sides of this equation by 150. Or they might "dilate" 150 by the scale factor of 4.5 without writing an equation. They know more about solving equations than when they made similar calculations in *Stretching and Shrinking*.)

If everyone is comfortable with the idea and solution strategy, you can proceed to the experiment and have students write up their results.

Reflecting on Student Learning

Use the following questions to assess student understanding at the end of the lesson.

- What evidence do I have that students understand the Focus Question?
  - Where did my students get stuck?
  - What strategies did they use?
  - What breakthroughs did my students have today?
- How will I use this to plan for tomorrow? For the next time I teach this lesson?
- Where will I have the opportunity to reinforce these ideas as I continue through this Unit? The next Unit?

ACE Assignment Guide

- **Applications:** 21, 22
- **Extensions:** 30, 31

Mathematical Reflections

Possible Answers to Mathematical Reflections

1. One could explain what it means for two geometric shapes to be similar:

a. In everyday words that could be understood by most people, it is probably most effective to simply say that the figures have the same shape but different size.

b. In the technical terms of mathematics, it means that one can transform one shape into an exact copy of the other by a dilation with some scale factor. To transform the first shape exactly onto the second, one might also need a sequence of reflections, rotations, and/or translations.

2. a. If a dilation transforms a polygon to a similar figure of a different size: (1) the side lengths will be related by the scale factor k; (2) the corresponding angles will be congruent; (3) the perimeters will be related by the scale factor k; (4) the areas of the two figures will be related by k^2; and (5) for dilations only, slopes of corresponding sides will be equal, meaning the sides are parallel.

b. We already knew all this information about similar figures from *Stretching and Shrinking*. In *Stretching and Shrinking*, we also used coordinate rules to make the dilations, but we called them stretches. One new idea was to match two pairs of angles to guarantee that two triangles are similar. This comes from the idea of nesting triangles and then thinking of the shared vertex as the origin of the dilation. We did something like this with rep-tiles in *Stretching and Shrinking*, but we could only do this with whole-number scale factors then.

3. The minimum amount of information needed to assure that two triangles are similar is congruence of two pairs of corresponding angles.

4. All strategies involve reasoning proportionally. You need one pair of corresponding side measures and one other side measure.

- You might then use one pair of corresponding sides to determine the scale factor, or dilation factor. Then multiply the remaining side measure by this dilation factor to find the measure of another corresponding side.
- You might set up a proportion with the given measures. Say side AB corresponds to side XY, side BC corresponds to side YZ, and you know the lengths of AB, XY, and BC. Then $\frac{AB}{XY} = \frac{BC}{YZ}$. So, $YZ = BC\left(\frac{XY}{AB}\right)$.
  Note: You can also set up a proportion that uses the internal ratios of corresponding lengths. $\frac{AB}{BC} = \frac{XY}{YZ}$.

Possible Answers to Mathematical Practices Reflections

Students may have demonstrated all of the eight Common Core Standards for Mathematical Practice during this Investigation. During the class discussion, have students provide additional Practices that the Problem cited involved and identify the use of other Mathematical Practices in the Investigation.

One student observation is provided in the Student Edition. Here is another sample student response.

> *We applied what we knew about similar triangles to explain why slope is the same between any two points on a slanted line. We related corresponding angles of similar right triangles formed on the line. These right triangles each had their hypotenuse as a segment of the line. This meant that the horizontal legs of two right triangles on the line are parallel. Also the vertical legs of two right triangles on the line are parallel. From either of these two facts and the right angle, the triangles are similar. Since the triangles are similar, their ratios of the length of the vertical leg to the horizontal leg are equal, which means that slope is a constant, m.*
>
> **MP2: Reason abstractly and quantitatively.**

Notes

Investigation 4

Dilations and Similar Figures

The Problems of the first three Investigations focused on ideas and techniques for recognizing and making symmetric patterns. They also focused on comparing figures to see if they have identical shape and size. You know, from earlier work in *Stretching and Shrinking*, that interesting things happen when you enlarge or reduce a figure.

For example, in one Investigation, you used a rubber band tool to enlarge the logo for a mystery club. In another Investigation, you compared various transformations of Mug Wump.

- Which characters are members of the Wump family, and which are impostors?

Common Core State Standards

8.EE.B.6 Use similar triangles to explain why the slope *m* is the same between any two distinct points on a non-vertical line in the coordinate plane . . .

8.G.A.4 Understand that a two-dimensional figure is similar to another if the second can be obtained from the first by a sequence of rotations, reflections, translations, and dilations; given two similar two-dimensional figures, describe a sequence that exhibits the similarity between them.

8.G.A.5 Use informal arguments to establish facts about the angle sum and exterior angle of triangles, about the angles created when parallel lines are cut by a transversal, and the angle-angle criterion for similarity of triangles.

Also 8.G.A.3

STUDENT PAGE

Notes

By measuring the figures that result from stretching or shrinking operations, you learned about **similarity transformations.** These are actions that change the size, but not the shape, of geometric figures. In this Investigation, you will review and extend your understanding of dilations and other similarity transformations.

4.1 Focus on Dilations

The key part of any similarity transformation is a **dilation.** The diagram below shows how a dilation, centered at point P with scale factor $\frac{3}{2}$ or 1.5, transforms triangle ABC to triangle XYZ. The two triangles are **similar figures.**

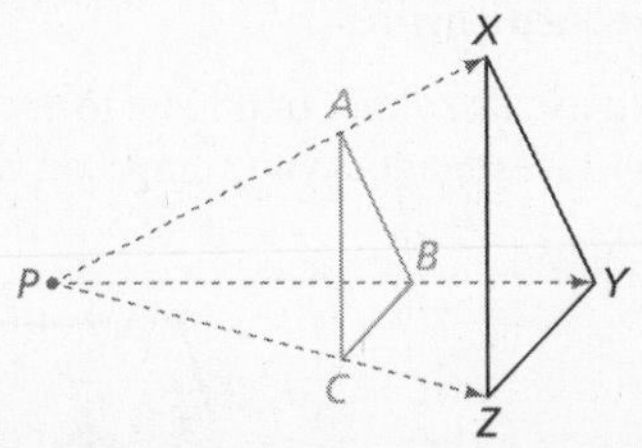

In everyday language, a "dilation" is usually an enlargement with a scale factor greater than 1. In mathematics, the scale factor of a dilation may be greater than or less than 1. A scale factor greater than 1 causes stretching, while a scale factor less than 1 causes shrinking. In fact, the diagram above also shows how a dilation with center P and scale factor $\frac{2}{3}$, or about 0.67, transforms triangle XYZ to triangle ABC.

How do dilations affect the size and shape of the figures they transform?

In this Problem, you will review the properties of stretching and shrinking transformations by working with figures on a coordinate grid.

Notes

Problem 4.1

A Copy the figure below onto grid paper. Draw the image of quadrilateral *PQRS* after a dilation with center (0, 0) and scale factor 3. Label corresponding points P', Q', R', and S'.

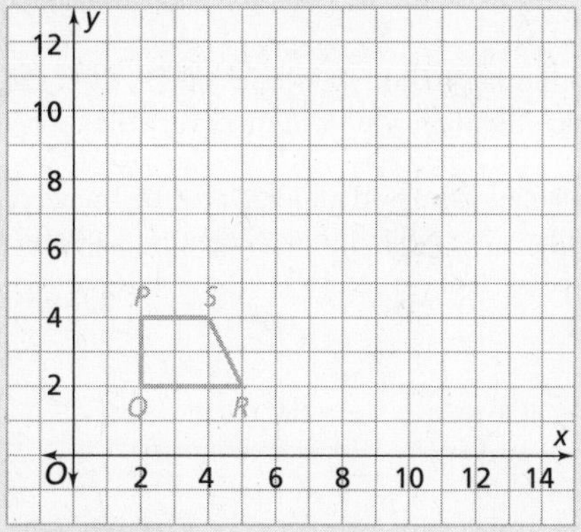

1. How do the side lengths of quadrilateral $P'Q'R'S'$ compare to those of quadrilateral *PQRS*?
2. How do the angle measures of quadrilateral $P'Q'R'S'$ compare to those of quadrilateral *PQRS*?
3. How does the perimeter of quadrilateral $P'Q'R'S'$ compare to that of quadrilateral *PQRS*?
4. How does the area of quadrilateral $P'Q'R'S'$ compare to that of quadrilateral *PQRS*?
5. How do the slopes of the sides of quadrilateral $P'Q'R'S'$ compare to the slopes of the sides of quadrilateral *PQRS*?
6. What rule of the form $(x, y) \rightarrow (\blacksquare, \blacksquare)$ shows how coordinates of corresponding points are related under a dilation with center (0, 0) and scale factor 3?

continued on the next page >

STUDENT PAGE

Notes

Problem 4.1 continued

B On the drawing from Question A, draw $\overline{OP}$, $\overline{OP'}$, $\overline{OQ}$, and $\overline{OQ'}$.

1. What similar triangles do you see? Explain.
2. a. Suppose point $Z = (2z, 4z)$. How are points P and Z related to each other?

   b. Use coordinates to find the slopes of $\overline{OP}$, $\overline{OP'}$, $\overline{OZ}$, and $\overline{PZ}$. What do you notice? Explain why your discovery makes sense.

C Copy the figure below onto grid paper. Draw the image of quadrilateral $PQRS$ after a dilation with center (0, 0) and scale factor $\frac{1}{2}$.

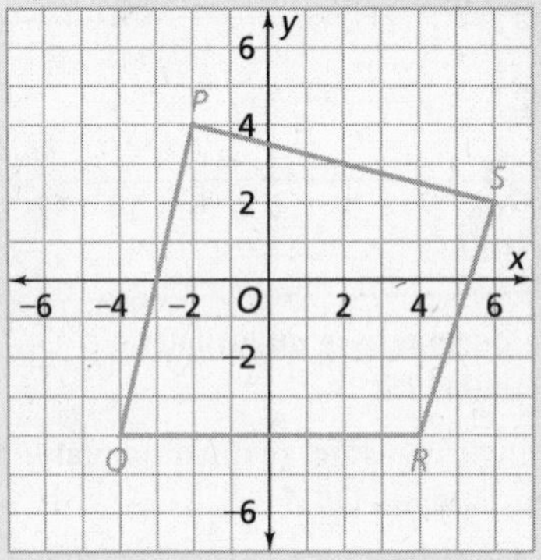

1. How do the side lengths of quadrilateral $P'Q'R'S'$ compare to those of quadrilateral $PQRS$?
2. How do the angle measures of quadrilateral $P'Q'R'S'$ compare to those of quadrilateral $PQRS$?
3. How does the perimeter of quadrilateral $P'Q'R'S'$ compare to that of quadrilateral $PQRS$?
4. How does the area of quadrilateral $P'Q'R'S'$ compare to that of quadrilateral $PQRS$?
5. How do the slopes of the sides of quadrilateral $P'Q'R'S'$ compare to the slopes of the sides of quadrilateral $PQRS$?
6. What rule of the form $(x, y) \rightarrow (\blacksquare, \blacksquare)$ shows how coordinates of corresponding points are related under a dilation with center (0, 0) and scale factor $\frac{1}{2}$?

Notes

Problem 4.1 continued

D Use your results from Questions A and B to write conjectures about the effects of a dilation with scale factor k on a polygon. If necessary, try dilating a few more figures.

Begin your conjectures with: "When two polygons are related by a dilation with scale factor k, . . . "

E If you dilate a figure with reflectional or rotational symmetry, will the resulting image have the same symmetry? Explain.

ACE Homework starts on page 86.

4.2 Return of Super Sleuth

Similarity Transformations

Dilations transform geometric figures to larger or smaller versions of the same shape. The diagram below shows two versions of the "Super Sleuth" logo for the P. I. Middle School Mystery Club. They appear to be similar, but there is no obvious center or scale factor for a dilation that would stretch or shrink one image onto the other.

? What strategies could you use to check the similarity of the two figures?

STUDENT PAGE

Notes

If you can find a sequence of reflections, rotations, and/or translations that "move" one figure onto the other, then the two figures are congruent. In this Problem, you will decide if the same strategy works for testing the similarity of figures.

Problem 4.2

For each pair of polygons:

- Inspect and measure the parts of the figures to determine whether they are similar.
- If the figures are similar, list the corresponding vertices.
- If the figures are similar, describe a sequence of reflections, rotations, translations, and/or dilations that would move and then stretch or shrink one figure onto the other.

A Are triangles *ABC* and *PQR* similar?

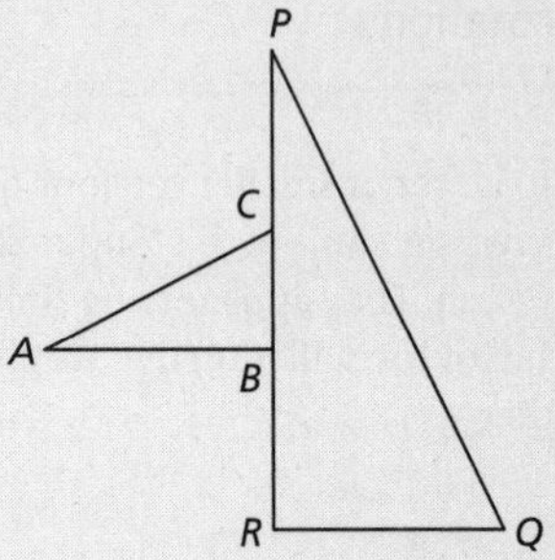

B Are rectangles *DEFG* and *STUV* similar?

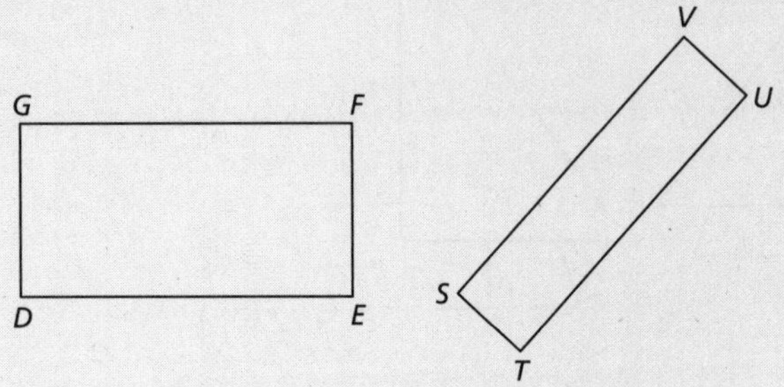

Notes

Problem 4.2 continued

C Are parallelograms *GHIJ* and *VWXY* similar?

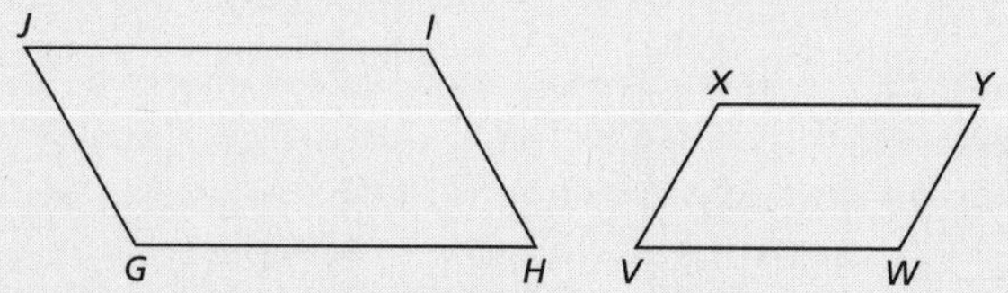

D What clues do you look for when identifying similar polygons?

ACE Homework starts on page 86.

4.3 Checking Similarity Without Transformations

In Investigation 2, you learned how to determine whether two triangles are congruent without actually "moving" one onto the other. That suggests there might be comparable strategies for testing the similarity of triangles.

If two triangles are similar, corresponding angles are congruent and the corresponding sides are related by a scale factor k.

For example, in triangles *ABC* and *XYZ*, you can measure to check that:

$\angle X \cong \angle A$	$XY = 2 \cdot AB$
$\angle Y \cong \angle B$	$YZ = 2 \cdot BC$
$\angle Z \cong \angle C$	$ZX = 2 \cdot CA$

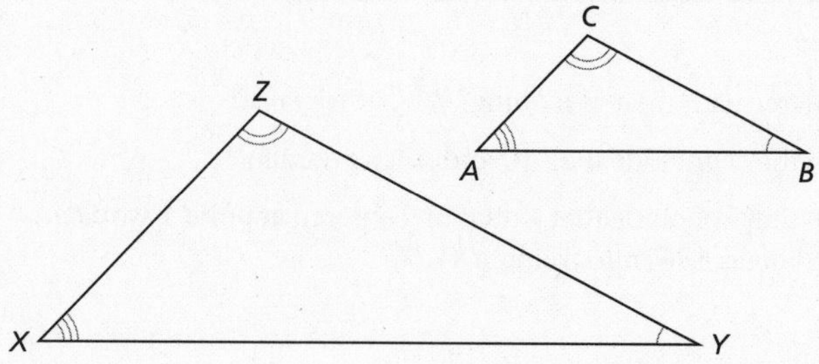

Notes

In this Problem, you will explore whether you need to measure all the sides and angles of the triangles to determine similarity.

Can you conclude that two triangles are similar if you know the measures of only one, two, or three pairs of corresponding parts? Explain.

Problem 4.3

The students at Palms Middle School have different ideas about whether they need to measure all the sides and angles of two triangles to determine similarity.

A Kevin and Ming think you only need to measure the angles of each triangle. They argue, "The angles give a polygon its shape. If two triangles have congruent corresponding angles, they will have the same shape and be similar."

Do you agree with their reasoning? Why or why not?

B Owen and Natasha agree that you need to measure angles, but have a different argument. They claim, "If two triangles have congruent corresponding angles, then you can flip, turn, and/or slide the smaller triangle onto the larger triangle as shown below. Then $\overline{AC}$ is parallel to $\overline{XZ}$, so a dilation centered at point Y will stretch triangle ABC exactly onto triangle XYZ. This proves that the original triangles are similar."

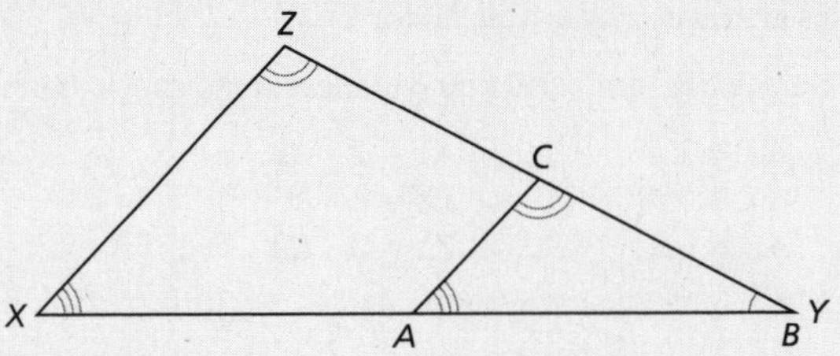

1. Do you agree with their reasoning? Why or why not?
2. How can they conclude that $\overline{AC}$ and $\overline{XZ}$ are parallel?
3. How can they conclude that a dilation centered at point Y would stretch triangle ABC onto triangle XYZ?

Notes

Problem 4.3 continued

C Kelly and Rico think you need to measure only two pairs of corresponding angles to guarantee similarity. They argue, "If you know the measures of two angles of a triangle, then you can subtract the sum of the two angles from 180° to find the measure of the third angle. If you know that the sum of two angles in one triangle is equal to the sum of two corresponding angles in another, then the third angles of those triangles must be equal in measure."

Do you agree with their reasoning? Why or why not?

D Complete this statement in a way that combines the ideas of the Palms Middle School students: If _____ angles in one triangle are equal in measure to _____ corresponding angles in another triangle, then . . .

E The shortcut for proving that two triangles are similar helps to verify other observations you might have made.

1. In the figure below, the equation of the line is $y = ax + b$ and points P, Z, and W are on the line. Copy the diagram and find similar triangles. Explain why they are similar.

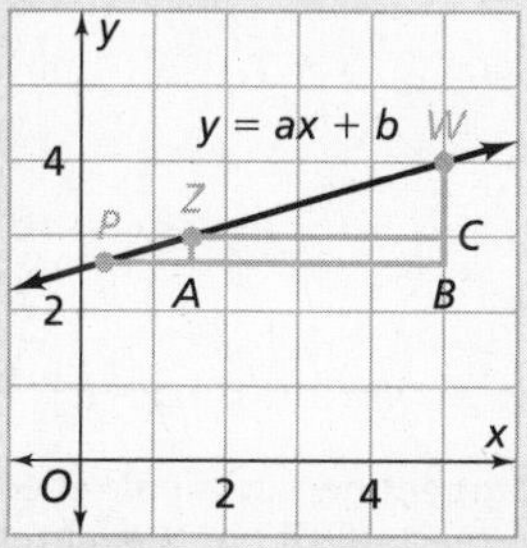

2. How can you use the similar triangles to explain why the slope of $\overline{PZ}$ equals the slope of $\overline{PW}$ (or the slope of $\overline{ZW}$)? Explain.

ACE Homework starts on page 86.

STUDENT PAGE

Notes

4.4 Using Similar Triangles

Similar triangles have the same shape, but are usually a different size. You can use the relationships between corresponding parts of similar triangles to solve measurement problems.

For example, the diagram below shows a method for calculating the height of an object that is difficult to measure directly. Place a mirror on a leveled spot at a convenient distance from the object. Back up from the mirror until you can see the reflection of the top of the object in the center of the mirror.

The two triangles in the diagram are similar. To find the object's height, you need to measure three distances and use similar triangles.

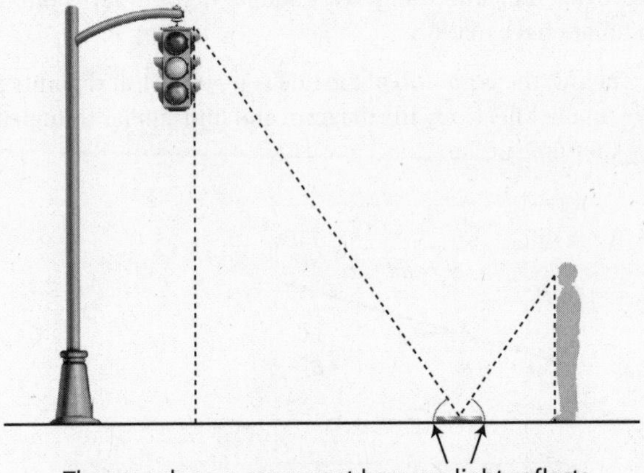

These angles are congruent because light reflects off a mirror at the same angle it hits the mirror.
Not drawn to scale

Notes

Problem 4.4

A Jim and Su use the mirror method to estimate the height of a traffic light near their school. They make the following measurements:

- height from the ground to Jim's eyes: 150 cm
- distance from the middle of the mirror to Jim's feet: 100 cm
- distance from the middle of the mirror to a point directly under the traffic signal: 450 cm

1. Sketch the situation to show the similar triangles formed. Label any parts of the triangles with the known measurements.
2. Explain how you know that the triangles are similar.
3. Use properties of similarity to estimate the height of the traffic light.

B Jim and Su also use the mirror method to estimate the height of the gymnasium in their school. They make the following measurements:

- height from the ground to Su's eyes: 130 cm
- distance from the middle of the mirror to Su's feet: 100 cm
- distance from the middle of the mirror to the gym wall: 9.5 m

1. Sketch the situation to show the similar triangles formed. Label any parts of the triangles with the known measurements.
2. Use properties of similarity to estimate the height of the gymnasium.

C Find an object that is too tall for you to measure directly. Use the mirror method to estimate its height. Make a sketch and explain how you used properties of similar triangles to estimate the height.

ACE Homework starts on page 86.

STUDENT PAGE

Notes

Applications | Connections | Extensions

Applications

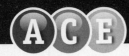

For Exercises 1–6, use the following figure.

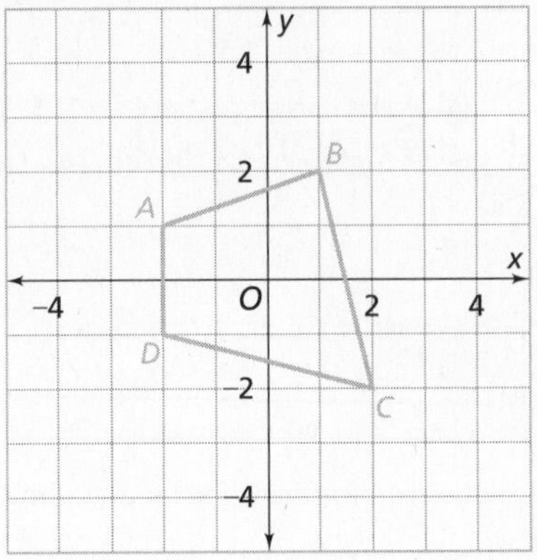

1. Copy the figure onto grid paper. Draw the image of quadrilateral *ABCD* under a dilation with center (0, 0) and scale factor 2. Label the image $A'B'C'D'$.

2. Find the side lengths of quadrilaterals *ABCD* and $A'B'C'D'$. How are the lengths of corresponding sides related?

3. Find the perimeters of quadrilaterals *ABCD* and $A'B'C'D'$. How are the two perimeters related?

4. Find the areas of quadrilaterals *ABCD* and $A'B'C'D'$. How are the two areas related?

5. Find the slopes of the sides of quadrilaterals *ABCD* and $A'B'C'D'$.
   a. How are the slopes of corresponding sides related?
   b. What does your answer to part (a) suggest about the relationship between a line and its image under a dilation?

6. What dilation would transform quadrilateral $A'B'C'D'$ to quadrilateral *ABCD*?

Notes

For Exercises 7–10, suppose you dilate quadrilateral *ABCD* by a scale factor of 2. Then you flip, turn, or slide the image to quadrilateral *A″B″C″D″*.

7. Describe how the side lengths of quadrilateral $A''B''C''D''$ are related to the side lengths of each quadrilateral.

a. $ABCD$

b. $A'B'C'D'$

8. Describe how the perimeter of quadrilateral $A''B''C''D''$ is related to the perimeter of each quadrilateral.

a. $ABCD$

b. $A'B'C'D'$

9. Describe how the area of quadrilateral $A''B''C''D''$ is related to the area of each quadrilateral.

a. $ABCD$

b. $A'B'C'D'$

10. Describe how the slopes of the sides of quadrilateral $A''B''C''D''$ are related to the slopes of the sides of each quadrilateral.

a. $ABCD$

b. $A'B'C'D'$

Notes

For Exercises 11–15, tell whether the polygons in each pair are similar. For those that are similar, describe a sequence of flips, turns, slides, and/or dilations that would transform one to the other.

11.

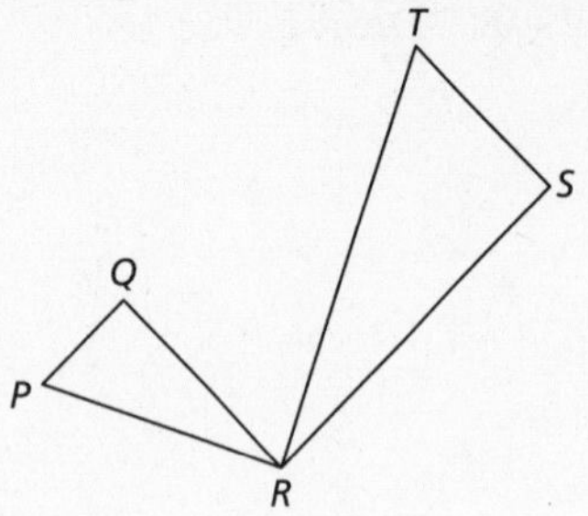

12.

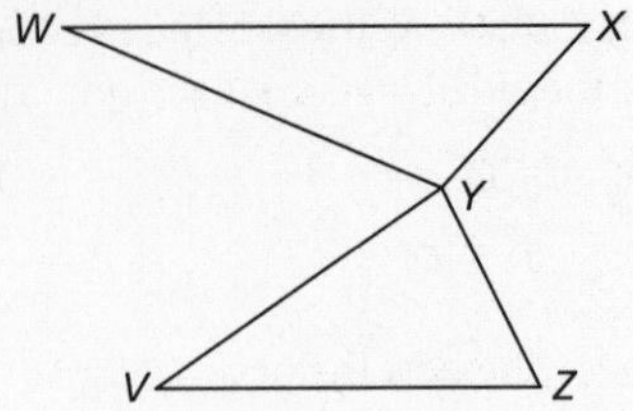

13.

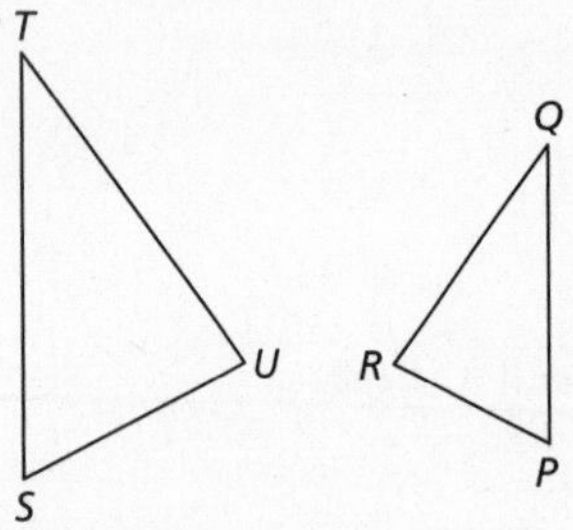

14.

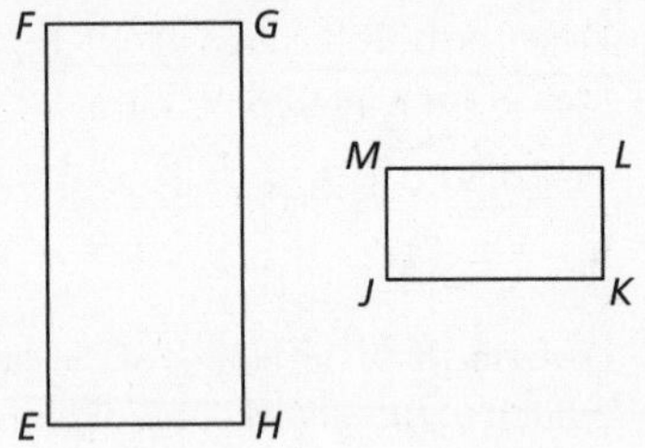

15.

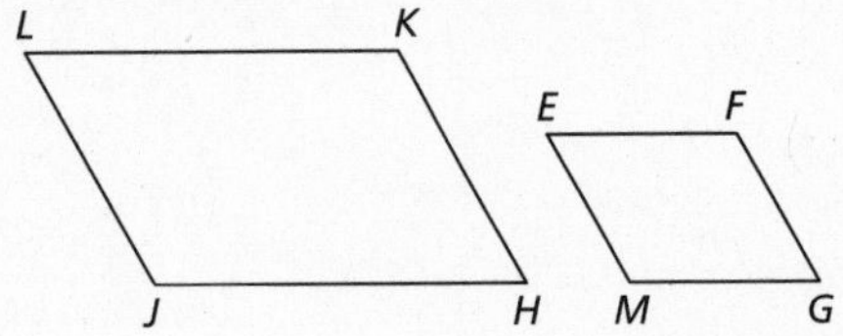

Notes

For Exercises 16–20, determine whether each statement is *true* or *false*. Justify your answer.

16. If $\angle P \cong \angle A$, $PQ = 2.5 \cdot AB$, and $PR = 2.5 \cdot AC$, you can conclude that the triangles are similar without measuring any more angles or sides.

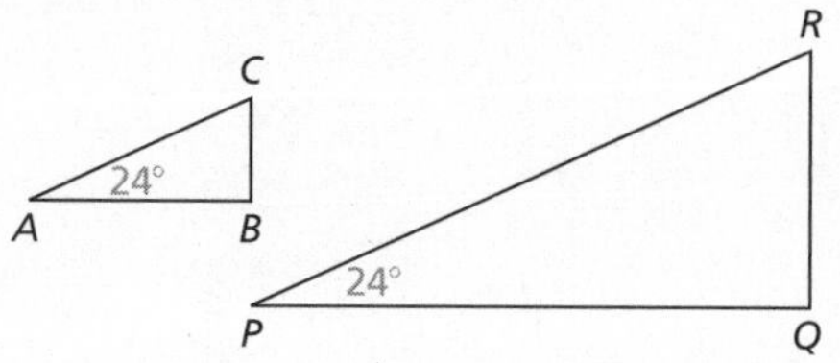

17. If $\overline{AB}$ is parallel to $\overline{DE}$, then triangles ABC and DEC are similar.

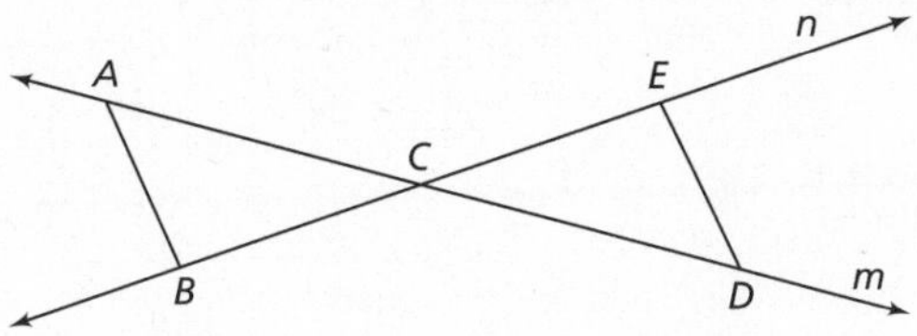

18. Any two equilateral triangles are similar to each other.

19. If corresponding angles of two polygons are congruent, then the polygons are similar.

20. Any two isosceles triangles are similar to each other.

STUDENT PAGE

Notes

21. Stan uses the mirror method to estimate the height of a building. His measurements are shown in the diagram below.

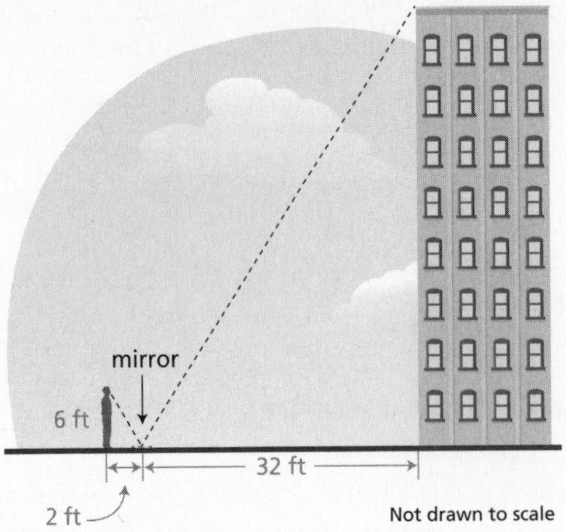

a. How tall is the building?

b. How do you know that your calculation is correct?

22. One afternoon, the building in Exercise 21 casts a shadow that is 10 feet long, while a nearby building casts a shadow that is 6 feet long.

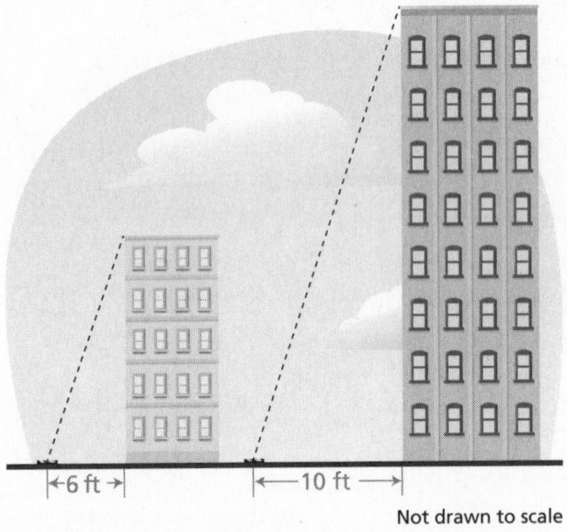

a. How tall is the shorter building?

b. How do you know that your calculation is correct?

Notes

Connections

23. A sphere has a radius of 5 centimeters.

a. What are the volume and surface area of the sphere?

b. The sphere is dilated by a scale factor of 2.

i. What is the surface area of the image?

ii. What is the volume of the image?

c. How can you find the answers to part (b) quickly by using your results from part (a)?

24. Consider the image of a figure after a dilation with center (0, 0) and scale factor 1.5, followed by a dilation with center (0, 0) and scale factor 4.

a. What is the simplest coordinate rule that relates each point of the figure to its image after the two dilations?

b. Suppose the order of the two dilations was reversed. Would the rule be different? Explain.

25. The figure below has reflectional symmetry in the *y*-axis.

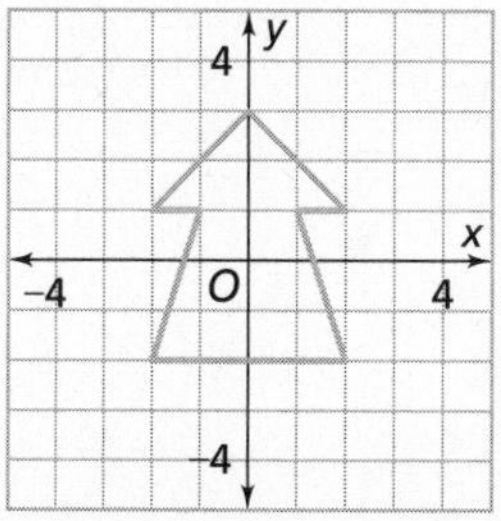

a. Suppose the figure is dilated with scale factor 1.5 and center (0, 0). Would the image have the same symmetry?

b. Would the result be different with a different scale factor?

c. Would the result be different if the center of dilation was outside the figure?

STUDENT PAGE

Notes

For Exercises 26 and 27, determine whether the given statement is *true* or *false*. Justify your answer.

26. Any two squares are similar to each other.

27. Any two rhombuses are similar to each other.

28. The diagram below shows triangle ABC and its three images under a rotation of 180° about midpoints M, N, and P.

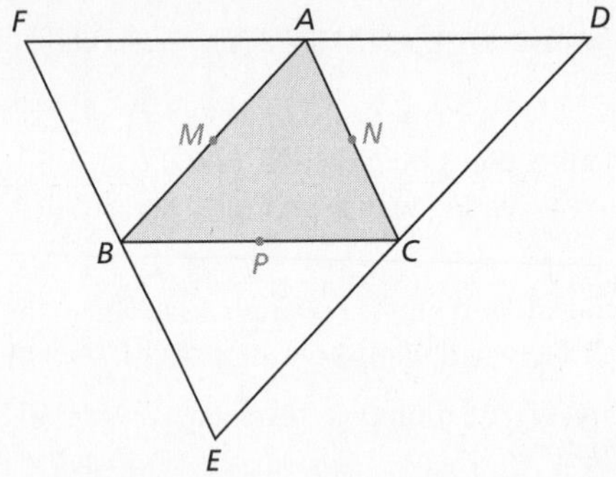

a. Are any of the triangles in the diagram similar? If so, what is the scale factor? Explain.

b. List all the parallelograms in the diagram. For each one, state why you think it is a parallelogram.

Notes

Extensions

29. Two students claim that you can determine whether two triangles are similar without measuring any angles. They say, "For example, if $XY = 2 \cdot AB$, $YZ = 2 \cdot BC$, and $ZX = 2 \cdot CA$, then triangles ABC and XYZ are similar."

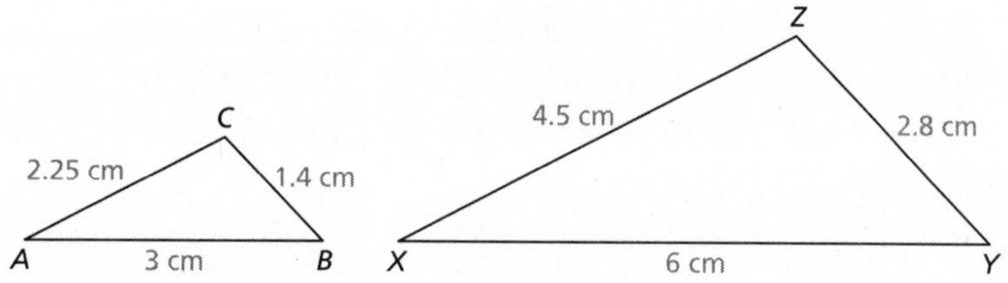

a. Do you think the students are correct? Explain.

b. Do you agree with their reasoning in the following proof? Explain why or why not.

> If triangles ABC and XYZ are similar, then the lengths of corresponding sides are proportional. That is, $\frac{XY}{AB} = \frac{YZ}{BC} = \frac{ZX}{CA} = 2$.
> If you dilate triangle ABC by a factor of 2, corresponding angles will be congruent. The image $A'B'C'$ will have side lengths that are congruent to those of triangle XYZ.
>
> So, triangle $A'B'C'$ will be congruent to triangle XYZ and have congruent corresponding angles. This means that the angles of triangle ABC must be congruent to those of triangle XYZ, and the two triangles must be similar.

STUDENT PAGE

Notes

30. Suppose that a figure is transformed by two dilations, one after the other. The scale factors and centers of the two dilations are different. Will the final result be a dilation of the original figure with a different third center and scale factor?

Explore some simple cases to help you answer the question. For example, you might start with transformations of a simple triangle. Use centers of dilation (0, 0) and (1, 0) and scale factors 2 and 3.

31. Consider a one-directional dilation with rule $(x, y) \rightarrow (2x, y)$ instead of the basic dilation centered at the origin that "moves" $(x, y) \rightarrow (2x, 2y)$.

Experiment with a figure like the one below to see how the one-directional dilation works.

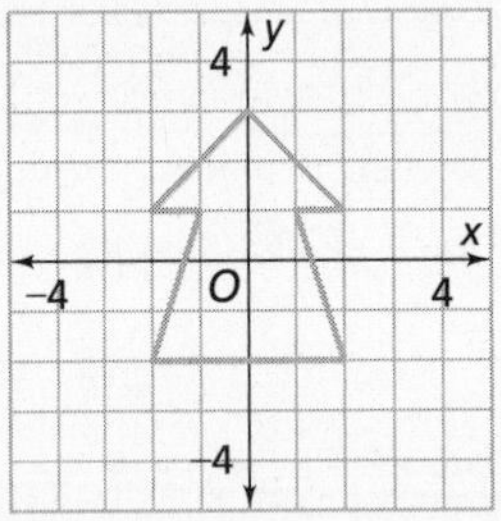

a. Does the transformation produce an image that is similar to the original figure?

b. How does the transformation affect the side lengths, angle measures, perimeter, and area of the figure?

c. How does the transformation affect the slopes of the sides of the figure?

Notes

Mathematical Reflections 4

In this Investigation, you used geometric transformations to study similarity of figures. The following questions will help you summarize what you have learned.

Think about these questions. Discuss your ideas with other students and your teacher. Then write a summary of your findings in your notebook.

1. **How** would you explain what it means for two geometric shapes to be similar using
   a. everyday words that most people could understand?
   b. technical terms of mathematics?
2. a. Suppose you dilate a polygon to form a figure of a different size. **How** will the side lengths, angle measures, perimeters, areas, and slopes of the sides of the two figures be alike? How will they be different?
   b. **How** has your knowledge of dilations changed or extended what you already knew about similarity?
3. **What** is the least amount of information you need in order to be sure that two triangles are similar?
4. **How** do you use similarity to find the side lengths of similar figures?

STUDENT PAGE

Notes

Common Core Mathematical Practices

As you worked on the Problems in this Investigation, you used prior knowledge to make sense of them. You also applied Mathematical Practices to solve the Problems. Think back over your work, the ways you thought about the Problems, and how you used Mathematical Practices.

Jayden described his thoughts in the following way:

> In Problem 4.4, we applied what we knew about similar triangles to solve real-world problems. My group found the height of the flagpole outside the school by using the mirror method. We drew a diagram that showed how similar triangles model the situation. Then, we labeled the diagram with all the measurements we could find directly. Another group found the height of the school the same way, so we were able to compare our results to see if they made sense.
>
> **Common Core Standards for Mathematical Practice**
> **MP4** Model with mathematics.

- What other Mathematical Practices can you identify in Jayden's reasoning?
- Describe a Mathematical Practice that you and your classmates used to solve a different Problem in this Investigation.

Notes

Notes

STUDENT PAGE

Looking Back

In this Unit, you learned how to recognize and make symmetric figures. You learned how to use geometric transformations to compare the size and shape of figures. You also learned how to use coordinate grids to locate and show motion of figures.

Use Your Understanding: Algebraic Reasoning

Test your understanding of symmetry, transformations, congruence, and similarity by solving these problems about a home improvement project.

1. The wallpaper design below has been selected for the kitchen.

   a. Describe the symmetries in the wallpaper pattern. Assume that the design continues in the same way horizontally and vertically.

   b. The wallpaper pattern is made of two basic design elements. What is the smallest angle you can rotate each design element so that it looks the same as in its original position?

Notes

2. One of the square tiles for the kitchen floor is shown below.

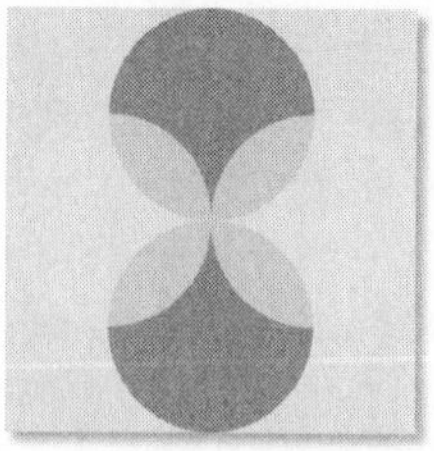

a. Describe all symmetries of the design on the tile.

b. Identify the smallest basic design element that can be transformed to produce the entire design. Explain the transformations that will map that basic element onto all other parts of the design.

3. The living room rug has copies of the design at the right along its border. Here, the design is shown on a coordinate grid. Copy the figure onto grid paper. Draw the image of the design after each transformation.

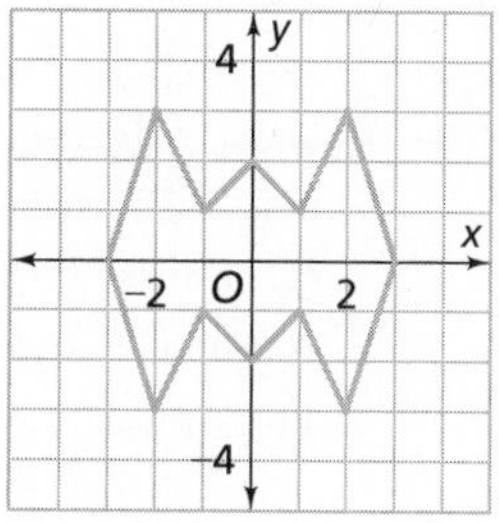

a. a 90° counterclockwise rotation about the origin

b. a reflection in the y-axis

c. a translation with rule $(x, y) \rightarrow (x, y + 3)$

4. Consider triangle ABC below.

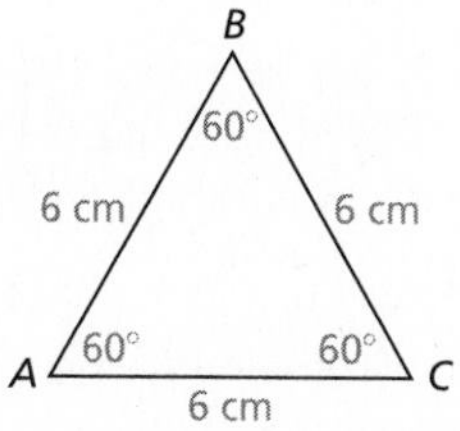

a. What is the least number of side and/or angle measures needed to make a congruent copy of triangle ABC? Explain.

b. What different combinations of side and angle measures could you use to make the congruent copy?

c. If a friend claims that he has drawn a similar copy of triangle ABC, what measurements could you make to check that claim?

Notes

5. Line k is a line of symmetry for triangle PQR. What, if anything, does this tell you about each pair of parts of the figure?

   a. $\overline{PR}$ and $\overline{PQ}$

   b. $\angle Q$ and $\angle R$

   c. point M and $\overline{QR}$

   d. $\angle RPM$ and $\angle QPM$

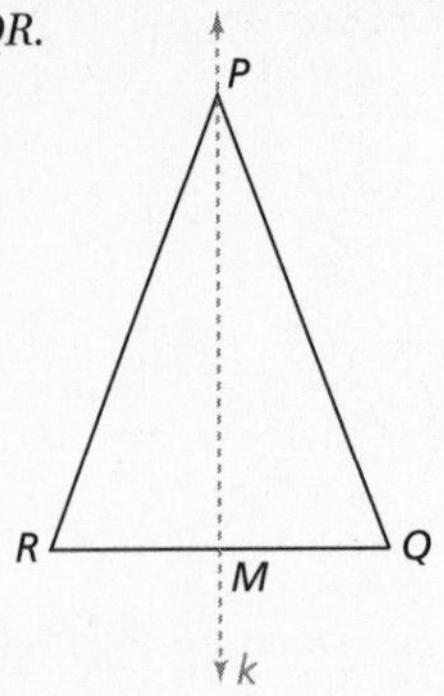

Explain Your Reasoning

Solving geometric problems requires using visual skills to see important patterns. However, you also need to be able to justify your conclusions.

6. How would you convince someone that a figure has the given symmetry?

   a. reflectional symmetry

   b. rotational symmetry

   c. translational symmetry

7. Suppose you have a figure and its image under a rotation. How could you find the center and angle of rotation that produced the image?

8. Suppose you have a figure and its image under a reflection. How could you find the line of reflection that produced the image?

9. Give some combinations of congruent sides and angles that will guarantee that two triangles are congruent. Then, give some combinations of congruent sides and angles that will *not* guarantee that two triangles are congruent.

10. Give some combinations of side and angle measures that will guarantee that two triangles are similar.

Notes

English / Spanish Glossary

A

angle of rotation The number of degrees that a figure rotates.

ángulo de rotación El número de grados que rota una figura.

B

basic design element A part of a pattern or design that, when transformed using at least one type of symmetry transformation, will produce the entire design.

elemento de diseño básico Parte de un patrón o diseño que, cuando se transforma usando un tipo de simetría de transformación, producirá el diseño completo.

C

center of rotation A fixed point about which a figure rotates.

centro de rotación Un punto fijo alrededor del cual rota una figura.

congruent figures Two figures are congruent if one is an image of the other under a translation, a reflection, a rotation, or some combination of these transformations. Put more simply, two figures are congruent if you can slide, flip, or turn one figure so it fits exactly on the other. The polygons below are congruent.

figuras congruentes Dos figuras son congruentes si una es la imagen de la otra sometida a una traslación, una reflexión, una rotación o a alguna combinación de estas transformaciones. Expresado de manera más sencilla, dos figuras son congruentes si puedes deslizar, voltear o rotar una figura para que coincida exactamente con la otra. Los siguientes polígonos son congruentes.

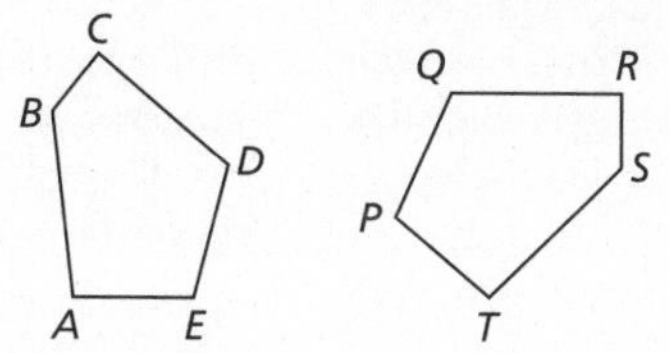

Notes

D

describe Academic Vocabulary To explain or tell in detail. A written description can contain facts and other information needed to communicate your answer. A diagram or a graph may also be included.

related terms *express, explain, illustrate*

sample Describe the reflectional and rotational symmetries for the figure.

The figure has one vertical line of reflectional symmetry through its center. The figure cannot be rotated less than one full turn to any position so that it looks the same as it does in its original position. The figure does not have rotational symmetry.

describir Vocabulario académico Explicar o decir con detalle. Una descripción escrita puede contener datos y otra información necesaria para comunicar tu respuesta. También se puede incluir un diagrama o una gráfica.

términos relacionados *expresar, explicar, ilustrar*

ejemplo Describe las simetrías de reflexión y de rotación de la figura.

La figura tiene una recta vertical de simetría de reflexión a través de su centro. La figura no puede rotarse menos de una vueita completa a cualquler posición de modo que se vea lgual que en su posición original. La figura no tiene simetría de rotación.

dilation A transformation that enlarges or reduces a figure by a scale factor about a center point so that the original figure and its image are similar. If the scale factor is greater than 1, the dilation is an enlargement. If the scale factor is less than 1, the dilation is a reduction.

dilatación Una transformación que aumenta o reduce la figura en un factor de escala sobre un punto central para que la figura original y su imagen sean similares. Si el factor de escala es mayor que 1, la dilatación es un aumento. Si el factor de escala es menor que 1, la dilatación es una reducción.

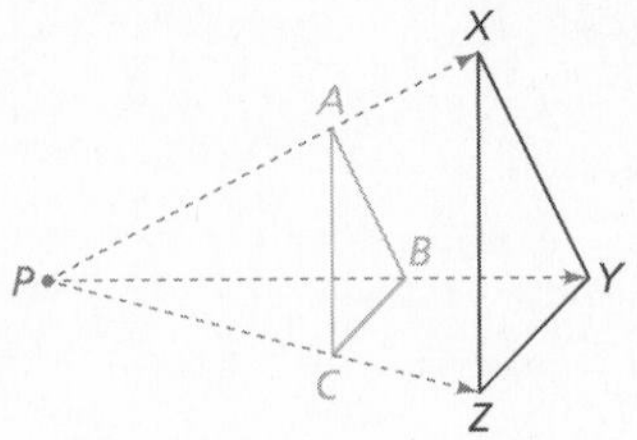

Notes

E

explain Academic Vocabulary To give facts and details that make an idea easier to understand. Explaining something can involve a written summary supported by a diagram, chart, table, or any combination of these.

related terms *analyze, clarify, describe, justify, tell*

sample Are the triangles below congruent? Explain.

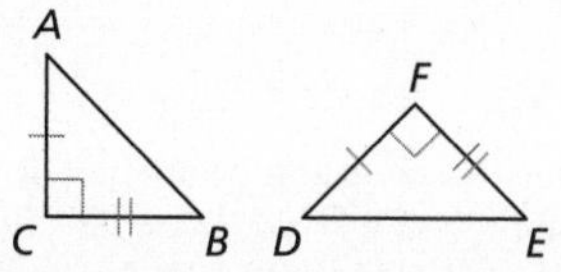

The two triangles are congruent because the sides and the included angle of $\triangle ABC$ are congruent to the two sides and the included angle of $\triangle DEF$.

explicar Vocabulario académico Dar datos y detalles que hacen que una idea sea más fácil de comprender. Explicar puede incluir un resumen escrito apoyado por un diagrama, una gráfica, una tabla o una combinación de estos.

términos relacionados *analizar, aclarar, describir, justificar, decir*

ejemplo ¿Son congruentes los triángulos siguientes? Explica tu respuesta.

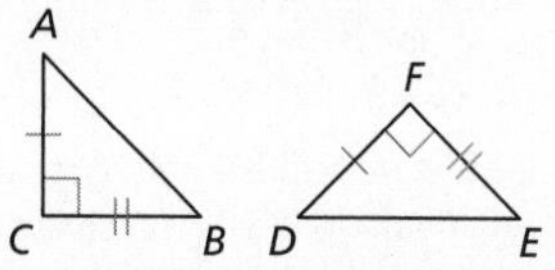

Los dos triángulos son congruentes porque los dos lados y el ángulo incluido del $\triangle ABC$ son congruentes con los dos lados y el ángulo incluido del $\triangle DEF$.

I

identify Academic Vocabulary To match a definition or a description to an object or to recognize something and be able to name it.

sample Identify the letter that has rotational symmetry.

A H V C

The letter H has rotational symmetry because it can be turned 180 degrees to a position in which it looks the same as it does in the original position.

identificar Vocabulario académico Relacionar una definición o una descripción con un objeto, o bien, reconocer algo y ser capaz de nombrarlo.

ejemplo Identifica la letra que tiene simetría de rotación.

A H V C

La letra H tiene simetría de rotación porque puede girarse 180 grados hasta una posición en la que se ve igual que en la posición original.

Notes

L

line of symmetry A line of symmetry divides a figure into halves that are mirror images. Lines *WY* and *ZX* below are lines of symmetry.

eje de simetría El eje de simetría divide una figura en dos mitades en la que una es el reflejo de la otra. Las rectas *WY* y *ZX* que aparecen abajo son ejes de simetría.

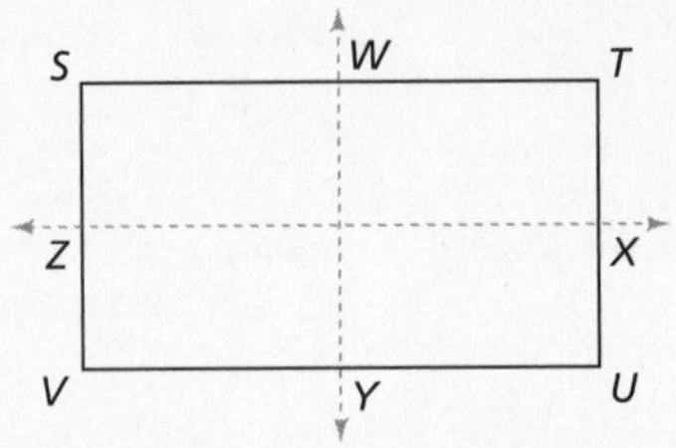

line reflection A transformation that maps each point of a figure to its mirror image, where a line acts as the mirror. Polygon $A'B'C'D'E'$ below is the image of polygon *ABCDE* under a reflection in the line. If you drew a line segment from a point to its image, the segment would be perpendicular to, and bisected by, the line of reflection.

reflexión sobre un eje Una transformación en la que cada punto de una figura coincide con su imagen reflejada sobre un eje. El polígono $A'B'C'D'E'$ que aparece abajo es la imagen del polígono *ABCDE* sometido a una reflexión sobre un eje. Si dibujaras un segmento de recta desde un punto hasta su imagen, el segmento sería perpendicular al eje de reflexión y estaría bisecado por este.

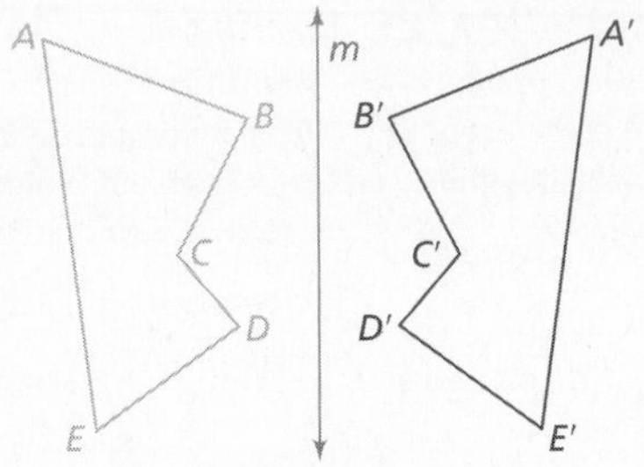

Notes

R **reflectional symmetry** A figure or design has reflectional symmetry if you can draw a line that divides the figure into halves that are mirror images. The line that divides the figure into halves is called the *line of symmetry*. The design below has reflectional symmetry about a vertical line through its center. Reflectional symmetry is sometimes referred to as *mirror symmetry* or *line symmetry*.

simetría de reflexión Una figura o diseño tiene simetría de reflexión si se puede dibujar una recta que divida la figura en dos mitades que sean imágenes reflejadas una de la otra. La recta que divide la figura en dos mitades se llama *eje de simetría*. El siguiente diseño tiene simetría de reflexión a ambos lados de una recta vertical que pasa por su centro. La simetría de reflexión a veces se conoce como *simetría axial*.

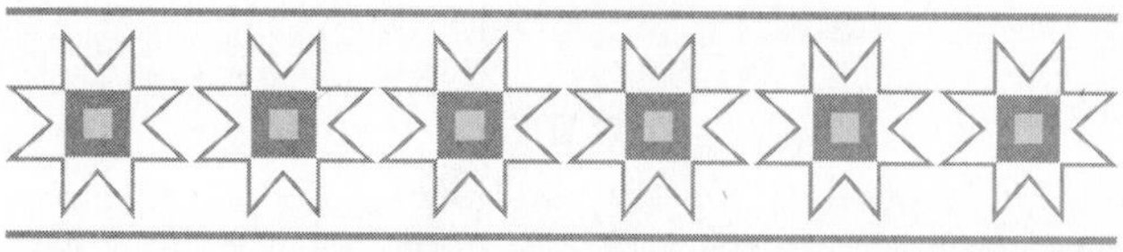

rotation A transformation that turns a figure counterclockwise about a point. Polygon $A'B'C'D'$ below is the image of polygon $ABCD$ under a 60° rotation about point P. If you drew a segment from a point on polygon $ABCD$ to point P and another segment from the point's image to point P, the segments would be the same length and they would form a 60° angle.

rotación Una transformación en la que una figura gira alrededor de un punto en sentido contrario a las manecillas del reloj. El polígono $A'B'C'D'$ que se muestra abajo es la imagen del polígono $ABCD$ después de una rotación de 60° alrededor del punto P. Si se dibujara un segmento desde un punto en el polígono $ABCD$ hasta el punto P y otro segmento desde la imagen del punto hasta el punto P, los segmentos tendrían la misma longitud y formarían un ángulo de 60°.

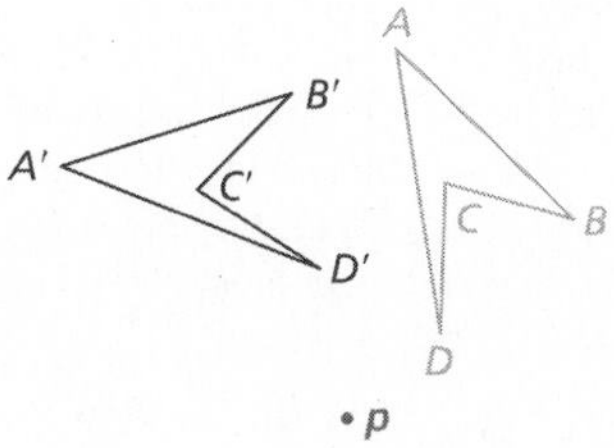

English / Spanish Glossary

END MATTER

STUDENT PAGE

Notes

rotational symmetry A figure or design has rotational symmetry if it can be rotated less than a full turn about a point to a position in which it looks the same as the original. The design below has rotational symmetry with its center as the center of rotation and a 60° angle of rotation. This means that it can be rotated 60°, or any multiple of 60°, about its center point to produce an image that matches exactly with the original.

simetría de rotación Una figura o diseño tiene simetría de rotación si se puede rotar casi por completo alrededor de un punto hasta llegar a una posición en la que quede igual al dibujo original. El siguiente diseño tiene simetría de rotación: su centro es el centro de rotación y tiene un ángulo de rotación de 60°. Esto significa que se puede rotar 60°, o cualquier múltiplo de 60°, alrededor de su punto central para crear una imagen que coincida exactamente con la original.

S

similar figures Two figures are similar if one is an image of the other under a sequence of transformations that includes a dilation. If the scale factor is greater than 1, the side lengths of the image are greater than the corresponding side lengths of the original figure. If the scale factor is less than 1, the side lengths of the image are less than the corresponding side lengths of the original figure. If the scale factor is equal to 1, then the two figures are congruent.

figuras semejantes Dos figuras son semejantes si una de ellas es una imagen reflejada de la otra en una secuencia de transformaciones que incluye una dilatación. Si el factor de escala es mayor que 1, las longitudes de los lados de la imagen son mayores que las longitudes de los lados correspondientes de la figura original. Si el factor de escala es menor que 1, las longitudes de los lados de la imagen son menores que las longitudes de los lados correspondientes de la figura original. Si el factor de escala es igual a 1, entonces las dos figuras son congruentes.

similarity transformation A transformation that produces similar figures. The image of a figure under a similarity transformation, such as a dilation, has the same shape as the original figure, but may be a different size. A similarity transformation can also be a sequence of a rigid motion (reflection, rotation, or translation) and a dilation.

transformación de semejanza Una transformación que produce figuras semejantes. La imagen de una figura en una transformación de semejanza, como la dilatación, tiene la misma forma que la figura original, pero puede ser un tamaño diferente. Una transformación de semejanza también puede ser una secuencia de un movimiento rígido (reflexión, rotación o traslación) y una dilatación.

Notes

sketch Academic Vocabulary To draw a rough outline of something. When a sketch is asked for, it means that a drawing needs to be included in your response.

related terms *draw, illustrate*

sample Sketch the lines of symmetry for the figure.

A line of symmetry divides a figure into halves that are mirror images. I can sketch two lines of symmetry for the given figure.

hacer un bosquejo Vocabulario académico Dibujar un esbozo de algo. Cuando se pide un bosquejo, quiere decir que se debe incluir un dibujo en la respuesta.

términos relacionados *dibujar, ilustrar*

ejemplo Haz un bosquejo de los ejes de simetría de la figura.

Un eje de simetría divide una figura en mitades que son imágenes reflejadas. Puedo hacer el bosquejo de dos ejes de simetría para la figura dada.

Notes

symmetry An object or design has symmetry if part of it, the basic design element, can be transformed repeatedly to produce the entire design. In this Unit, you learned about three types of symmetry. The butterfly below has *reflectional symmetry*, the pinwheel has *rotational symmetry*, and the wallpaper design has *translational symmetry*.

simetría Un objeto o diseño tiene simetría si una parte del mismo, el elemento de diseño básico, se puede transformar repetidamente para producir el diseño completo. En esta Unidad, aprendiste tres tipos de simetría. La mariposa que ves a continuación tiene *simetría de reflexión*, el molinete tiene *simetría de rotación* y el diseño del papel tapiz tiene *simetría de traslación*.

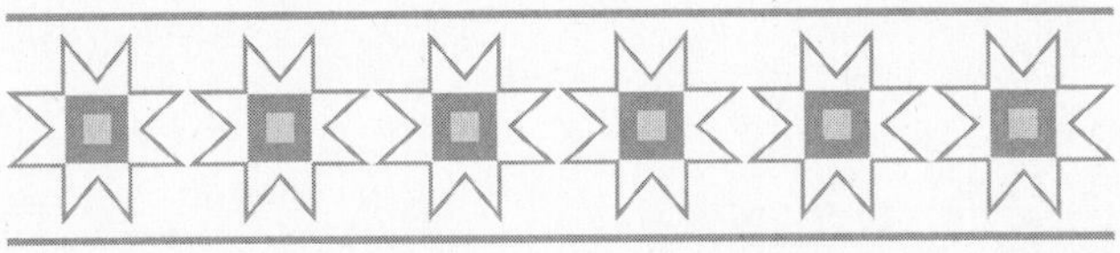

T

transformation A geometric operation that relates each point of a figure to an image point. The transformations you studied in this Unit—reflections, rotations, and translations—are symmetry transformations. A symmetry transformation produces an image that is identical in size and shape to the original figure.

transformación Una operación geométrica en la que cada punto de una figura coincide con un punto de su imagen. Las transformaciones que estudiaste en esta Unidad—reflexiones, rotaciones y traslaciones—son transformaciones de simetría. Una transformación de simetría da como resultado una imagen con el mismo tamaño y la misma forma que la figura original.

Notes

translation A transformation that slides each point on a figure to an image point a given distance and direction from the original point. Polygon $A'B'C'D'E'$ below is the image of polygon $ABCDE$ under a translation. If you drew line segments from two points to their respective image points, the segments would be parallel and they would have the same length.

traslación Una transformación que desliza cada punto de una figura hacia un punto de su imagen a determinada distancia y dirección del punto original. El polígono $A'B'C'D'E'$ que se observa a continuación es la imagen del polígono $ABCDE$ sometido a una traslación. Si dibujaras segmentos de recta desde dos puntos hasta los puntos correspondientes en su imagen, los segmentos serían paralelos y tendrían la misma longitud.

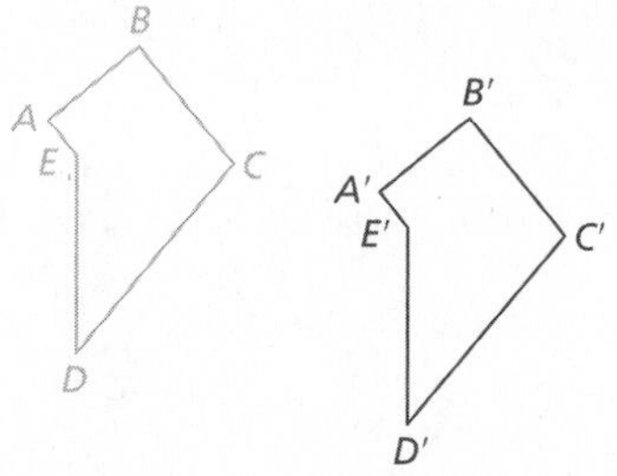

translational symmetry A design has translational symmetry if you can slide it to a position in which it looks exactly the same as it did in its original position. To describe translational symmetry, you need to specify the distance and direction of the translation. Below is part of a design that extends infinitely in all directions. This design has translational symmetry.

simetría de traslación Un diseño tiene simetría de traslación si se puede deslizar a una posición en la que luce exactamente igual que en la posición original. Para describir la simetría de traslación se debe especificar la distancia y la dirección de la traslación. La figura de abajo es parte de un diseño que se extiende infinitamente en todas las direcciones. Este diseño tiene simetría de traslación.

English / Spanish Glossary

END MATTER

Notes

Index

Notes

Notes

Notes

Acknowledgments

Cover Design

Three Communication Design, Chicago

Photographs

Photo locators denoted as follows: Top (T), Center (C), Bottom (B), Left (L), Right (R), Background (Bkgd)

003 Jeffrey Greenberg/Photo Researchers, Inc.; **007** Florian Monheim/Roman von Götz/Bildarchiv Monheim GmbH/Alamy; **023** Nieuwenhoven/Fotolia; **032** rabbit75_fot/Fotolia.

Notes

Notes

 Problem 1.1 Pacing 1 Day

1.1 Butterfly Symmetry: Line Reflections

Focus Question What does it mean to say that a figure has flip or reflectional symmetry? How is each point related to its image under transformation by reflection in a line?

Launch

You might consider launching this Problem by asking students to describe what they see as similarities and differences among the three designs pictured in the Student Edition (or others of your choosing).

- *What is the basic element for each design?*
- *Where is the line of symmetry?*
- *How many copies do you need to make the complete pinwheel?*
- *Where is the center of rotation?*
- *What is the direction and distance of the translation?*

Tell the students that by the end of the Problem, they will be able to answer the following questions.

- *What is the relationship between each pair of symmetric points and the line of symmetry?*
- *How can you use that relationship to draw designs with line symmetry?*

Explore

For Question A, if students do not immediately see that the line of symmetry bisects BB', CC', and DD', you may want to ask:

- *You have measured all the segments AA', BB', CC', DD', and EE'. Which one is the longest? Why is that?*
- *How far is D from the line of symmetry compared to how far is D' from the line of symmetry? Why does that make sense?*
- *Which points are in the same location as their images? Why is that?*

For Question B, if students try drawing the line of symmetry without joining points to images, you may want to ask:

- *I see you guessed where the line of symmetry would be. How can you check that the line is correct?*
- *If you think your line of symmetry could be improved upon, would it help to join points to their images as in Question A?*

For Question C,

- *How did you measure the distance from the line of symmetry to K'?*
- *What shape is the original figure? Is the image the same shape?*

Key Vocabulary

- basic design element
- line of symmetry
- line reflection
- reflectional symmetry
- symmetry
- transformation

Materials

Labsheet

- 1.1: Questions A–C Diagrams

Teaching Aids

- 1.1A: Getting Ready
- 1.1B: A Basic Design Element
- ruler
- angle rulers or protractors
- miras or mirrors
- Transformations

Summarize

You could prompt the discussion of the focus questions by referring to Question C.

- *What steps did you have to take to find the images of points J, K, L, M?*
- *What do you notice about JJ′ and KK′? What do you notice about JK and J′K′?*
- *In mathematics, when you talk about a distance from a point to a line, the distance is assumed to be the perpendicular distance. Why is this important?*
- *What characteristics of trapezoid JKLM is preserved in trapezoid J′K′L′M′? What is not preserved?*
- *Can we start with any figure and make a design with reflectional symmetry? Do we have to choose a particular line of symmetry?*

ACE

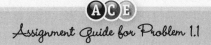

Assignment Guide for Problem 1.1

Applications: 1–7 | Connections: 19–20
Extensions: 30–35

Answers to Problem 1.1

A. For parts (1)–(3), the basic result of this work should be the discovery that the line of reflection is the perpendicular bisector of each segment joining a point to its image. Although the students' observations might not be expressed in this technical language, they should recognize that the line of reflection is perpendicular to each segment at its midpoint.

4. *A* is in the same location as *A′*, and *E* is also in the same location as *E′*.

B. To reverse the process of Question A, students should suggest connecting pairs of corresponding points on each part of the design and drawing a line that is the perpendicular bisector of each such segment. (Only one pair of corresponding points is actually needed).

C. 1. To find the image quadrilateral, students should suggest drawing lines from each point *J*, *K*, *L*, and *M* perpendicular to the line of reflection and marking points on the opposite side of that line that are equidistant from the line of symmetry. For example, if the perpendicular from *J* meets line n at point *X*, one looks for a point *J′* on ray *JX* so that *JX* = *J′X*.

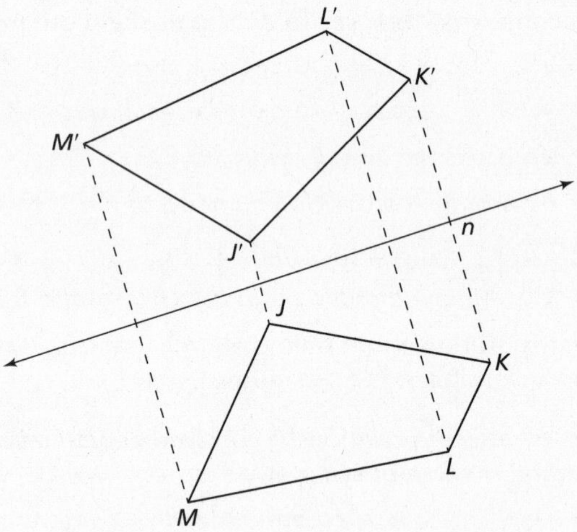

2. Yes; if I choose a point on *KL* and then find the image of that point, the image will be on *K′L′*. Therefore, it is sensible to say that if *K* → *K′* and *L* → *L′*, then each point between *K* and *L* "moves" to a location on *K′L′*.

3. The size and shape of the figure is retained; *KL* and *JM* are parallel sides in the original figure and *K′L′* and *J′M′* are parallel sides on the image figure.

D. Students will use a variety of wordings to complete the definition of a flip or line reflection. Possible answer: A reflection in line *m* matches each point *X* on a figure to an image point *X′* so that $\overline{XX'}$ is perpendicular to line *m* and points *X* and *X′* are equidistant from line *m*.

1.2 In a Spin: Rotations

Focus Question What does it mean to say that a figure has turn or rotational symmetry? How is each point related to its image under transformation by rotation?

Launch

You might choose to start the work on this Problem by asking students how the pinwheel is different from the butterfly in Problem 1.1.

- *How many copies do you need to make?*
- *Is there a different basic design element that you could copy?*
- *How is each point X related to its image point X′, the center of the rotation O, and the angle of rotation?*

Explore

To help students see that different angles of rotation are possible, you might ask about the basic design element.

- *You said you "moved" A to G. How much of a turn is that?*
- *How many rotations will it take for A to "move" back to the starting position?*
- *What part of the design would you have to copy 3 times so that the basic design element and the 3 copies make the complete design?*

You may want to explain that other centers of rotation are possible by displaying Teaching Aids 1.2A and 1.2B.

- *What is the center for your rotation? How do you use this?*
- *Can you keep track of the way point R is moving as you rotate the tracing paper?*
- *How many copies do you have to make? How can you predict the number of copies needed?*
- *Can you choose any point for the center of rotation?*

Key Vocabulary

- angle of rotation
- center of rotation
- rotation
- rotational symmetry

Materials

Labsheet

- 1.2: Question B

Teaching Aids

- 1.2A: Finding the Center
- 1.2B: Where is the Center
- ruler
- angle rulers or protractors
- tracing paper
- Transformations

Summarize

Ask students to share their drawings from Question B.

- *What is the center of rotation and angle of rotation for this design?*
- *As you rotate the basic design element around P to make an image, what point is the image of point R? Can you show the path that R moves along?*
- *Are points Q and S "moving" along the same circle as R in this rotation?*
- *When you rotate Q around P and R around P, what happens to QR?*

- *What do you think is preserved in Question C? What is not preserved?*
- *Are there any other center points we could have chosen?*

Note: You may want to display Teaching Aid 1.2A to demonstrate other possible choices for the center point. You could also use it to prompt a class discussion.

- *Does it look like the drawing could be completed to make a symmetric design? What difficulty would you have in completing this?*
- *Can you guess where the center might be?*
- *How do these arcs help us figure out where the center is?*

ACE

Assignment Guide for Problem 1.2

Applications: 8–10 | Connections: 21–26
Extensions: 29

Answers to Problem 1.2

A. **1.** 90°

2. **a.** The point → image matches are: $A \rightarrow G$, $G \rightarrow E$, $E \rightarrow C$, $C \rightarrow A$, $H \rightarrow F$, $F \rightarrow D$, $D \rightarrow B$, and $B \rightarrow H$.

b. $AO \rightarrow GO$; $HO \rightarrow FO$.

3. Each point moves along an arc of a circle with center at *O*. The radius of the circle is the constant distance between *O* points *A*, *G*, *E*, and *C*. Likewise, points *H*, *F*, *D*, and *B* move along the arc of a circle with the same center but a different radius.

4. Points *X*, *X′*, and the center of the compass star *O* determine a right angle $\angle XPX'$ and line segments *XP* and *X′P* have the same length.

5. Yes, this compass star also reflectional symmetry about any of the line segments drawn through the center point *O*.

B. The different ways to create rotation symmetries with the pictured flag as a basic design element essentially amount to choosing different centers of rotation. The most likely choice for the center is point *P*, but any point of the plane could be chosen. Students who choose other center points will have different designs. **Note:** If the class doesn't draw a variety of designs, refer to the Suggested Questions in the Summarize section and display Teaching Aids 1.2A and 1.2B.

1. For 120° rotations, two possible designs are:

C. To create a design with reflectional symmetry, you need a basic design element and a line of symmetry. You can choose any basic element and any position for the line of symmetry. Likewise, to create a figure with rotational symmetry, you can choose any basic design element, any center of rotation, and any angle of rotation. The difference, however, is the number of images needed to complete the symmetric design. A design with reflectional symmetry only needs one image plus the basic design element to complete it. The number of images needed to complete a design with rotational symmetry depends on the angle size chosen.

D. The essence of the students' answers should be similar to the following: A rotation of *d* degrees about a point *P* matches any point *X* on a figure to an image point *X′* so that $XP = X'P$ and the measure of $\angle XPX' = d$.

Problem 1.3 Pacing 1 Day

1.3 Sliding Around: Translations

Focus Question *What does it mean to say that a figure has slide or translational symmetry? How is each point related to its image under transformation by translation?*

Launch

Start with an open question asking the students to describe how each point of a basic design element "moves" under a translation that preserves appearance of the wallpaper design.

- *How would you explain the exact translation that creates an image of a basic design element?*
- *How many images of the basic design element would you have to make so that the completed design has translational symmetry?*

Key Vocabulary

- translation
- translational symmetry

Materials

Labsheet

- 1.3: Questions A and B Diagrams
- rulers
- angle rulers or protractors
- tracing paper
- Transformations

Explore

For Question A, it is helpful for students to connect corresponding vertices of a polygon and its translation image.

- *You noticed that GG′, HH′, and JJ′ are all the same length so the distance of the translation is constant. What else is the same about GG′, HH′, and JJ′?*
- *There are a lot of parallel line segments as a result of this translation: GG′, HH′, JJ′, etc. What else do you notice about the original figure and its image?*
- *When you say the image is the same size and shape, what do you mean?*
- *Looking at segments GM and G′M′, what else do you notice about the figure and its image? Why does this happen?*
- *You say that angle G is the same size as angle G′. Does that have anything to do with your claim that GM is parallel to G′M′?*

In Question B, we revisit the idea of parallel segments created by a translation. Watch for student strategies that can be usefully shared in the Summary.

- *What does that arrow tell you about the translation needed? How can you apply the same translation to all points on the polygon?*

Student may not make the connection that if you "move" *A* and *B* the same distance and direction, then you will also "carry" along all the intermediate points on the line segment *AB*. This is an important and useful idea, so it needs to be explicitly stated.

Summarize

The main point of the summary is to agree on a definition of translation.

- *What equal segments does your strategy create? What parallel segments?*
- *How is translational symmetry like or unlike reflectional and rotational symmetry?*
- *What parallelograms do you see on the finished figure?*
- *If you draw a figure on a piece of paper, you can think of the piece of paper as a plane that goes on forever. When you do a translation, every point in the plane has an image point. You can picture a copy of the plane being translated and carrying the figure with it. Are there any points unmoved by a translation?*

ACE

Assignment Guide for Problem 1.3

Applications: 11–13 | Connections: 27
Extensions: 36

Answers to Problem 1.3

A. **1.** In both Diagram 1 and Diagram 2, the connecting segments made by connecting corresponding vertices, GG', HH', etc. will be equal in length and parallel to each other.

2. I would need an infinite number of copies to make a design with translational symmetry.

B. After the indicated translation, the image will look as in the following sketch. (For questions about drawing a translation image, it is not essential that students copy the given figure exactly. They can sketch one of their own that is similar to what is given.)

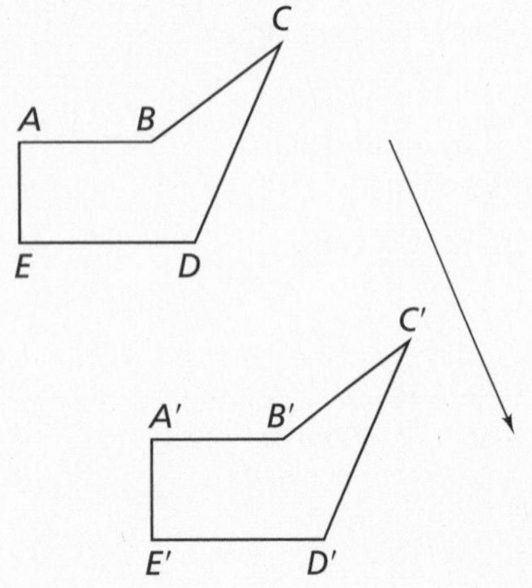

1. The segments joining points and their images are all the same length as the translation arrow and parallel to it.

2. Because of a special property of translations, corresponding sides of the original polygon and its image are the same length and parallel. Corresponding angles are also the same measure.

3. $ABB'A'$ is a parallelogram. AB and $A'B'$ are the same length and parallel. AA' and BB' are the same length and parallel to the translation arrow.

4. Yes; if we find the midpoint X of AB and apply the same translation, then its image X' will be on $A'B'$.

C. In each case, any basic design element plus a transformation will make an image. In the case of reflection, only one image is needed to complete the symmetric design. In the case of rotation, the number of images needed depends on the angle of rotation. In the case of translation, infinite images are required. In all cases size and shape are preserved. Translation also preserves orientation.

D. The student's language in completing the translation definition will vary. An acceptable answer should have the elements of the statement: A translation matches any two points X and Y on a figure to points X' and Y' so that $\overline{XY}$ and $\overline{X'Y'}$ are the same length and parallel to each other. This definition is not quite precise enough to be fully rigorous, because there is an element of directionality in the rigid motion. One way to cope with this detail is to require that the figure $XX'Y'Y$ is a parallelogram. At this point in students' development of geometry, this definition is sufficient.

Problem 1.4 Pacing $1\frac{1}{2}$ Days

1.4 Properties of Transformations

Focus Question How, if at all, will the shape, size, and position of a figure change after each of the transformations—reflection, rotation, or translation?

Launch

Referring to the graphic in the Student Edition to start a discussion.

- *What is the shape of the original figure?*
- *What transformations were used?*
- *How can you describe the details of each transformation?*
- *How is the shape, size, and position?*

Labsheet 1.4 gives students the opportunity to collect together all the information gleaned in Problems 1.1, 1.2, and 1.3.

Materials

Labsheet

- 1.4: Transformation Properties

Accessibility Labsheet

- 1ACE: Exercises 14–17

Assessment

- Check Up 1

- rulers
- angle rulers or protractors
- Tessellations

Explore

For Question A, students may need help finding the center of a rotation.

- *What seems to be the angle of rotation for the middle transformation? How do you know?*
- *How can we go about finding the center of the rotation? Would sketching the arcs followed by X as it "moves" to X′, and Y as it "moves" to Y′, help?*
- *We are trying to find a point O so that OX and OX′ are the same distance, and OY and OY′ are the same. Suppose we join XX′ and YY′. Do these segments suggest where to look for point O?*

Some students may need more direction to complete Question A because they haven't yet developed tips or shortcuts for identifying a transformation. Provide them with Labsheet 1ACE: Exercise 14–17.

In Question B, the question of which points or lines are "unmoved" by various transformations is non-trivial. You might want to assign each group the responsibility of summarizing their findings for each part of the Problem.

Summarize

Review the students' answers of each part of Questions. The key result is that flips, turns, and slides all "move" lines onto lines, angles onto angles of the same size, and segments onto segments of the same length. Lines that are parallel in the original figure are "moved" onto parallel lines in the image figure. Line segments and their images are also parallel under translation. Area and perimeter are preserved by all three transformations.

- *When are points or lines "unmoved" under a reflection?*
- *If we look at the completed diagram you made for the reflectional symmetry example, are there any points or lines "unmoved"?*
- *Let's look at the example of a rotation. Imagine the whole plane is rotating around the center while carrying the trapezoid along with it. What points or lines are "unmoved"?*
- *Let's look at the translation example. Imagine the entire plane is translated carrying along the trapezoid. What points or lines are unmoved?*

ACE

Assignment Guide for Problem 1.4

Applications: 14–18 | Connections: 28
Extensions: 37–39

Answers to Problem 1.4

A.

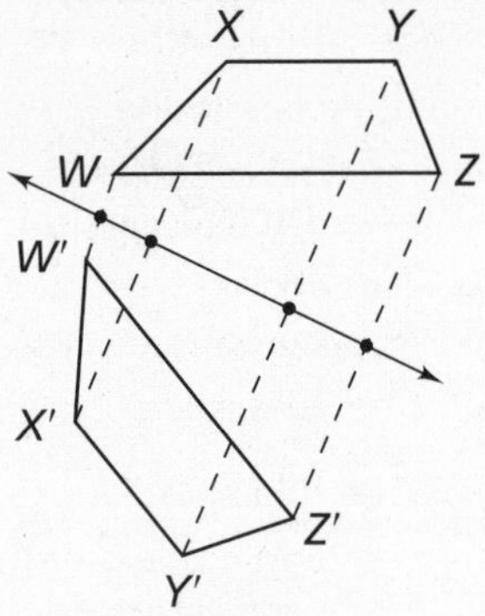

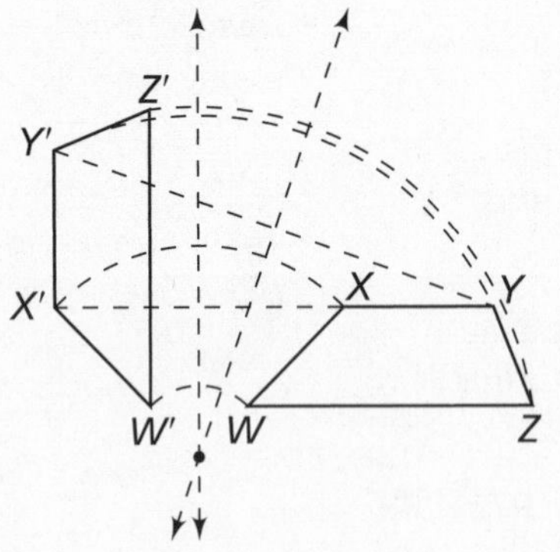

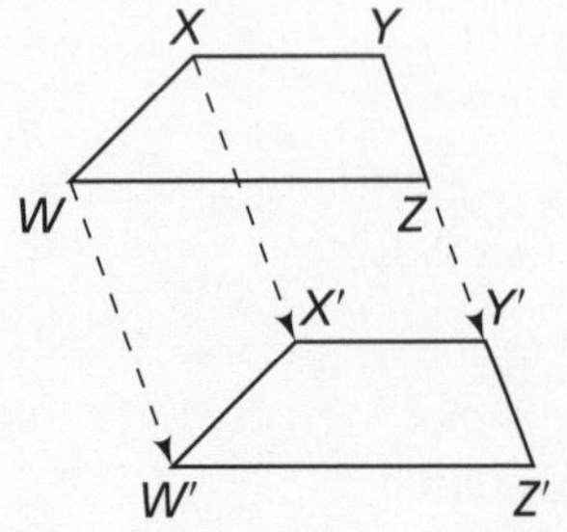

B. **1.** For all the three transformations, the distances between the vertices in the original figure are equal to the distances between the corresponding vertices in the image figure. In addition, the distance XX', YY', etc. are equal under translation.

2. For all the three transformations, the angle measures at the vertices of the original figure are equal to angle measures of the corresponding vertices in the image figure. In addition, angles XOX' and YOY' are the same under rotation about the center O.

3. Any line segments that is parallel in the original figure is parallel on the image figure. In addition, segments that join a point on the original figure to the corresponding point on the image figure are parallel to each other under translation.

4. Refer to the discussion posed in the Summarize section.

5. All three transformations retain the lengths of segments, the measures of angles, and any parallel relationships. They also retain the area and perimeter of the figure. Translation is the only transformation that retains the orientation of the figure.

Problem 2.1 Pacing 1 Day

2.1 Connecting Congruent Polygons

Focus Question What does it mean to say that two geometric shapes are congruent to each other? How could you show congruence with movable copies of the figures?

Launch

You might consider launching the Problem by asking students to study each of the given kaleidoscope designs and identify the basic design element. They should explain how a transformation strategy could be used to replicate that basic design element and complete the full figure. Use Teaching Aid 2.1: Kaleidoscope Designs to facilitate the discussion.

Suggested Questions

- *What transformations have been used to make these designs?*

Before students start to work on Problem 2.1, you may want to inspect the given quadrilaterals, *ABCD* and *PQRS*, as a class. Explain that since the text says *ABCD* and *PQRS* are congruent, they must have corresponding sides of the same length and corresponding angles of the same measure.

- *How do you know which sides are the same length? Which angles are the same measure?*

Tell students that to visually match up sides and angles, it helps to imagine a series of transformations that "move" one polygon onto the other. The goal is to make the correct match and name the exact transformations.

Key Vocabulary

- congruent figures

Materials

Labsheet
- 2.1: Question D

Accessibility Labsheet
- 2ACE: Exercises 1–4

Teaching Aid

2.1: Kaleidoscope Designs

- rulers
- angle rulers or protractors
- tracing papers
- Transformations

Explore

The questions of this Problem introduce notational conventions for describing congruence. Some students will take more time than others to match congruent sides. Point out that it helps to notice the relative positions of these sides. They may benefit from Labsheet 2ACE: Exercises 1–4 (accessibility) to practice this tip. While they work on Question D, you may want to have tracing paper and Labsheet 2.1: Question D available. Watch for students who make incorrect matches and use the opportunity to discuss their reasons. They should be taking advantage of the shortest sides, longest sides, etc.

Suggested Questions

- *I see that you have matched AB to QR. Are these the longest sides in each figure?*
- *Notice that QR is adjacent to PQ, the shortest side. Is AB also adjacent to the shortest side in the other figure?*

- *Would it help to start with the short sides and match them?*
- *The angles at P and Q looks very similar to the angles at C and D. How can we figure out the corresponding angles?*

For Question D, you might ask:

- *Can you use your tracing to be sure that your answers for Questions A, B, and C are correct?*
- *What transformations did you use?*

Watch for alternative transformation sequences and share them during the summary.

Summarize

If students were working on this Problem in groups, it will be useful to check their answers to Questions A–C. You can refer to Teaching Aid 2.1 during the discussion. When you finish checking the details of each Question, you could revisit the focus question and have selected students or groups explain their transformation sequences.

Suggested Questions

- *Why did some people start with a slide?*
- *Did anyone start by rotating the polygon? If you did, how did you find the center and angle of rotation?*
- *Did anyone rename PQRS? If you did, how did the new name tell you how sides and angles are matched?*
- *What do you mean when you say side RS corresponds to side AB, or $\angle S$ corresponds to $\angle B$, etc?*
- *Would you say that side RS corresponds to side BA?*

ACE

Assignment Guide for Problem 2.1

Applications: 1–4 | Connections: 27–29

Answers to Problem 2.1

A. $A \rightarrow R$ $B \rightarrow S$ $C \rightarrow P$ $D \rightarrow Q$

B. $\overline{AB} \cong \overline{RS}$ $\overline{BC} \cong \overline{SP}$ $\overline{CD} \cong \overline{PQ}$ $\overline{DA} \cong \overline{QR}$

C. $\angle A \cong \angle R$ $\angle B \cong \angle S$ $\angle C \cong \angle P$ $\angle D \cong \angle Q$

D. 1. There are many different ways to transform *ABCD* onto *PQRS*. One sequence of flips, turns, and slides is to slide $C \rightarrow P$ and then rotate the figure around *P* until *CD* matches *PQ*. The turn and the slide could be done in reverse order by starting with a turn about *C* and then sliding.

2. $ABCD \cong RSPQ$ lists the vertices in the order that indicates correspondence of parts in the two figures.

Problem 2.2 Pacing 1 Day

2.2 Supporting the World: Congruent Triangles I

Focus Question How much information do you need to decide that two triangles are congruent? How do you plan the transformations that "move" one triangle onto another?

Launch

To launch this Problem, remind the students of what they learned in the Grade 7 Unit Shapes and Designs about the importance of triangles in building structures. Then, pose the question of how one could go about establishing that two triangles are identical in shape and size.

Review the directions that apply to each part of this Problem. You could use Question A and Labsheet 2.2: Questions A–F as a reference to ask:

- *Do the two triangles look congruent? How do you know?*
- *Did you measure all sides and angles?*
- *Can you slide triangle ABC onto triangle XYZ? Why or why not?*
- *If you decide to do the slide first, how far is the slide and what direction?*
- *If you decide to do a rotation, what details should you give?*

After this discussion, the class is now set to finish Question A and complete other parts of the Problem.

Materials

Labsheet
- 2.2: Questions A–F

Accessibility Labsheet
- 2ACE: Exercise 39

- rulers
- tracing paper
- angle rulers or protractors

Explore

The class may find it helpful to have access to transparencies or tracing paper. Encourage each group to test their transformation ideas with physical movements of triangles. You should also remind them to write down their transformation plans for the pairs of congruent triangles. When the students identify a pair of triangles as non-congruent, press them to explain their reasoning behind that decision.

For Question B, the students should give the details for the necessary reflection. Have them demonstrate their ideas as they describe them.

- *I see you flipped your tracing paper of triangle DEF over. What line of symmetry are you thinking of?*
- *After you flip your tracing over this line do you need any other transformations?*

For Question D, the students should also give the details for the necessary slide, rotation, and reflection.

- *What did you do first in Question D?*

The triangles are not congruent in Questions C and E. Push students to explain why the triangles are not identical in shape and size.

- *How can you be sure that the triangles in Question C are not congruent? Did you measure all the angles and sides?*

- *If the angles of the two triangles in Question E match each other, why do you say that the triangles are not congruent?*

Summarize

Different groups of students can demonstrate their sequences of transformations for Questions A, B, D and F, using Labsheet 2.2. After each demonstration, ask:

- *Did another group use a different order? Did that make any difference to the details of your transformations?*
- *Did you measure all the sides and angles before you decided the triangles were congruent? Or did you use shortcuts?*
- *How should you name the triangles to show the corresponding congruent parts? Explain.*

For the pairs of non-congruent triangles, ask:

- *How did you know that the triangles in Question C are not congruent?*
- *How many sides do you have to measure to know that a pair of triangles are not congruent?*
- *How do you know the triangles in Question E are not congruent? How are they different?*
- *What is the least number of parts you would have to measure to be sure that a pair of triangles are not congruent?*

ACE

Assignment Guide for Problem 2.2

Applications: 5–6, 13–18

Connections: 30–32 | Extensions: 36–39

Answers to Problem 2.2

A. These two figures certainly appear to be congruent with the correspondence $\triangle ABC \cong \triangle ZYX$. A possible sequence of transformations would be to slide *B* onto *Y* and then do a 180° rotation centered at *Y*.

B. These two figures also appear congruent with the correspondence $\triangle DEF \cong \triangle UTS$. A possible transformation would be to reflect one of the triangles across a line that is the perpendicular bisector of $\overline{FS}$.

C. These two figures are not congruent.

D. These two figures appear congruent with the correspondence $\triangle JKL \cong \triangle ONM$. A possible sequence of transformations would be to slide *K* onto *N*, rotate $\triangle JKL$ 90° counter-clockwise around *N*, and then reflect across line $\overline{KJ}/\overline{NO}$.

E. These two triangles are not congruent (however, they are similar).

F. These two figures appear congruent with the correspondence $\triangle ABC \cong \triangle RQP$. A possible sequence of transformations would be to slide *C* onto *P* and then reflect across a vertical line (perpendicular to $\overline{PQ}$ at *P*).

2.3 Minimum Measurement: Congruent Triangles II

Focus Question What is the smallest number of side and/or angle measurements needed to conclude that two triangles are congruent?

Launch

You may want to discuss the congruent triangles *ABC* and *PQR* pictured in the introduction. Ask them to explain what the term *corresponding* means. Refer back to Problem 2.2:

- *Did you need to measure all parts of each triangle before you were confident that they could be matched by a sequence of transformations?*
- *How do you show that two triangles are NOT congruent? Do you have to measure all the sides and angles?*

Begin Question A as a class so that students have a model of the sort of evidence to look for or construct for disproving a claim.

- *If I tell you that I have drawn two triangles, and each of them has a longest side length of 3 inches, might the triangles be congruent? Must they be congruent?*
- *Suppose I say that, "Triangles ABC and PQR are congruent because AB and PQ are corresponding sides where AB = PQ." How can you prove that this statement is not true?*
- *One counterexample is enough to disprove that a statement is always true. If you cannot draw a counterexample, does that mean that the claim is always true?*

Materials

Labsheet
- 2.3: Questions C–E

Teaching Aid
- 2.3: Congruence Criteria

Assessment
- Partner Quiz

- rulers
- angle rulers or protractors

Explore

Monitor the answers they write down to see that each yes or no answer includes a brief explanation.

- *For Question C part (1), how would you describe the matching information about sides and angles? What transformations "move" triangle GHI onto triangle JKL?*
- *How can you be sure that this will work for any size of angles at H and K?*
- *You have explained how the direction of side HI has to match the direction of side KL, and how the direction of side IG has to match the direction of side LJ. How can you be sure that the lengths will also match?*
- *For Question D part (1), how would you describe the matching information? Does Amy's reasoning convince you that all corresponding sides and angles must match?*
- *For Question D part (2), what are the two parallelograms? How do we know that these quadrilaterals have parallel sides? What do we know about parallelograms that might identify equal sides and angles?*

Summarize

Choose students or groups to present their arguments for Questions C, D, and E part (1) and encourage the class to critique the explanations.

- *In Question C part (1), which congruence criterion is described by the information provided?*
- *In Question C part (2), which congruence criterion is described by the information provided?*
- *What information is the group giving us about the pairs of triangles? Are you convinced that the argument presented by this group guarantees congruence?*

ACE

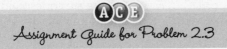

Assignment Guide for Problem 2.3

Applications: 7–12, 19–26
Connections: 33–35 | Extensions: 40

Answers to Problem 2.3

A. Discovering one pair of congruent corresponding parts is not sufficient evidence to justify a conclusion that the triangles are congruent.

1. In the triangles shown here, $AB = DE$, but the triangles are clearly not congruent.

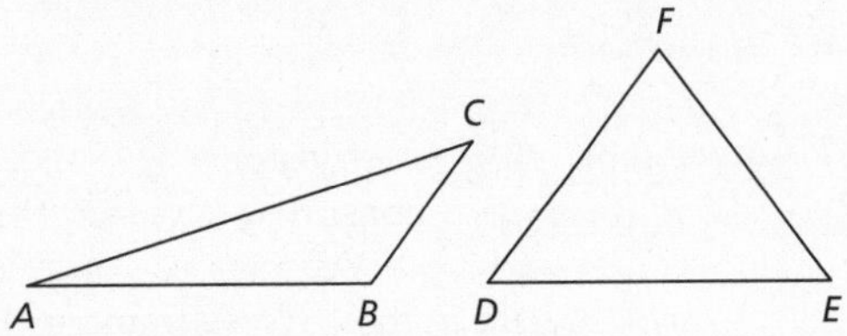

2. In the triangles shown here, $\angle A \cong \angle D$, but the triangles are clearly not congruent.

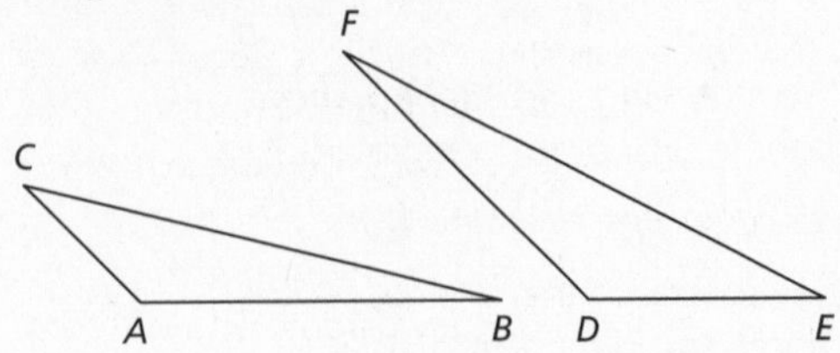

B. Discovering two pairs of congruent corresponding parts is not sufficient evidence to justify a conclusion that the triangles are congruent.

1. In the triangles shown here, $AB = DE$ and $AC = DF$, but the triangles are clearly not congruent.

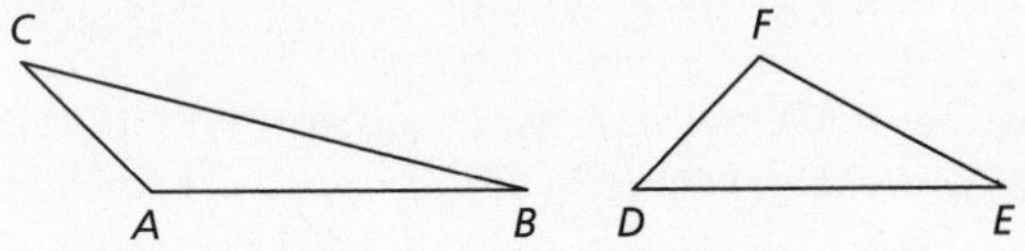

2. In the triangles shown here, $\angle A \cong \angle D$ and $\angle B \cong \angle E$ but the triangles are clearly not congruent. In fact, because all triangles have the same angle sum, if two pairs of angles are congruent, the third pair must be congruent also. But this doesn't imply congruence because the sides can be of different (but proportional) lengths.

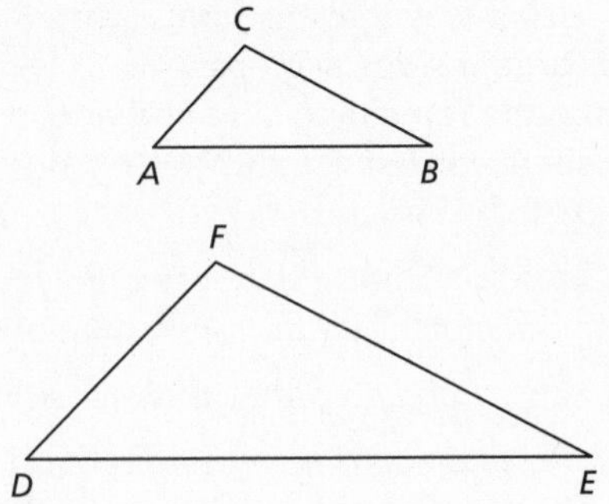

3. In the triangles shown here, $\angle A \cong \angle D$ and $AB = DE$ but the triangles are clearly not congruent.

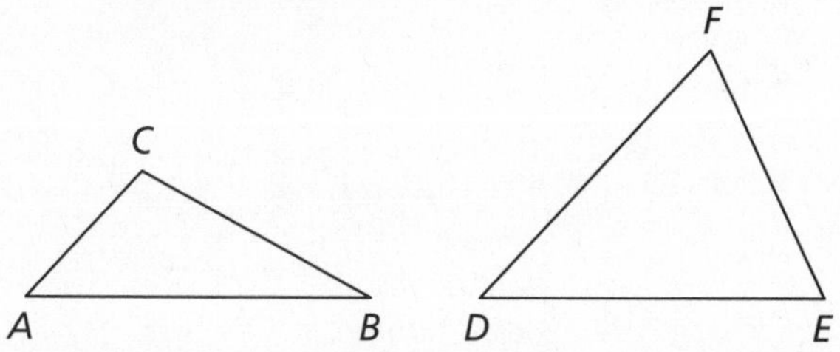

C. Three pairs of congruent corresponding parts will often be sufficient evidence to conclude that two triangles are congruent. But it makes it difference what the combinations of parts are.

1. The angle side angle (ASA) condition does guarantee triangle congruence. For example, in the given diagram one can imagine moving $\triangle GHI$ onto $\triangle JKL$ in such a way that side $\overline{GH}$ falls onto side $\overline{JK}$, $\angle G$ onto $\angle J$, and $\angle H$ onto $\angle K$. This will force the sides $\overline{HI}$ and $\overline{IG}$ to fall onto rays $\overrightarrow{KL}$ $\overrightarrow{QP}$ and $\overrightarrow{LJ}$ respectively and their intersection point I to fall onto of L.
2. If two sides and the included angle of one triangle are congruent respectively to two sides and the included angle of another triangle, the two figures will be congruent. The intuitive reasoning that justifies this conclusion is that it will always be possible to 'move' one angle onto its congruent corresponding angle in such a way that the corresponding congruent sides align as well. This will force the remaining side and angles to be positioned exactly onto their congruent corresponding parts. For example, in the sketch shown, if $G \rightarrow J$, $H \rightarrow K$, and $I \rightarrow L$, then $\overline{IH} \rightarrow \overline{LK}$, $\angle I \rightarrow \angle L$ and $\angle H \rightarrow \angle K$. This means that all six pairs of corresponding parts are congruent

D. 1. Amy's reasoning leaves us with $H \rightarrow K$ and $G \rightarrow J$, so $HG \rightarrow KJ$, but she makes no argument for why other sides are congruent, particularly HI and KL. Nor does she explain why the angles are matched. Her explanation is not complete.

2. $GJLI$, and $HKLI$ are parallelograms. (See Explore for explanation about why we know these are parallelograms.) The sides of a parallelogram are parallel and congruent, so $HI \cong KL$. Because $HI \parallel KL$, $\angle H = \angle K$; these are corresponding angles for parallel lines. Lastly, $\angle I = 180$ degrees $- (\angle G + \angle H) = 180$ degrees $- (\angle J + \angle K) = \angle L$. So, the facts about this translation help us match all the sides and angles of the triangle.

E. 1. Congruence of angles does not guarantee congruence of the triangles (though it might look like that in the given drawing. One triangle can simply be bigger than the other, but similar in shape. Students might refer back to Part E of Problem 2.2 for a counterexample.

2. See TA 2.3 for SSS and AAS (and why SSA is not a guarantee of congruence.)
3. There are several ways to prove that two triangles are not congruent. For example, students might propose that they could measure all three sides of one triangle and then start measuring side lengths of the other triangle. As soon as you find a side length in the second triangle that is not equal to any of the side lengths in the first triangle, you know that the two figures cannot be congruent. You could try a similar strategy with angle measurement, but it is possible to have three pairs of congruent corresponding angles and still not be sure whether the figures are congruent or not. That would require measuring one pair of corresponding sides. The general question of what is the minimum number of measurements required to be sure that two triangles are not congruent doesn't seem to have a simple answer.

Notes

Problem 3.1 Pacing 1 Day

3.1 Flipping on a Grid: Coordinate Rules for Reflections

Focus Question How can you describe how points "move" under a reflection with coordinate rules in the form (x, y) → (■, ■) when the reflection line is: (1) the x-axis? (2) the y-axis? (3) the line y = x?

Launch

Have students study the flag and identify coordinates of the key points that could be used to give directions for drawing the figure.

- *What are the coordinates of points A, B, C, D, and E?*
- *How might you make a design with reflectional symmetry, using this basic element?*
- *Are there any other lines of symmetry we might choose?*
- *How could you make a design with rotational symmetry using the flag as a basic element?*
- *Can you choose any other point as the center of the rotation?*

Explore

Ask students questions that help them generalize the patterns they see.

- *In Question A, how did you know where to locate the images of each point on the original flag? If so, how did you know where to draw the image points?*
- *How do you know how far C is from the y-axis (reflection line) without counting?*
- *If we had point W at (13, 14), where would you look for W′?*
- *A reflection like this reflects the whole plane over the line of symmetry and not just the key points we choose to track. So, where is the image of the point in the center of the flag? The point (x, 10)? The point (−10, y)? The x-axis? The y-axis?*
- *Describe what happens to the coordinates of a point when it is reflected over the y-axis.*
- *Is every point in a different location from its image, under this reflection?*
- *In Question C, how can you find the image of B with coordinates (2, 4) in the line y = x? Do you see a pattern in the relationship between the original point and its image?*
- *Which points do not "move"? Why is this?*
- *Remember that a reflection really "moves" all the points in the plane, not just the key points we choose to track. What would be the reflection of (5, 0) in the line y = x? (0, 6)? (−1, 0)? The x-axis? The y-axis?*

Materials

Labsheets
- 3.1 Reflection
- 3ACE: Exercise 26
- Quarter-Inch Grid Paper

Accessibility Labsheets
- 3ACE: Exercises 1–3
- 3ACE: Exercise 8
- 3ACE: Exercise 16

Teaching Aid
- 3.1 Reflection Over the y- and x-axis

- graph paper
- Transformations

Summarize

If time becomes an issue, begin the Summarize after Questions A and B.

- *Do the flag images from Question A and B with the original figure produce a design with reflectional symmetry?*
- *Does this show a design with rotational symmetry?*
- *Give the coordinates for a point and its image under a reflection in the y-axis.*
- *Name another point, not on the flag, and its image under this reflection.*
- *What coordinate rule lets you name a point and its reflection in the y-axis?*
- *Does this rule work for any point, say (−3, −5)?*

Repeat with reflection in the x-axis and in the line $y = x$.

ACE

Assignment Guide for Problem 3.1

Applications: 1–3, 8 | Connections: 16
Extensions: 26

Answers to Problem 3.1

A. (See Figure 1.)

1. $(x, y) \rightarrow (-x, y)$
2. The rule works in all quadrants.
3. **a.** Points on the y-axis are not "moved" by this reflection.

   b. The flag and its image in the y-axis make a symmetric design.

B. (See Figure 2.)

1. $(x, y) \rightarrow (x, -y)$
2. The rule works in all quadrants.
3. **a.** Points on the x-axis are not "moved" by this reflection.

   b. The flag and its image in the x-axis make a symmetric design.

C. (See Figure 3.)

1. $(x, y) \rightarrow (x, y)$
2. The rule works in all quadrants.

Figure 1

Point	*A*	*B*	*C*	*D*	*E*
Original Coordinates	(0, 0)	(2, 4)	(5, 4)	(6, 6)	(3, 6)
Coordinates After Reflection	(0, 0)	(–2, 4)	(–5, 4)	(–6, 6)	(–3, 6)

Figure 2

Point	*A*	*B*	*C*	*D*	*E*
Original Coordinates	(0, 0)	(2, 4)	(5, 4)	(6, 6)	(3, 6)
Coordinates After Reflection	(0, 0)	(2, –4)	(5, –4)	(6, –6)	(3, –6)

Figure 3

Point	*A*	*B*	*C*	*D*	*E*
Original Coordinates	(0, 0)	(2, 4)	(5, 4)	(6, 6)	(3, 6)
Coordinates After Reflection	(0, 0)	(4, 2)	(4, 5)	(6, 6)	(6, 3)

 Problem 3.2 Pacing 1 Day

3.2 Sliding on a Grid: Coordinate Rules for Translations

Focus Question What kind of coordinate rule $(x, y) \rightarrow (\blacksquare, \blacksquare)$ tells how to "move" any point to its image under a translation?

Launch

You can probably launch this Problem by asking what students recall about the Mug Wumps in Problem 2.1 from *Stretching and Shrinking*.

Suggested Questions

- *Why did we compare the results of the Wump drawing with different coordinate rules?*
- *What did you find out?*

Tell students that they are going to find coordinate rules for translations. Now your students know how translations work, i.e., that a translation preserves the shape of a figure and changes its position, they can explore how these characteristics appear in coordinate models.

You can give Labsheet 3.2 to students to help them organize their answers. This can allow them to remain focused on the mathematics of the Exercises and save time.

Materials

Labsheets

- 3.2: Translation Rules
- 3ACE: Exercise 9
- 3ACE: Exercise 20
- Quarter-Inch Grid Paper

Accessibility Labsheets

- 3ACE: Exercises 4 and 5
- 3ACE: Exercise 17
- 3ACE: Exercise 18

- graph paper
- Transformations

Explore

Distribute Labsheet 3.2 to students as they collect and organize the data from the four Mugs. Students might need some help figuring out how to inspect this data to find the requested patterns for each translation. If they seem lost in the data, you might ask the following:

- *Focus on the motion of points on Mug 1 to corresponding points on Mug 2. How are the corresponding x-coordinates related for each point?*
- *How are the corresponding y-coordinates related for each point?*
- *How can you use these patterns to write a coordinate rule* $(x, y) \rightarrow (\blacksquare, \blacksquare)$*?*

For Question D, help students relate these examples of translations to the general characteristics of a translation.

- *How can you show that AF is parallel to A′F′?*
- *How does the translation rule that produced A′F′ guarantee it will be parallel to AF?*
- *What else is always true about translations? Can we show how the coordinate rules for translations relate to this?*

AT A GLANCE 3

Summarize

You will probably want to check the rules students come up with in each Question A–C and then pose the general Questions D and E. Ask about Question E first:

- *If a translation of a figure on a coordinate grid moves the figure a units horizontally and b units vertically, what rule will show how the coordinates of each point on the figure will change?*

If you have had a conversation with students about Question D during the Explore, then you can call on them to explain how a particular coordinate rule, for Mug 2 for example, relates to the ideas about translations. Under translations, segments "move" to parallel segments, and the distance and direction of the translation is the same for every point. Help students extend this to the general case. Students in an algebra class should be able to generalize from the slopes and distances in examples.

- *If the general rule for a translation is (x, y) → (x + a, y + b), how does rule guarantee that for any two points (x, y) and (w, z) the distance of the translation is the same? The direction of the translation is the same?*
- *How does this rule guarantee that sides "move" to parallel sides?*

ACE

Assignment Guide for Problem 3.2

Applications: 4, 5, 9 | Connections: 17–20

Answers to Problem 3.2

A. (x, y) → (x + 8, y + 2)

(See Figure 1.)

B. (x, y) → (x − 2, y + 8)

C. (x, y) → (x − 9, y − 2)

D. 1. Answers will depend on whether students choose an image on Mug 2 or Mug 3 or Mug 4. Slope of $\overline{AF}$ is $\frac{-4-(-7)}{-4-(-5)} = \frac{3}{1}$. Slope of $\overline{A'F'}$ on Mug 2 $= \frac{-2-(-5)}{4-3} = \frac{3}{1}$.

2. Answers may be at different levels of generality. For a segment joining two general points (x, y) and (w, z), and the translation rule (x, y) → (x + a, y + b), the slope of the original segment is $\frac{y-z}{x-w}$, and the slope of the image is $\frac{(y+b)-(z+b)}{(x+a)-(w+a)}$, which is again, $\frac{y-z}{x-w}$.

E. (x, y) → (x + a, y + b) since a and b will be either positive or negative depending on the direction of the "move."

Figure 1

Point	A	B	C	D	E	F
Coordinates of Mug 1	(−5, −7)	(−1, −7)	(−2, −4)	(−2, −3)	(−4, −3)	(−4, −4)
Coordinates of Mug 2	(3, −5)	(7, −5)	(6, −2)	(6, −1)	(4, −1)	(4, −2)
Coordinates of Mug 3	(1, 3)	(5, 3)	(4, 6)	(4, 7)	(2, 7)	(2, 6)
Coordinates of Mug 4	(−8, 1)	(−4, 1)	(−5, 4)	(−5, 5)	(−7, 5)	(−7, 4)

Problem 3.3 Pacing 1 Day

3.3 Spinning on a Grid: Coordinate Rules for Rotations

Focus Question What are the coordinate rules that describe "motion" of points on a grid under turns of 90° and 180°?

Launch

You might launch this Problem by showing the picture in the text.

- *In which quadrant is the image after a quarter turn counterclockwise?*
- *How can you be sure you have made a rotation angle, say BAB′, that is 90°, and that BA = B′A?*
- *This reminds me of trying to draw a tilted square in Looking for Pythagoras. How did we draw perpendicular lines then?*
- *In which quadrant is the image after a half turn counterclockwise?*
- *How can you be sure you have made a rotation angle, say BAB′, that is 180°?*

Pose the Problem of finding coordinate rules that could accomplish these "motions" in a computer graphics program.

Explore

Ask about the rotation images students sketch.

- *In Question A, what is the image of B? How did you find B′?*
- *From the center A, we count 2 to the right and 4 up to locate B. Does that help us think about the location of B′?*
- *The slope of AB is $\frac{4}{2} = 2$. What is the slope of AB′?*

If students' images are incorrect, you can suggest they check them using rulers and protractors or you can continue to ask about slopes.

- *It looks like C′ (for example) is not in the right place. Remember that spinning C around A means there is a radius AC that spins around and becomes AC′. AC and AC′ should be the same length and form a 90° angle. Are they the same length? Do they form a 90° angle?*

In Question B, a turn of 180° should be simpler to accomplish, but students might not be consistent. For example, they might make *BAB′* a straight angle, but not do the same for *CAC′*, because *CA* is not joined.

- *The angle of rotation is 180°. Is BAB′ 180°? Is CAC′ 180°? How about DAD′?*

Summarize

The Summarize for this Problem can be initiated by two questions:

- *What coordinate rules show how points "move" under quarter- and half-turns?*
- *How do you know that the rules you arrived at are correct?*

Materials

Labsheets
- 3.3: Rotations of 90° and 180°
- 3ACE: Exercise 27
- Quarter-Inch Grid Paper

Accessibility Labsheet
- 3ACE: Exercises 6 and 7

Teaching Aid
- 3.3: Rotations of 90° and 180°

- graph paper
- rulers
- protractors or angle rulers
- tracing paper
- Transformations

For the second question, if you observed students using slopes, have them share their work. Teaching Aid 3.3 is provided to facilitate the discussion.

- *How do slopes help you locate the image of B? of D?*
- *Do we have a design with rotational symmetry after doing these two rotations?*

Help your students connect the rules they find from the patterns in the tables to the general characteristics of rotations.

- *Choose a point not on the flag, say (5, 0), what would be the image after a rotation of 90° counterclockwise? What would be the image of (10, 0)? (0, 5)? (0, 10)? (5, 5)?*
- *We all found that the rule for a 90-degree rotation counterclockwise around A is (x, y) → (−y, x). How does this relate to the observations you made that a rotation of a point X around a center A makes an image X′ that is the same distance from A and the angle XAX′ is the angle of rotation?*
- *Suppose the center is not (0, 0). Would the same rule work?*
- *We all found that the rule for a 180 degree rotation around A is (x, y) → (−x, −y). How does this relate to the observations you made about how rotations work?*

ACE

Assignment Guide for Problem 3.3

Applications: 6, 7 | Connections: 21, 22
Extensions: 27

Answers to Problem 3.3

A. (See Figure 1.)

1. (x, y) → (−y, x)
2. Same rule applies regardless of where the flag starts.
3. a. A; the center of the rotation does not "move."
   b. We would need two more images to make a complete design with rotational symmetry.

B. (See Figure 2.)

1. (x, y) → (−x, −y)
2. Same rule applies regardless of where the flag starts.

Figure 1

Point	*A*	*B*	*C*	*D*	*E*
Original Coordinates	(0, 0)	(2, 4)	(5, 4)	(6, 6)	(3, 6)
Coordinates After a 90° Rotation	(0, 0)	(−4, 2)	(−4, 5)	(−6, 6)	(−6, 3)

Figure 2

Point	*A*	*B*	*C*	*D*	*E*
Original Coordinates	(0, 0)	(2, 4)	(5, 4)	(6, 6)	(3, 6)
Coordinates After a 180° Rotation	(0, 0)	(−2, −4)	(−5, −4)	(−6, −6)	(−3, −6)

3.4 A Special Property of Translations and Half-Turns

Focus Question How are lines and their images under translations and half-turns related to each other?

Launch

You might choose to launch the Problem by asking students to study the diagram.

- *Do the pentagons all look congruent? How could you check this? How would you name them to show this correspondence?*
- *What sequence of transformations will "move" ABCDE onto FGHIJ? Could you write a coordinate rule for this?*
- *What sequence of transformations will "move" FGHIJ onto KLMNO? Is there another way to do this?*
- *What sequence of transformations will move ABCDE onto KLMNO? Is there another way to do this?*
- *What does it mean for the pentagons to be congruent?*
- *What special relationships are there among the sides of the pentagons?*
- *How can you use coordinates to prove your conjectures?.*

Materials

Labsheets

- 3.4: Special Property of Translations and 180° Rotations
- 3ACE: Exercise 28
- Quarter-Inch Grid Paper

Teaching Aid

- 3.4: Special Property of Translations and 180° Rotations
- graph paper
- Transformations

Explore

- *What are the coordinates of points A and B? How can you use these to find length AB? Slope AB?*
- *How can you use the coordinates of F and G to show that FG is parallel to AB and the same length?*

In Question B, students may focus on the equal lengths of the segments, since that is what is expected after any rigid transformation, including rotation.

- *I see you have used the coordinates of the endpoints to confirm AB = KL. What else is true about these sides? How can you prove they are parallel?*
- *We found that the coordinate rule for a half turn about the origin is $(x, y) \rightarrow (-x, -y)$. Suppose you have a segment joining two general points (x, y) and (w, z). What are the images of these two points under a half turn around $(0, 0)$? What is the slope of the segment joining these two points? What is the slope of the image of the segment?*

Since Question C is really the summary of the Problem discoveries, you can start a summary discussion when most students have had a chance to at least think about the questions given there. Question D can be viewed as an "extra for experts." Labsheet 3.4 is available for this. It does not need to be done by all students prior to beginning the Summarize.

Summarize

The Summarize can focus on the Question C in the Problem.

- *What evidence do you have that your statements are true in these examples?*
- *Does showing that this statement is true for the sides of these pentagons constitute a proof that this will be true for all segments (or lines)?*

For Question D, you might use Labsheet 3.4 or Teaching Aid 3.4 and ask:

- *I can see how to translate line n onto line m. But, how would I achieve this by rotating line n? What would be the center of rotation?*
- *Suppose I wanted to move segment AB onto segment A″B″. How would I do that?*
- *So I can "move" segment AB anywhere onto line m using a half-turn. What do all the centers have in common?*

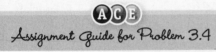

ACE

Assignment Guide for Problem 3.4

Applications: 10 | Connections: 23
Extensions: 28–30

Answers to Problem 3.4

A. Comparing $\overline{AB}$ and its image after translation, $\overline{FG}$.

1. The segments are parallel (or lie on parallel lines).

   Both slopes are −2. The slope from (−1, 5) to (1, 1) is $\frac{1-5}{1-(-1)} = \frac{-4}{2} = -2$ and the slope from (−8, 4) to (−6, 0) is $\frac{0-4}{-6-(-8)} = \frac{-4}{2} = -2$.
   Distance *AB* can be found by applying Pythagorean Theorem to a right triangle with *AB* as the hypotenuse: $\sqrt{(2^2+4^2)} = \sqrt{20}$. Likewise for *FG*.

2. Other pairs of corresponding sides are parallel, a fact that can be confirmed by checking slopes of each segment in each pair.

B. Comparing $\overline{AB}$ and its image after half-turn, $\overline{KL}$.

1. The segments are congruent and parallel (or lie on parallel lines).
2. Both slopes are −2. The slope from (−1, 5) to (1, 1) is $\frac{1-5}{1-(-1)} = \frac{-4}{2} = -2$ and the slope from (−1, −1) to (1, −5) is $\frac{-5-(-1)}{1-(-1)} = \frac{-4}{2} = -2$.
3. Other pairs of corresponding sides are parallel, a fact that can be confirmed by checking slopes of each segment in each pair.

C.

1. *Any translation "moves" every line m to a line n so that m and n are parallel.*
2. *Any half turn "moves" every line m to a line n so that m and n are parallel.*

D. If two lines are parallel, it is always possible to construct a translation and a half-turn to "move" one onto the other. To give the required translation, one need only to pick a point on each line and use those two points to define the direction and distance of translation. To give the required half-turn, locate the midpoint of the segment joining the chosen points and use it as the center of the half-turn.

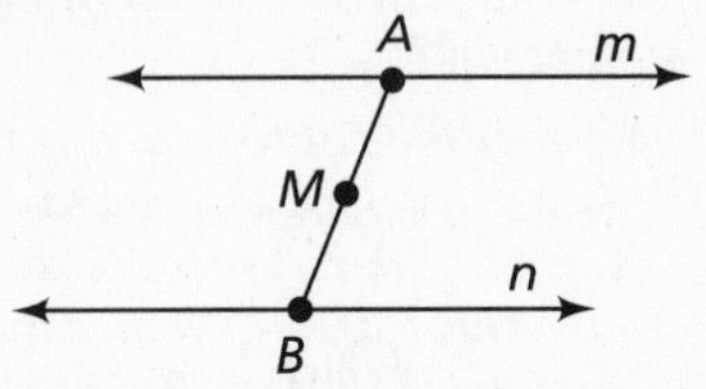

3.5 Parallel Lines, Transversals, and Angle Sums

Focus Question When two parallel lines are cut by a transversal, what can be said about the angles formed? What is always true about the angle measures in a triangle? How do you know that your answers are correct?

Launch

You might choose to launch the two Problems by presenting only the two drawings in the introduction and asking students:

- *How did you show that when a transversal cuts two parallels it makes 2 groups of 4 congruent angles? What unit were you studying?*
- *How did you show that the angle sum of a triangle is 180°?*
- *What are the interior angles of a triangle? The exterior angles?*

Materials

Labsheet
- 3.5: 180° Rotation Around Midpoints

Assessment
- Check Up 2

- tracing paper
- rulers
- angle rulers
- protractors
- Transformations

Explore

- *Why are angles 1 and 3 congruent?*
- *Are you sure that if you translate angle 5 it will "move" exactly onto angle 1? Explain why this shows that angles 1, 3, 5, and 7 are all congruent. Would it help if you started with an example?*
- *How are you rotating the triangle about M_1? What do we know about the result of a half turn?*
- *Which segments are parallel to AC?*
- *I see Erin has marked the exterior angles on this triangle. They each seem to be made of two other angles. How does that help us?*

Summarize

For Question A, display the drawing and ask students :

- *Who can explain why all four angles are equal?*
- *Is this result true for only this example or is it true for all cases where a transversal cuts two parallel lines?*
- *What other transformation, if any, would match? Explain.*

Focus on why there is only one line through *B* parallel to *AC* in Question C.

ACE Assignment Guide for Problem 3.5

Applications: 11–15 | Connections: 24, 25
Extensions: 31

Answers to Problem 3.5

A. Proving congruence of alternate interior and alternate exterior angles formed by a transversal cutting two parallel lines:

1. Angles 1 and 3 are congruent because they are opposite or vertical angles formed when two lines intersect. If this basic result is not something that students have established before, they can provide a proof-within-a-proof by noting that $\angle 1 + \angle 2 = 180°$ and $\angle 3 + \angle 2 = 180°$, so $\angle 1 = \angle 3$.
2. Angles 5 and 7 are congruent for the same reasons given in Step 1.
3. There is a translation that "moves" angle 5 exactly onto angle 1. Sliding line *n* along line *t* will take line *n* onto parallel line *m*, so the sides of angle 5 will be "moved" onto those of angle 1.
4. From the previous parts we have $\angle 3 \cong \angle 1$ and $\angle 5 \cong \angle 7$. Since translations preserve angle measures, we also have $\angle 5 \cong \angle 1$. Thus, $\angle 3 \cong \angle 1 \cong \angle 5 \cong \angle 7$.

B. Proof of the congruence for other angles can be almost identical in form to that given in Question A. It might look like this:

1. Angles 2 and 4 are congruent because they are opposite or vertical angles formed when two lines intersect.
2. Angles 6 and 8 are congruent for the same reasons given in Step 1.
3. There is a translation that "moves" angle 6 exactly onto angle 2. Sliding line *n* along line *t* will take line *n* onto parallel line *m*, so the sides of angle 6 will be "moved" onto those of angle 2.
4. Angles 6 and 2 are congruent because translations preserve angle measures.
5. The facts established in 1–4 imply that angles 2, 4, 6, and 8 must all be congruent because we have shown $\angle 4 \cong \angle 2 \cong \angle 6 \cong \angle 8$.

C. Using transformations.

1. After one rotation, we have *AC* is parallel to *C′B* because half turns "move" segments to parallel segments. Also, angle *C′BA* is the image of angle 1.

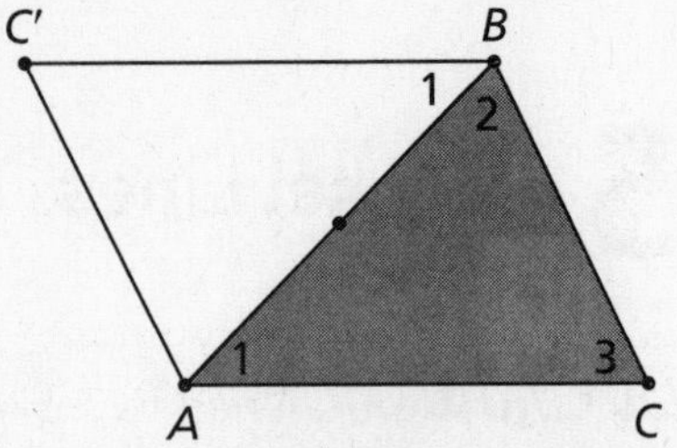

2. After the second rotation, we have *AC* is parallel to *BA′* because half turns "move" segments to parallel segments. Also, angle *A′BC* is the image of angle 3.

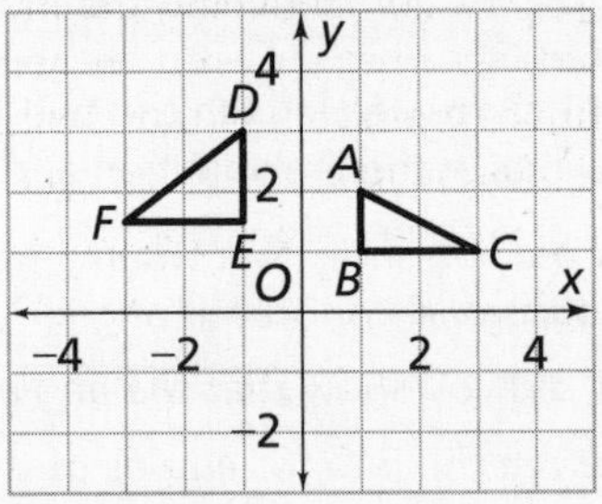

3. The two images of *AC* are each parallel to *AC* and they share an endpoint, *B*. So, they must lie in one straight line since there is only one line through *B* parallel to *AC*.
4. The angles 1, 2, and 3 make a straight angle at *B* as shown.
5. There was nothing specific about this triangle, and the characteristics of half turns we used are always true.

D. Each marked angle is an exterior angle of the central triangle. The exterior angles are made from $\angle 3 + \angle 1$, $\angle 2 + \angle 3$, and $\angle 1 + \angle 2$. If you add these you get: $(\angle 3 + \angle 1) + (\angle 2 + \angle 3) + (\angle 1 + \angle 2) = 2(\angle 1 + \angle 2 + \angle 3) = 2(180°) = 360°$.

E. An alternate proof of the triangle sum theorem:

1. In the figure, $\angle BAC \cong \angle 1$ because they are alternate interior angles formed when two parallel lines are cut by a transversal. $\angle BCA \cong \angle 3$ for the same reason as Step 1.
2. The sum of the angles in triangle *ABC* is 180° because the angles of the triangle are congruent respectively to angles 1, 2, and 3, and these angles can be arranged to form a straight angle.

Problem 4.1 Pacing $1\frac{1}{2}$ Days

4.1 Focus on Dilations

Focus Question What coordinate rules model dilations? How do dilations change or preserve characteristics of the original figure?

Launch

You might consider launching the Investigation and this Problem by asking students what they remember about the Wump family—who were the legitimate members of the family and what kinds of characters were imposters. Segue into the challenge of Problem 4.1 by asking about the dilation pictured in the introduction.

- *What is meant by a dilation?*
- *How is this kind of transformation different from reflections, rotations, and translations?*
- *Which triangles seem to be similar?*
- *What is meant by a dilation with a scale factor of $\frac{3}{2}$?*
- *Can you see a dilation of $\frac{2}{3}$ in this figure? What is being compared?*

Now ask students to look at the figure in Question A. Ask:

- *How does the idea of a dilation connect to this figure drawn on a coordinate grid?*

Tell students they are going to look for coordinate rules for dilations.

Explore

In order to answer Question A, parts (1)–(6) correctly, they will need to locate the image points from the starting figure accurately. Check on this work early to see that students are on the right track.

- *How do you know that points P′, Q′, R′, and S′ are 3 times as far from the origin (0, 0) as P, Q, R and S, the points from which they "moved"?*
- *How are you able to compare side lengths for the figure and its image?*
- *How are you able to compare angle sizes?*
- *How can you check and compare the perimeters? Areas?*
- *I see that you have checked slopes and found that the slopes of the sides of the image are the same as the slopes of the sides of the original. What does that mean about a pair of corresponding sides?*

For Question B, students make the distances from the origin explicit, and the underlying similar triangles become apparent.

- *What similar triangles can you see? How do you know they are similar?*

Key Vocabulary

- dilation
- similarity transformation

Materials

Labsheets

- 4.1: Dilation
- 4ACE: Exercises 1–6
- 4ACE: Exercises 7–10
- 4ACE: Exercise 25
- rulers
- angle rulers
- protractors (optional)
- Transformations

Students may not see that point $Z(2z, 4z)$ must lie on the line OP. Help them connect $(2z, 4z)$ to the coordinate rule for the dilation in Question A.

- *The coordinate rule for the dilation in Question A was $(x, y) \rightarrow (3x, 3y)$. What rule would move $P(2, 4)$ to $Z(2z, 4z)$? What does this mean about O, P, and Z?*

Summarize

Questions D and E address the points that you want to make from this Problem, so use those questions in the Summarize. Connect back to their work on specific dilation examples in Questions A–C by asking what evidence supports their generalizations about all dilations.

- *What statements did you make for Question D?*

Ask about Question E. Push for the coordinate rule that connects corresponding points: $(x, y) \rightarrow (kx, ky)$.

- *How did you come up with statements for Question E?*

Be sure to ask students whether the two specific cases they have studied give them confidence that their conjectures will be true for other shapes and other scale factors. Two specific cases are not enough to prove a conjecture. But, because of their earlier experience with dilations, there is little reason to suspect that they have met examples here that do not illustrate a general pattern.

You might have another example ready to test using a different scale factor. Apply scale factors of $\frac{3}{2}$ and $\frac{2}{3}$ to these figures using the origin for the center of dilation.

ACE

Assignment Guide for Problem 4.1

Applications: 1–10 | Connections: 23–25

Answers to Problem 4.1

A. Dilation effects with scale factor 3 gives a picture like this:

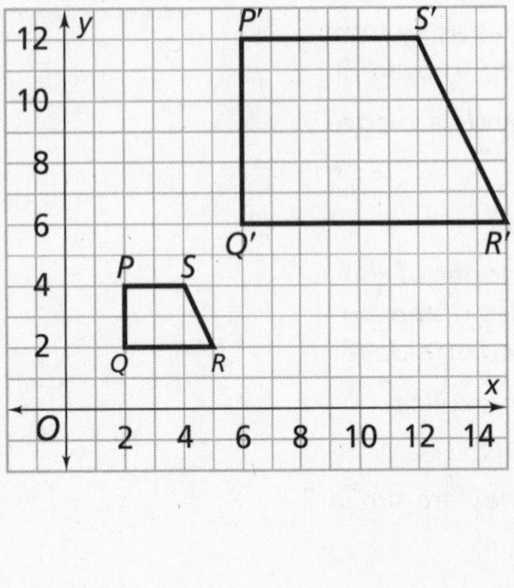

1. The side lengths of $P'Q'R'S'$ are 3 times those of $PQRS$.
2. The measures of angles in $P'Q'R'S'$ are equal to those of $PQRS$.
3. The perimeter of $P'Q'R'S'$ is 3 times that of $PQRS$.
4. The area of $P'Q'R'S'$ is $3^2 = 9$ times that of $PQRS$.
5. The slopes of the sides of $P'Q'R'S'$ are equal to the slopes of corresponding sides of $PQRS$, making the lines of those sides parallel.
6. The rule $(x, y) \rightarrow (3x, 3y)$ shows how coordinates of corresponding points are related under dilation with center at the origin (0, 0) and scale factor 3.

B. 1. Triangles OPQ and $OP'Q'$. Scale factor is $\frac{3}{1} = 3$; $OP' = 3OP$. The sides are related by this scale factor; the corresponding angles are equal.

3. a. Z is the image of $P(2, 4)$ under a dilation with scale factor z: $(2, 4) \rightarrow (2z, 4z)$. Also, O, P, and Z are in a straight line, i.e., collinear.

b. Using endpoints, slope of $OP = \frac{4}{2} = \frac{2}{1} = 2$; slope of $OP' = \frac{12}{6} = \frac{2}{1} = 2$; slope of $OZ = \frac{4z}{2z} = \frac{2}{1} = 2$; slope of $PZ = \frac{4z-4}{2z-2} = \frac{4(z-1)}{2(z-1)} = \frac{4}{2} = \frac{2}{1} = 2$.

C. Dilation with scale factor $\frac{1}{2}$.

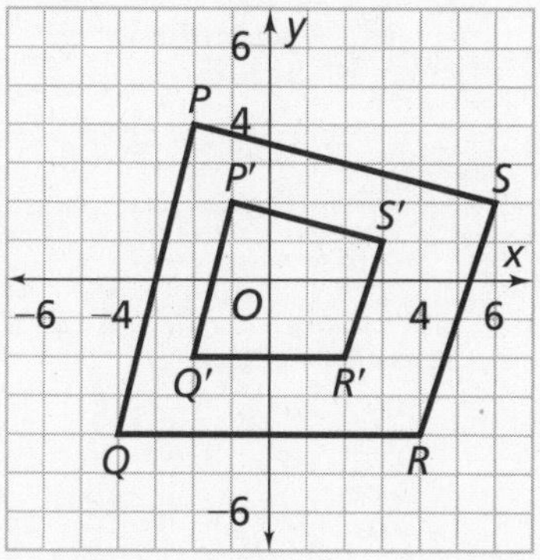

1. The side lengths of $P'Q'R'S'$ are $\frac{1}{2}$ those of $PQRS$.
2. The measures of angles in $P'Q'R'S'$ are equal to those of the corresponding angles in $PQRS$.
3. The perimeter of $P'Q'R'S'$ is $\frac{1}{2}$ that of $PQRS$.
4. The area of $P'Q'R'S'$ is $\left(\frac{1}{2}\right)^2 = \frac{1}{4}$ that of $PQRS$.
5. The slopes of the sides of $P'Q'R'S'$ are equal to the slopes of corresponding sides of $PQRS$, meaning that the lines with those sides are parallel.
6. The rule $(x, y) \rightarrow (\frac{1}{2}x, \frac{1}{2}y)$ shows how coordinates of corresponding points are related under dilation with center at the origin (0, 0) and scale factor $\frac{1}{2}$.

D. When two polygons are related by a dilation with scale factor k,

1. corresponding side lengths are related by the same factor k;
2. corresponding angles are congruent;
3. perimeters of the two figures are related by the same factor k;
4. areas of the two figures are related by the factor k^2;
5. corresponding sides are parallel.
6. A rule of the form $(x, y) \rightarrow (kx, ky)$ shows how coordinates of corresponding points are related under dilation with center at the origin (0, 0) and scale factor k.

E. If a figure with some kind of symmetry is stretched or shrunk by a dilation, the resulting image will have the same symmetry. **Note:** The image of a parallelogram, for example, will be a similar parallelogram, and in both cases the parallelograms will have rotational symmetry, about the points where the diagonals meet—which will, of course, not be the same point for both parallelograms.

Notes

Problem 4.2 Pacing 1 Day

4.2 Return of Super Sleuth: Similarity Transformations

Focus Question How can you use transformations to check whether two figures are similar or not?

Launch

You might launch the Problem by reminding students how they checked two triangles for congruence:

Suggested Questions

- *In Investigation 2, how did you show that two triangles were congruent?*
- *What were some of the discoveries that made some sequences easier to describe than others?*

You can segue into the Problem by asking about the drawings of "Super Sleuth."

- *Do these figures look similar?*
- *How can you check?*
- *What transformations do you think will "move" one onto the other? Does the order of the transformations matter?*
- *What might be a key point to locate?*
- *How do you think we can show that these figures are similar?*
- *How can we figure out the scale factor?*

When you are sure that your students understand the challenge, then set them loose on the Problem.

Materials

Labsheets

- 4.2: Similarity
- 4ACE: Exercises 11–15
- rulers
- angle rulers
- protractors (optional)
- Transformations

Explore

This Problem gives students the challenge of judging "same shape" for figures using informal reasoning. They might be tempted to simply look at the given pairs of polygons and make a snap judgment that the figures are similar or not. It is important that they measure with a ruler and an angle ruler/protractor to check their intuition. Labsheet 4.2 can be used to facilitate this.

- *How did you make the judgment that the figures were similar?*
- *How did you decide that the figures were not similar?*
- *Could you have just used angle measures to check if two figures are similar? Explain.*
- *Once you establish that you think figures are similar, how do you decide which transformations to use? Does deciding on corresponding angles or sides help?*

Check that students are naming figures correctly so that intended correspondences are obvious.

Summarize

The focus question is actually given as Question D, so after checking to see that groups agree on which figures are similar in Questions A and C and which are not in Question B, ask how they made those decisions and what evidence they can offer to support their claims. Also, ask them to describe the sequence of transformations, flip, turn, and slide, and final dilation that will map one figure exactly onto the other. Have groups critique each other's ideas and push each other to be exact in their descriptions.

Suggested Questions

- *Do you think that other sequences are possible? Explain.*
- *If corresponding angles of a figure are congruent, are the figures guaranteed to be similar? Explain.*
- *If corresponding sides of a figure are scaled copies of each other, are the figures guaranteed to be similar? Explain.*

ACE

Assignment Guide for Problem 4.2

Applications: 11–15 | Connections: 26–27

Answers to Problem 4.2

A. The two triangles appear to be similar. The smaller one can be "moved" onto the larger by translating it so that *B* goes to *R*. Then, the smaller triangle can be rotated 90° clockwise or 270° counterclockwise about *R*. Finally, dilate the smaller triangle with a center at *R* and a scale factor of 2.

B. The two rectangles are not similar; corresponding sides have unequal ratios.

C. The two parallelograms appear to be similar. The smaller parallelogram can be "moved" onto the other parallelogram by reflecting across a line that is the perpendicular bisector of $\overline{HV}$. This "moves" *V* onto *H*. Finally, dilate the smaller with a scale factor of approximately $\frac{3}{2}$ centered at *H*.

D. Students will probably say that they look for figures that seem to have the same general shape but a different size. To test their ideas about same shape, they might suggest measuring angles and comparing what appear to be corresponding sides. They should note with the example in Question B that simply having congruent corresponding angles is not enough to guarantee the similarity of polygons, though it will turn out to be sufficient for triangles.

Problem 4.3 Pacing 1 Day

4.3 Checking Similarity Without Transformations

Focus Question What information about the sides and angles of two triangles will guarantee that they are similar?

Launch

Have students study triangles *ABC* and *XYZ* in the text.

- *Do you think it would be sufficient to know that one pair of corresponding angles are congruent? Explain.*
- *Suppose you knew the ratio of the longest sides in a pair of triangles was 1 : 2. Would that be enough to guarantee similarity? Explain.*
- *Suppose that two sides of one triangle were related by the same scale factor to two sides of a second triangle. Do you think you could conclude that the triangles were similar? Explain.*

Materials

Labsheets

- 4.3: Similar Triangles and Slope of a Line
- 4ACE: Exercise 28

- rulers
- angle rulers
- protractors (optional)
- Transformations

Explore

In Question A:

- *Do you agree with the general idea that it is the angles that give a polygon its shape? Think about shapes you know a lot about, triangles and quadrilaterals.*
- *Do you think that what you found with triangles having angles 30°, 70°, and 80° will be true for all triangles with corresponding congruent angles?*

For Question B, you might draw the two triangles separately.

- *What are the two triangles in Question B? Would it help to see these triangles drawn separately?*
- *When you "move" triangle ABC onto XYZ, why does C end up on side YZ and A end up on side YX?*
- *How can we find the scale factor of the dilation?*
- *What other ratios are equal?*

For Question C:

- *Would it help to think of some examples? Say, we know that two angles of one triangle are 40° and 60°, and two angles of another triangle are also 40° and 60°. Would the third angles also be equal? Can you think of a counterexample when the third angles would not be equal?*

For Question E, a requirement of the CCSSM:

- *Where are your similar triangles? How do you know these are similar?*
- *What ratios would give the slopes of PZ? PW? Why are they equal?*

Summarize

You can conduct a class summary after completing Questions A–C. Question E could be done as a large group activity as part of the Summarize. After discussing Question B, push students to explain why this reasoning would always work.

- *Will this reasoning work for all triangles? Acute angled? Right angled? Obtuse angled?*
- *How does this relate to the rep-tile triangles you made in Stretching and Shrinking?*

Then share student statements for Question D, and either apply this new knowledge to solve Question E as a class or have students share their explanations.

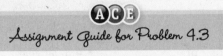

ACE

Assignment Guide for Problem 4.3

Applications: 16–20 | Connections: 28
Extensions: 29

Answers to Problem 4.3

A. Kevin and Ming have good instincts about the importance of angles in setting the shape of polygons, triangles in particular. But, the counterexample rectangles in Problem 4.2 should give pause to their claim that measuring angles alone is sufficient to conclude that two triangles are similar.

B. Owen and Natasha give an argument that utilizes the concept of transformations to compare figures.

1. Students should agree that it will always be possible to "move" angle *B* onto the congruent angle *Y*, and that they could flip triangle *ABC* if needed to assure that $\overline{BC}$ lies on $\overline{YZ}$ and $\overline{BA}$ lies on $\overline{YX}$.
2. $\overline{AC}$ and $\overline{XZ}$ are parallel because of the corresponding angles formed by transversal $\overline{YZ}$. **Note:** Actually we are invoking the converse of the theorem about angles formed when parallel lines are cut by a transversal. That is, we are assuming that if the angles formed are congruent, then the lines will be parallel. This assertion is dependent on the Euclidean parallel axiom.
3. Any dilation "moves" lines onto parallel lines, so a dilation that "moves" *C* to *Z* will take $\overline{AC}$ onto $\overline{XZ}$.

C. Kelly and Rico are correct because if $a + b + c = 180 = x + y + z$ and $a + b = x + y$, then $c = z$.

D. If two angles in one triangle are equal in measure to two corresponding angles in another triangle, then the triangles are similar.

E. Students will have to name points so they can name pairs of similar triangles.

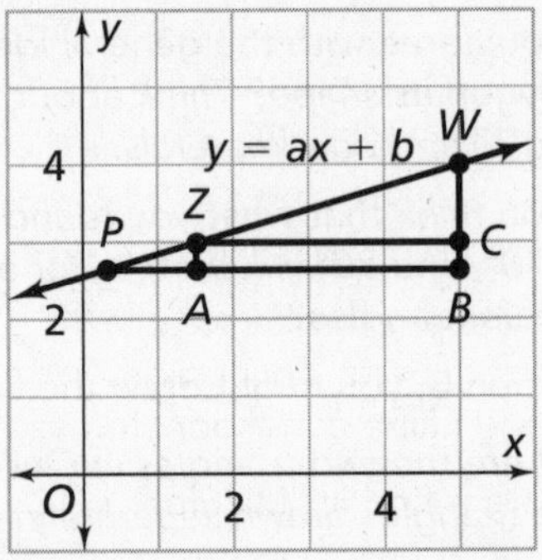

1. Triangles *PAZ*, *PBW*, and *ZCW* are similar. The parallel horizontal and parallel vertical grid lines are cut by the transversal $y = ax + b$. In the triangles, there are two pairs of congruent angles.
2. Slope of $PZ = \frac{rise}{run} = \frac{ZA}{AP}$; slope of $PW = \frac{rise}{run} = \frac{WB}{BP}$. But, $\frac{ZA}{AP} = \frac{WB}{BP}$, because these are internal ratios of corresponding sides of triangle *PZA* and *PWB*.

4.4 Using Similar Triangles

Focus Question What facts about similar triangles allow you to find lengths in very large figures that you are unable to reach?

Launch

Discuss briefly why the two triangles pictured in the introduction are similar.

Materials

Assessments
- Unit Test
- Self-Assessment
- Notebook Checklist
- mirrors
- meter sticks

Suggested Questions

- *Where are the equal angles?*
- *Now that you know the triangles are similar, what else do you know?*

You might confirm the concept of the equal angles at the mirror by placing a mirror on the floor of your classroom and having two students of very different heights stand where they can see each other's faces in the mirror. The key physical principle is that the angle of incidence equals the angle of reflection in the mirror. Once that idea is clear to students, they can apply what they have learned about similar triangles to solve the Problem.

Explore

You might choose to do a summary of Questions A and B before students apply the same reasoning to their own experimental data in Question C.

The critical fact about similar triangles that allows calculation of unmeasured parts is that there is a common scale factor (or proportionality constant) relating pairs of corresponding parts. Encourage your students to mark all the known lengths on their sketches and name corresponding vertices of triangles so the discussion is clearer.

If students are find it difficult to set up helpful proportions, you might ask about the scale factor.

Suggested Questions

- *You know the triangles are similar. What is the scale factor from the small triangle to the larger? How do you find this?*
- *What lengths are in the ratio 450 : 100?*
- *What other sides must also be related by the same scale factor?*
- *How can you write that as an equation?*

Push students to see that the method will always work.

- *Suppose we had a shorter person than Jim. Then the height to the person's eyes would not be the same. Would that wreck your calculations?*

For Question C, you might assign two groups to find the measure of the same object. This will demonstrate that, while the specifics of the similar triangles may differ, the result will be the same, except for measurement error.

Summarize

Since this Problem is really only one application of the ideas developed throughout the Investigation, the Summarize that is needed probably should focus on the student reasoning to solve either Question A or B. Ask a group to explain their reasoning.

Suggested Questions

- *How did you know the triangles were similar?*
- *What was the scale factor? Did you use this in your solution?*

If everyone is comfortable with the idea and solution strategy, you can proceed to the experiment, and have students write up their results.

ACE

Assignment Guide for Problem 4.4

Applications: 21, 22 | Extensions: 30, 31

Answers to Problem 4.4

A. Measuring the height of a traffic light.

1. The situation looks like this:

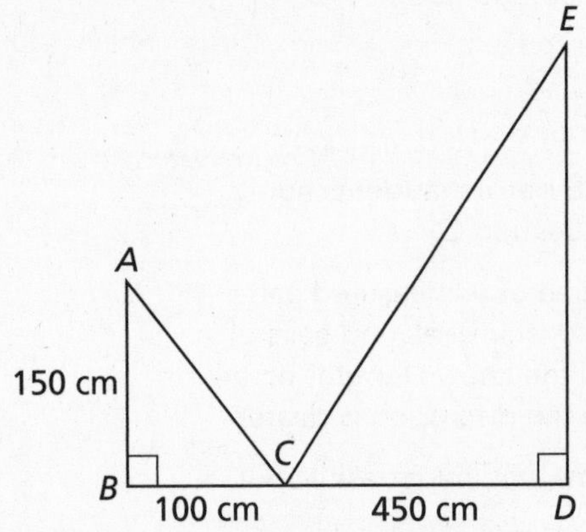

Not drawn to scale

2. The triangles are similar because each has a right angle and $\angle BCA \cong \angle DCE$.

3. The scale factor relating the triangle side lengths is $\frac{450}{100} = 4.5$, so the traffic light is $4.5(150) = 675$ cm or 6.75 m tall.

B. Gymnasium height.

1. The situation is depicted in this sketch:

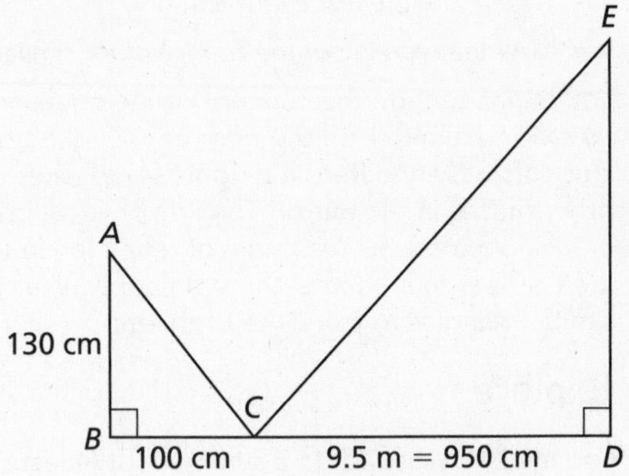

Not drawn to scale

2. The triangles are similar because each has a right angle and $\angle BCA \cong \angle DCE$.

3. The scale factor relating the triangle side lengths is $\frac{950}{100} = 9.5$, so the gymnasium ceiling is $9.5(130) = 1235$ cm or 12.35 m high.

C. If asked to complete this task, students will have a variety of situations and data, but the basic diagram will always be the same as in Question A and B, part (1).

At a Glance

Pacing ☐ Day

Mathematical Goals

Launch

Materials

Explore

Materials

Summarize

Materials

Notes

Applications

1. The basic design element is a fourth of the design. The design has rotational symmetry of 90° about the center of the design. There is no reflectional symmetry.

2. The basic design element is any sixth of the design (most clearly one of the sectors bounded by the blue radii) that can be replicated after successive rotations of 60°. It has six lines of symmetry defined by lines through the center of the square and lying along the blue sector boundaries or splitting those sectors in half.

3. This figure has as the most natural basic design element one of the eight-pointed 'stars.' However, one could argue that a smaller piece of such a 'star' could actually be used to generate a whole 'star' and then all of the other 'stars.' Using a whole 'star' as basic design element, one could generate the total strip pattern by replication following translation left and right.

4. This figure has basic design element any set of adjacent four hands with the four colors included. That design element can be replicated by translation up, down, left, right, and along diagonals to give the whole figure.

   The figure has no reflectional symmetries (for example, all blue hands are left hands) and no rotational symmetries (blue hands must point to the 'northeast' after any acceptable transformation).

Note: In the drawing exercises that follow, it is not essential that students make exact copies of the given figures. They should start work with drawings of their own that are approximately the same as those given in the text. They key point is that they should know what geometric transformations do to those figures.

5. The completed diagram will look like that below, with line *m* the perpendicular bisector of the segment joining each pair of corresponding points.

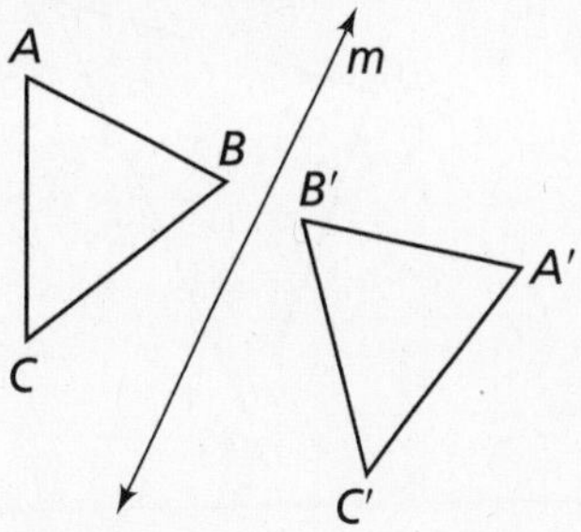

6. **a.** The line of reflection is the common perpendicular bisector of segments $\overline{AA'}$, $\overline{BB'}$, and so on.

   b. Each point on the original figure and its image on $A'B'C'D'$ are equidistant from the line of reflection, and the segment joining them is perpendicular to the line of reflection.

7. **a.** The resulting figure will look like this (without labels):

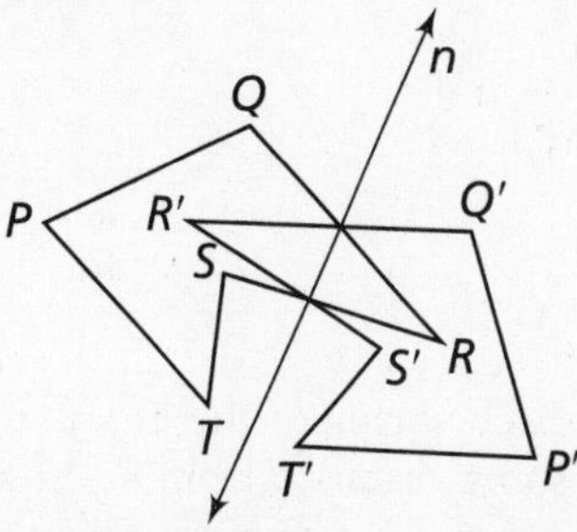

   b. The resulting figure does have reflectional symmetry because it was created to make that happen. The reflection of a reflection is the original.

8. a. The resulting figure will look like this:

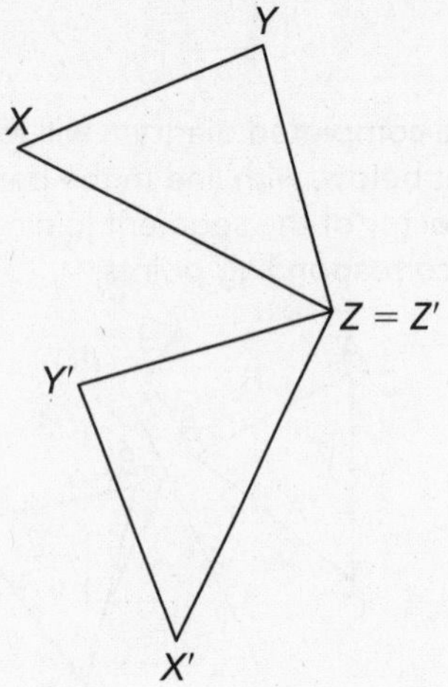

b. Each vertex of the image triangle is the same distance from *Z* as the point from which it 'moved.' The angle formed by a point, center *Z*, and the image point measures 90°.

9. a. The original triangle and its image will look like this:

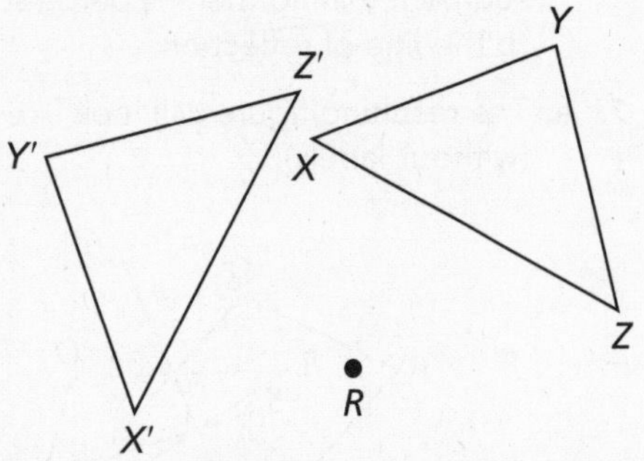

b. Each vertex of the image triangle is the same distance from *R* as its pre-image point. Each original point, the center *R*, and the image point form an angle measuring 90°.

10. a. The original figure and its image after a half-turn will look like this:

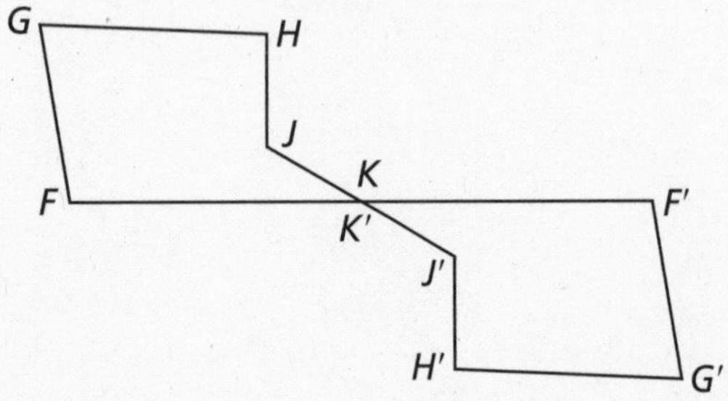

b. Each vertex of the image figure is the same distance from *K* as its pre-image point. Point *K* is the midpoint of each line segment joining a point of the original figure to its image.

11. a. The resulting figure will look like that below.

b. The segments connecting points and their images are the same length and parallel to each other.

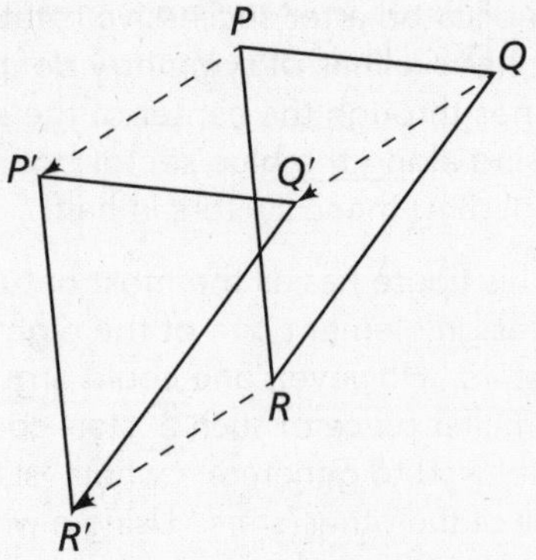

12. a. The resulting figure will look like this:

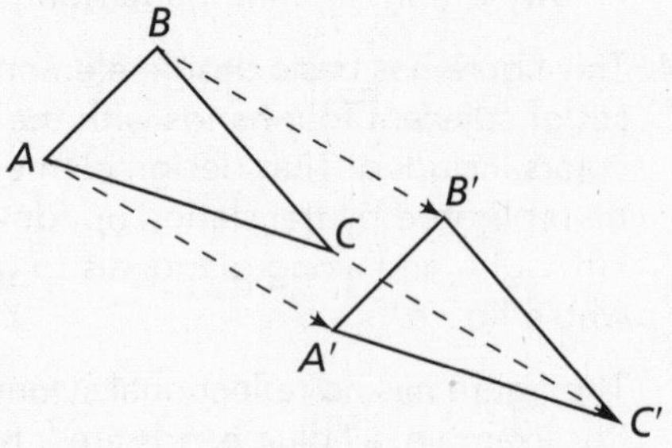

b. The segments joining points and their images will be of equal length and parallel to each other.

13. a. The result of reflection in line *m* will look like this:

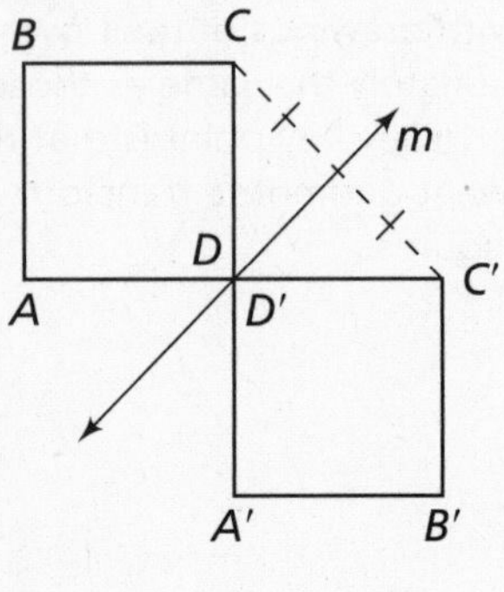

b. The result of 45° counterclockwise rotation about A will look like this:

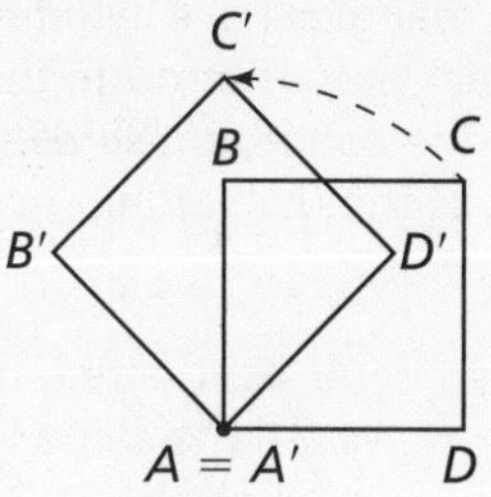

c. The result of the translation from D to D' will look like this:

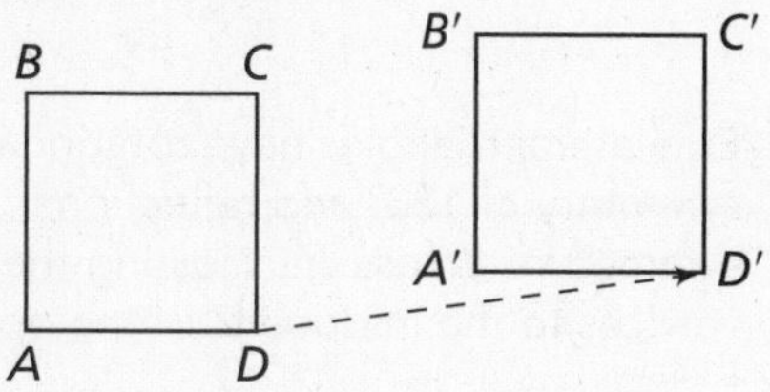

14. Translation on a slant that slides 1 to 1′, 2 to 2′, and 3 to 3′

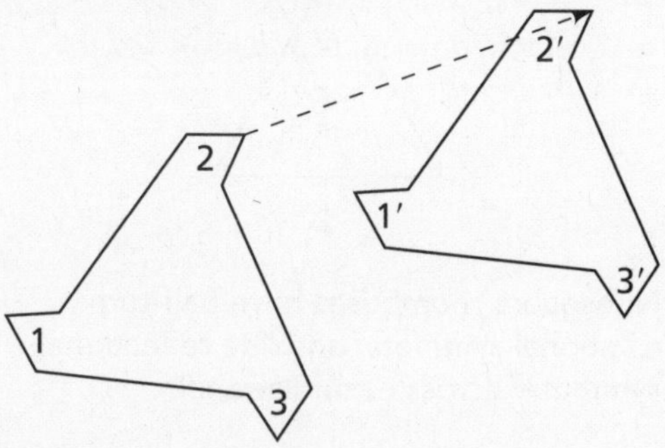

15. Line reflection about the perpendicular bisector of any segment joining corresponding points.

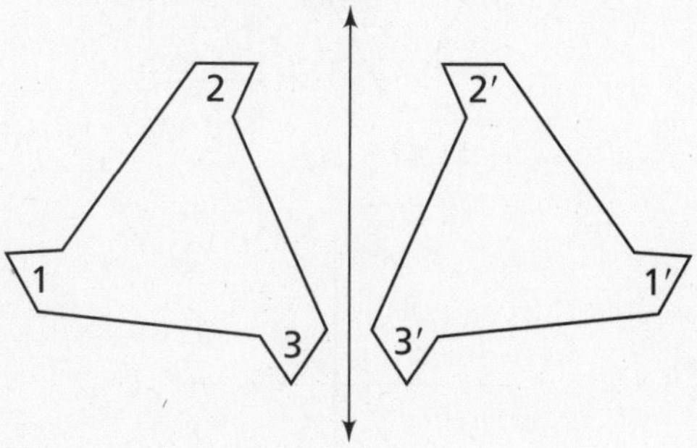

16. Half-turn about the point where 3 and 3′ touch.

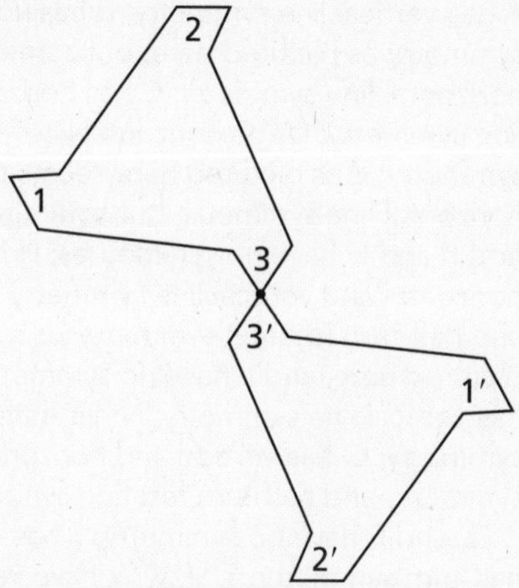

17. Translation downward that slides 1 to 1′, 2 to 2′, and 3 to 3′.

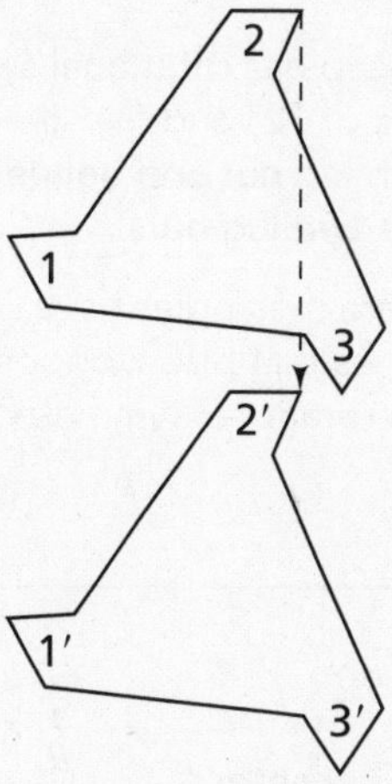

18. $PS = QR = 3$ cm; $PQ = SR = 4$ cm; $\angle S = \angle Q = 140°$. The fact that $\angle P = \angle R = 40°$ is a consequence of properties of parallelograms, not directly from the transformation of $ABCD$ onto $PQRS$.

Connections

19. A has vertical line symmetry; B has not symmetry as pictured here, but sometimes horizontal line symmetry; C has horizontal line symmetry; D has horizontal line symmetry; E as pictured here seems to have horizontal line symmetry, but sometimes not; F and G have no symmetries; H has horizontal and vertical line symmetry and half-turn rotation symmetry; J, K as pictured here, and L have no symmetry; M has vertical line symmetry; N has half-turn symmetry; O has vertical and horizontal line symmetry and half-turn rotation symmetry; P, Q, and R have no symmetry; S has half-turn symmetry; T, U, V, W have vertical line symmetry; X has vertical and horizontal line symmetry and half-turn symmetry; Z has half-turn symmetry.

20. The hubcap has rotational symmetry multiples of 72° and five lines of symmetry thru each lug nut and between the opposite two lug nuts.

21. Nonsquare rectangles have line symmetries across lines that bisect opposite sides and half-turn rotational symmetry.

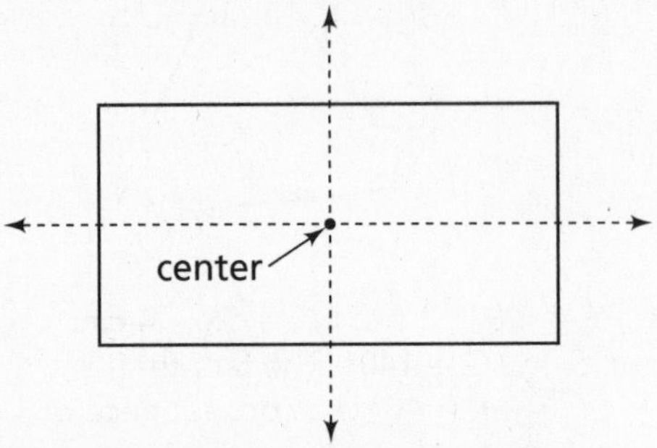

22. Nonrectangular parallelograms (that are not rhombuses) have only half-turn rotational symmetry.

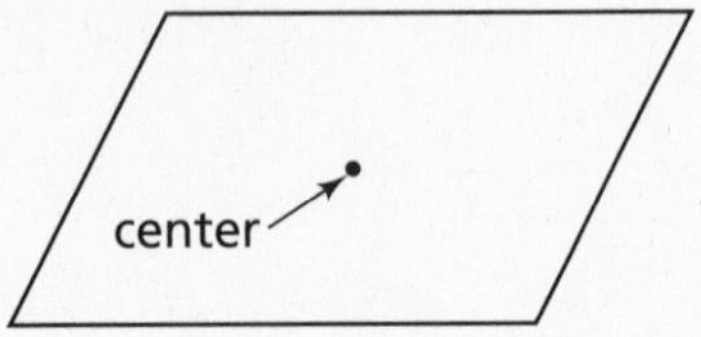

23. Isosceles triangles have symmetry across the line that passes through the common vertex of the congruent sides and the midpoint of the third side.

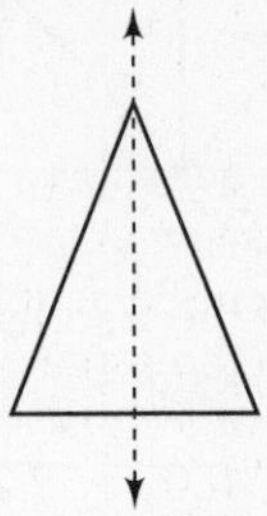

24. Equilateral triangles have rotational symmetry of 120° and reflectional symmetries across lines joining the vertices to the midpoints of the opposite sides.

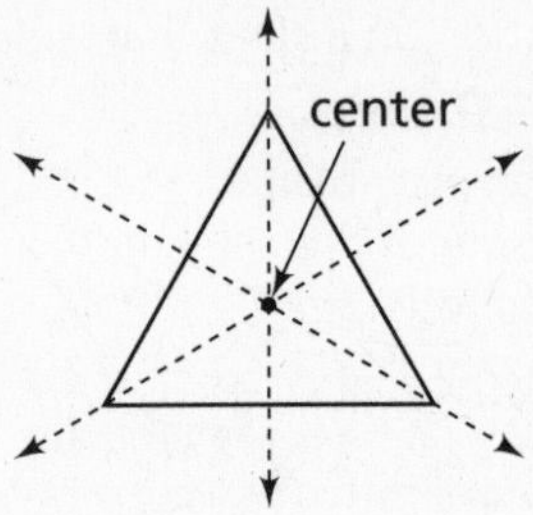

25. Nonsquare rhombuses have half-turn rotational symmetry and line reflectional symmetry across each diagonal.

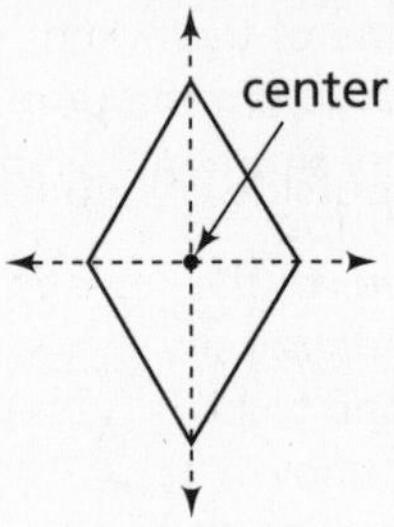

26. An isosceles trapezoid has one line of symmetry that joins midpoints of the parallel sides.

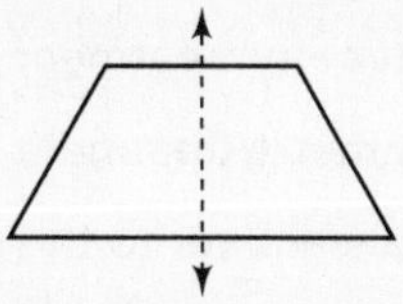

27. a. The prism is actually a cube. It has reflectional symmetry across 'mirror' planes that cut through each face of the figure in the same way lines set up symmetries of a square. It can also be rotated 90°, 180°, and 270° around axes that are perpendicular to each face at its midpoint.

The cylinder has rotational symmetry of any degree measure about the center of the base. Any plane that cuts the cylinder perpendicular to and through the center of the base will be a plane of reflectional symmetry for the cylinder. A horizontal plane that cuts through the middle of the cylinder is also a plane of symmetry.

b. 4 layers will fill the prism

c. The volume of the prism is 64 cubic centimeters.

d. Covering the cylinder base will require the equivalent of $\pi(2^2) = 4\pi$ cubes.

e. The volume of the cylinder is 16π or about 50 cubic centimeters.

28. Symmetries outside of geometry.

a. The answer to this question depends on whether you want 'tick marks' on a number line to have number labels that appear unmoved after a transformation. Without tick mark labels, a number line has reflectional and half-turn rotational symmetry about any point and translational symmetry of any length in either positive or negative direction.

With tick marks labeled, a number line has a kind of natural reflectional symmetry about 0 if one wants any number to match up with its opposite. The same pairing of numbers with their opposites can be accomplished by a half-turn centered at 0. Translation left or right will not change the appearance of the number line, only its position in front of your unmoving eyes.

b. A four-quadrant graph has reflectional symmetry about each axis and the lines $y = x$ and $y = -x$. It has rotational symmetry through 90°, 180°, and 270° around the origin. It can be translated in any direction without changing its basic appearance, only the location of the axes in relation to the viewer's eyes.

c. The graph of $y = x^2$ is symmetric about the y-axis.

d. The commutative properties of addition have a kind of reflectional symmetry across the equal sign as in $a + b = b + a$ and $ab = ba$. **Note:** The Distributive Property does not have this kind of symmetry because the two operations involved play asymmetric roles in the calculation.

ACE ANSWERS 1

Extensions

29. Rotating a rectangle about an external point.

   a. The result will look like this:

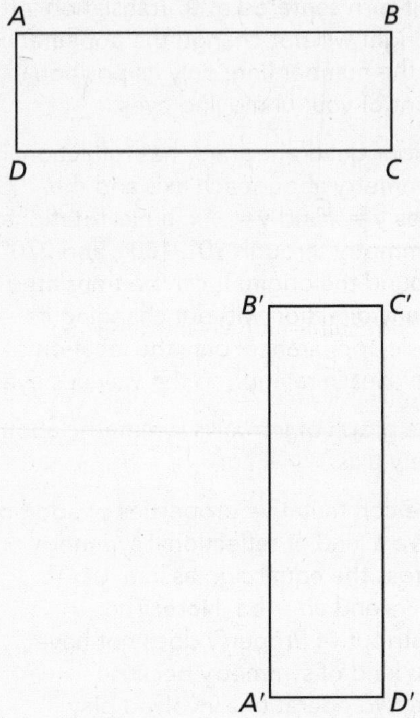

   b. Each point moves along a 90° arc of a circle with center P and radius equal to the distance from the starting point to P.

   c. Measurements in the table will vary, depending on the dimensions of the rectangle and the location of point P.

   d. In the table, there are certain values that are repeated. $PX = PX'$ and $\angle XPX' = 90°$ for $X = A, B, C,$ and D. Students might also note that the image of a side in the original triangle always lies on a line perpendicular to the original side.

   e. If the rotation angle were 120°, the pattern in the table would show that $PX = PX'$ and $\angle XPX' = 120°$ for $X = A, B, C,$ and D.

30. Line reflectional symmetry treatment of Zane

31. Line reflectional symmetry treatment of Yvette

32. Line reflectional symmetry treatment of Eve

33. Half-turn symmetry treatment of Quincy

34. Half-turn symmetry treatment of Michael

35. No predictable answer to this artistic invitation.

36. This figure has what is called glide reflectional symmetry (as well as translational symmetry). That is, one can translate the figure to the right and reflect it over a horizontal axis to match the endless strip pattern.

   a. Using only translations to replicate the basic design element, one needs at least a piece like this (though other cuts are possible):

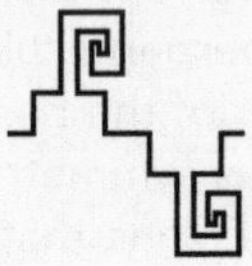

   b. A smaller basic design element that would be replicated by translations and reflections could look like this:

37. Opposite angles formed when two lines intersect.

   a. The result figure will look like this:

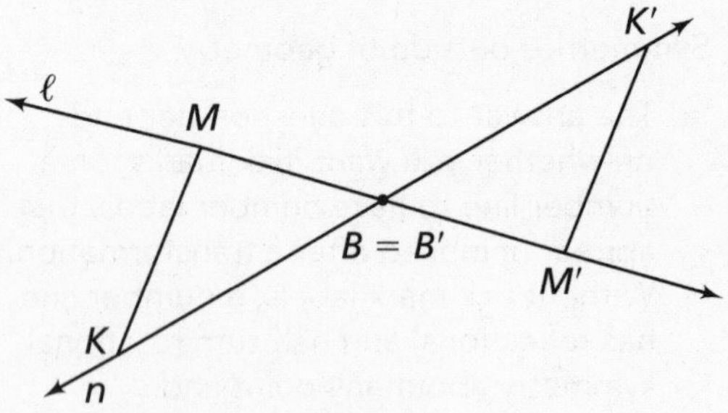

   b. $\angle MBK \cong \angle M'BK'$

   c. When any two lines intersect, the opposite angles formed are congruent in pairs.

38. The result of two reflections will be as shown in this diagram:

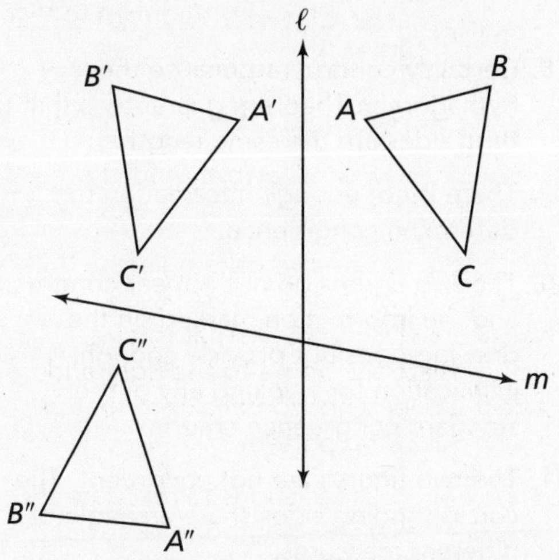

a–b. The result is actually equal to a rotation through twice the angle at which the lines meet (measured from first to second line) about the point of intersection as center.

39. Composition of line reflections in parallel lines will give a result that looks like this:

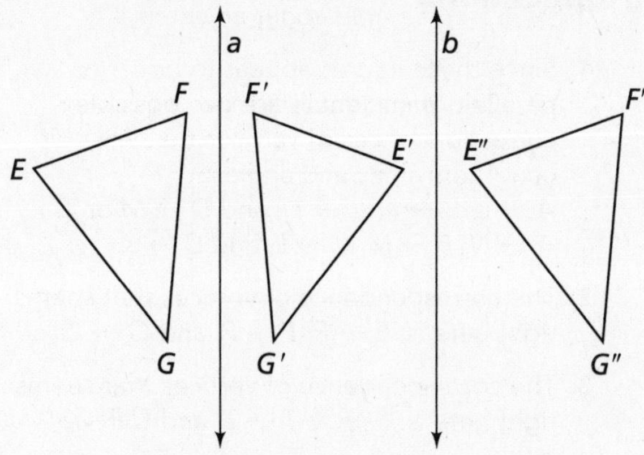

a–b. The result is actually a translation defined by a vector that is perpendicular to the two reflecting lines and twice as long as the distance between those lines.

ACE Answers Investigation 2

Applications

1. Since these figures appear to be parallelograms, there are two possible correspondences of vertices that will pair congruent sides and angles: $A \rightarrow L$, $B \rightarrow K$, $C \rightarrow N$, and $D \rightarrow M$ or $A \rightarrow N$, $B \rightarrow M$, $C \rightarrow L$, and $D \rightarrow K$.

2. The correspondence of vertices that seems right here is: $E \rightarrow R$, $F \rightarrow P$, and $G \rightarrow Q$.

3. The correspondence of vertices that seems right here is: $S \rightarrow X$, $T \rightarrow Z$, and $U \rightarrow Y$.

4. The correspondence of vertices that seems right here is: $A \rightarrow R$, $B \rightarrow S$, $C \rightarrow T$, $D \rightarrow P$, and $E \rightarrow Q$.

5. There are many pairs of congruent triangles in the given figure: $\triangle JNM \cong \triangle LNK$, $\triangle JNM \cong \triangle KNL$, $\triangle JNK \cong \triangle MNL$, $\triangle JNK \cong \triangle LNM$, and $\triangle JLM \cong \triangle KML \cong \triangle LJK \cong \triangle MKJ$.
Note: We've listed what are essentially the same triangles several times with vertices in different order since there is symmetry in the design that allows more than one correspondence of vertices consistent with congruence.

6. There are several different combinations of congruent triangles that can be paired up in response to this question. We give several responses to indicate the types of answers that could be given. There are essentially only two transformations needed—line reflections and half-turn rotations about N.

   $\triangle JNM \cong \triangle LNK$ and $\triangle KML \cong \triangle MKJ$ can be shown by half-turn rotation centered at N. That point must be the midpoint of each diagonal due to the symmetry of the rectangle.

   $\triangle JNM \cong \triangle KNL$ and $\triangle JLM \cong \triangle KML$ can be shown by reflection in a vertical line through point N, again due to the symmetry of the rectangle.

7. Certainly congruent by the Side-Side-Side criterion.

8. Certainly congruent because the Pythagorean Theorem guarantees that the third sides are the same length.

9. There is not enough information to determine congruence.

10. The two figures do not appear congruent, and the information marked on the drawing does not provide enough justification for invoking any of the standard congruence criteria.

11. The two figures are not congruent. The corresponding sides share an angle of different measures.

12. The two figures are not congruent. Three corresponding angles do not guarantee congruence.

13. In this figure it appears that $\triangle ABC \cong \triangle EBD$, a congruence that could be established by a line reflection in the bisector of $\angle ABE$ or by a combination of a counterclockwise rotation of 90° centered at B and reflection in the line that contains points B and D.

14. In this figure it appears that $\triangle PQR \cong \triangle UTS$, a congruence that could be established by translation that carries Q to T (also P to U and R to S).

15. Measurement evidence should suggest that the given triangles are not congruent.

16. In this figure it appears that $\triangle ABC \cong \triangle EDF$, a congruence that could be established most easily by a line reflection in the perpendicular bisector of $\overline{BD}$.

17. In this figure it appears that $\triangle JKL \cong \triangle TSR$, a congruence that could be established in several sequences of transformations. One such sequence would slide L to R, rotate that image of $\triangle JKL$ counterclockwise by 90° centered at R, and reflection in the line that contains $\overline{RT}$.

18. In this figure it appears that $\triangle JKL \cong \triangle MNO$, a congruence that could be established by a line reflection in $\overline{JL}$ and translation to the right. Of course, other sequences of transformations are possible.

Note: For Exercises 19–22, the instructions do not imply that the parts of triangle *ABC* necessarily correspond to parts of triangle *DEF* by the order of the vertex labels; in other words, triangle *ABC* could be congruent to triangle *DFE*.

19. It is possible, but not certain, that the two triangles are congruent. One could be larger than the other.

20. It is not possible for the two triangles to be congruent. If they were, then $DE = 3$ cm and $\triangle DEF$ would have to be an isosceles triangle with congruent base angles. $\triangle ABC$ cannot be isosceles, because $\angle B$ has measure of 30°.

21. The two triangles must be congruent because the Pythagorean Theorem implies that the third sides of each must be $\sqrt{15.6^2 - 8.2^2} \approx 13.3$ cm.

22. These two triangles are congruent by the Side-Angle-Side criterion.

23. Without any information about side lengths, the directions are unlikely to produce a congruent copy of the given figure.

24. Although the given information is not in one of the standard congruence criterion forms, the recipient could deduce that the measure of $\angle A$ has to be 35° and thus he/she will have Angle-Side-Angle data to construct a triangle that must be congruent to Figure 2.

25. Definitely congruent by the Angle-Side-Angle criterion.

26. Again, this information satisfies the Side-Angle-Side criterion for congruence.

Connections

27. a. The most natural basic design element would be a 120° sector bounded by two 'radii' of the hexagon, though there are several ways to choose the sector boundaries.

b. Rotations of 120° and 240° will do the job.

28. a. The design will appear unmoved after slides left or right, up or down, or along slanted lines, all assuming the appropriate distance of slide is chosen thoughtfully.

b. One needs a basic design element including at least two adjacent fish—one pointing in each direction.

c. If flips are allowed, one fish can be replicated to fill in each spot of the wallpaper design.

29. The circles are congruent because one can imagine sliding or reflecting one center onto the other. Since the circles have the same radius and diameter, they are identical size (and, of course, shape).

30. a. Rectangle perimeter is 30 cm and area is 36 cm^2; parallelogram perimeter is 34 cm and area is 36 cm^2.

b. Congruence, area, and perimeter.

i. No, you could have a square with sides 7.5 cm making perimeter of 30 cm and that figure would not be congruent to the given rectangle.

ii. No, the rectangle and parallelogram given have the same area but are not congruent.

iii. No, the rectangle shown and the square with sides 7.5 cm have the same perimeter, but the rectangle area is 36 cm^2 and the square area would be 56.25 cm^2.

iv. No, the given rectangle and parallelogram have the same area but not the same perimeter.

31. a. No

b. This is sufficient information because opposite sides and opposite angles of a parallelogram are congruent and consecutive angles are supplementary.

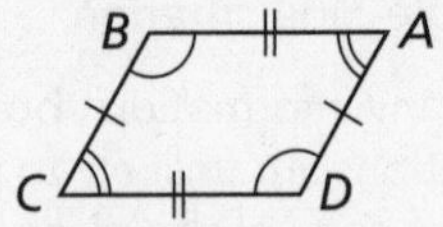

c. There are several different combinations of sufficient information to determine the shape and size of a quadrilateral. Side-Angle-Side-Angle-Side is one; Angle-Side-Angle-Side-Angle is another. Less information won't work.

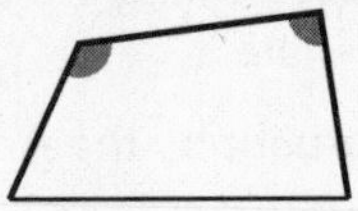

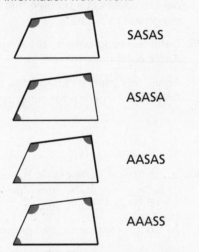

SASAS

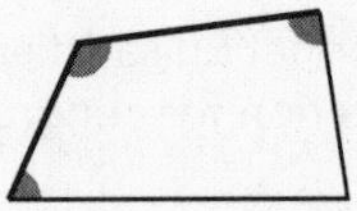

ASASA

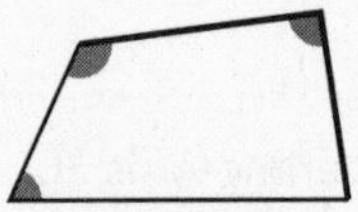

AASAS

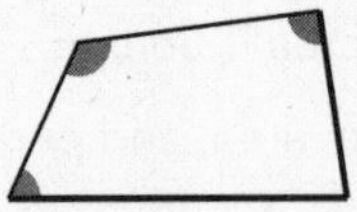

AAASS

32. a. It makes sense to locate point D on $\overrightarrow{AC}$ so that $AC = DC$. Then locate point E on a line that is perpendicular to $\overline{CD}$ so that points B, C, and E are collinear. This will mean that the two triangles are congruent by the Angle-Side-Angle criterion (angles at A and D are right angles, sides $AC = DC$, and $\angle BCA \cong \angle ECD$ because they are vertical or opposite angles formed by intersecting lines).

b. $DE = AB$.

33. a. This congruence is true for a variety of reasons. For instance, the angles at O are both right angles by construction of the coordinate grid, $OB = OC$ because both are length 3, and $AO = AO$.

b. $\overline{AC} \cong \overline{AB}$, $\overline{OC} \cong \overline{OB}$, $\angle OAC \cong \angle OAB$, and $\angle ACO \cong \angle ABO$.

34. a. $\overline{PS}$ and $\overline{QR}$ are hypotenuses of right triangles that have legs 2 and 3 units or one could reason that reflection in the y-axis would 'move' point R to S and point Q to P.

b. The angles are congruent because they are images under the reflection in the y-axis.

35. a. To build a physical triangle you have to make sides of definite lengths. Those lengths determine exactly one triangular shape, so unless the anchors at each vertex break, the figure cannot be distorted into any other shape.

b. Bracing a quadrilateral by connecting opposite vertices with a diagonal essentially creates two triangles that are rigid figures (joined together by the common side).

Extensions

36. Two sides and an angle of one triangle congruent to two sides and an angle of another triangle guarantee congruence only if the angle is include between the sides.

37. This question is equivalent to asking 'If you know the sum and the product of two numbers, do you know individual numbers?' The answer is, "Yes." Proof of this fact is beyond the level of this course, but some students might get hooked trying to find a counterexample!

38. a. All three angles are the same size.

b. All three sides are the same length.

39. a. The angle measures of the pentagon must all be 108° because each triangle has one 72° and two others that add to 108°.

b. The side lengths must all be the same.

c. The segments from C to the vertices must all be the same length.

40. In addition to the sides and angles given to be congruent, $\overline{AD}$ is a side of both triangles, and it sets up a Side-Angle-Side congruence condition for $\triangle ABD \cong \triangle DEA$. This means that angle $B \cong$ angle E because these are corresponding angles in the two triangles just shown to be congruent. And we know that angle $BCA \cong$ angle ECD because these are vertical angles. Since we have two pairs of congruent corresponding angles and one pair of congruent corresponding sides in $\triangle ABC$ and $\triangle DEC$, $\triangle ABC \cong \triangle DEC$ (using the Angle-Angle-Side condition).

Applications

1. Coordinates of key points and their images are shown in Figure 1.

   a. For Exercises 1–3, the figure and its image after reflection in the *y*-axis (top right), the *x*-axis (bottom left), and both axes (bottom right) will look like this:

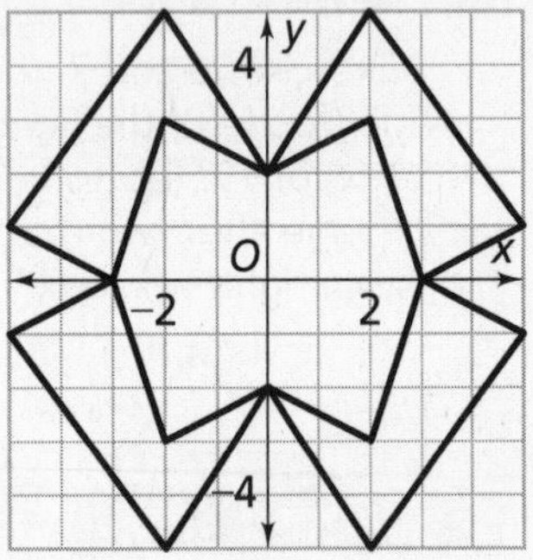

   b. $(x, y) \rightarrow (-x, y)$

2. Coordinates of key points and their images are shown in Figure 2.

   a. See diagram in Exercise 1, bottom left figure.

   b. $(x, y) \rightarrow (x, -y)$

3. Coordinates of key points and their images are shown in Figure 3.

   a. See diagram in Exercise 1, bottom right figure.

   b. $(x, y) \rightarrow (-x, -y)$

   c. The composite of successive line reflections in perpendicular lines is always equal to a half-turn.

Figure 1

Point	*A*	*B*	*C*	*D*	*E*
Original Coordinates	(–5, 1)	(–2, 5)	(0, 2)	(–2, 3)	(–3, 0)
Coordinates After a Reflection in *y*-axis	(5, 1)	(2, 5)	(0, 2)	(2, 3)	(3, 0)

Figure 2

Point	*A*	*B*	*C*	*D*	*E*
Original Coordinates	(–5, 1)	(–2, 5)	(0, 2)	(–2, 3)	(–3, 0)
Coordinates After a Reflection in *x*-axis	(–5, –1)	(–2, –5)	(0, –2)	(–2, –3)	(–3, 0)

Figure 3

Point	*A*	*B*	*C*	*D*	*E*
Original Coordinates	(–5, 1)	(–2, 5)	(0, 2)	(–2, 3)	(–3, 0)
Coordinates After a Reflection in *x*-axis	(5, –1)	(2, –5)	(0, –2)	(2, –3)	(3, 0)

4. A table that shows coordinates of key points on the figure and their images after the translation that "moves" point *B* to the point with coordinates (3, 4) will look like Figure 4.

a. For Exercises 4 and 5, the figure and its images after the two translations will look like this (right figure first and then bottom figure second):

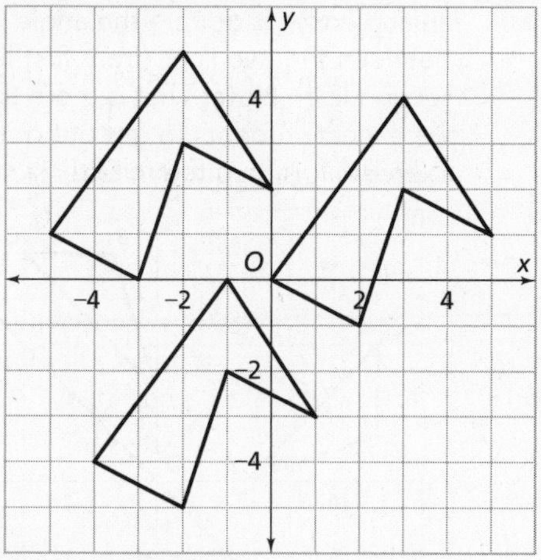

b. $(x, y) \rightarrow (x + 5, y - 1)$.

5. The table will look like Figure 5 for the second translation.

a. See bottom figure in Exercise 4.

b. $(x, y) \rightarrow (x - 4, y - 4)$.

c. $(x, y) \rightarrow (x + 1, y - 5)$.

d. The composite is a translation that moves every original point 1 unit to the right and down 5 units.

6. The table will look like Figure 6.

a. For Exercises 6 and 7, the original image (top left), the image after one rotation of 90° (bottom left), and the image after two rotations of 90° (bottom right) will look like this:

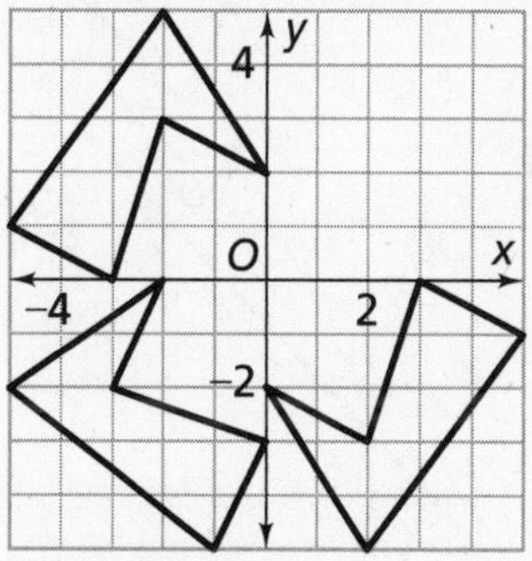

b. $(x, y) \rightarrow (-y, x)$.

Figure 4

Point	*A*	*B*	*C*	*D*	*E*
Original Coordinates	(−5, 1)	(−2, 5)	(0, 2)	(−2, 3)	(−3, 0)
Coordinates After Translating *B* to (3, 4)	(0, 0)	(3, 4)	(5, 1)	(3, 2)	(2, −1)

Figure 5

Point	*A*	*B*	*C*	*D*	*E*
Original Coordinates	(−5, 1)	(−2, 5)	(0, 2)	(−2, 3)	(−3, 0)
Coordinates after translating *B* to (3, 4)	(0, 0)	(3, 4)	(5, 1)	(3, 2)	(2, −1)
Coordinates After Translating *B′* to (−1, 0)	(−4, −4)	(−1, 0)	(1, −3)	(−1, −2)	(−2, −5)

Figure 6

Point	*A*	*B*	*C*	*D*	*E*
Original Coordinates	(−5, 1)	(−2, 5)	(0, 2)	(−2, 3)	(−3, 0)
Coordinates After a 90° Rotation	(−1, −5)	(−5, −2)	(−2, 0)	(−3, −2)	(0, −3)

7. The table of coordinates for key points will look like Figure 7.

   b. $(x, y) \rightarrow (-x, -y)$.

   c. The composite is a half-turn.

8. Composites of line reflections.

   a. The table (after both reflections) will look like Figure 8.

   b–c. The image of the triangle after reflection in $y = x$ is the top right figure; the image after a subsequent reflection in the x-axis is the bottom right figure.

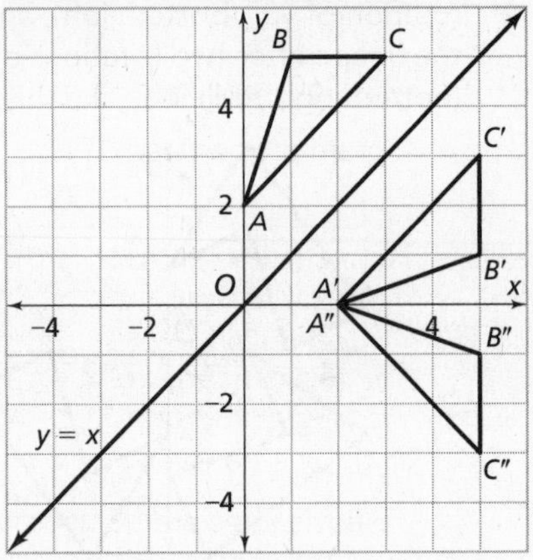

d–e. The image after first reflecting in the x-axis is the bottom right figure and then after reflecting in the line $y = x$ is the left figure. Comparing this drawing to that in parts (a)–(c) shows that composition of line reflections is not commutative. It is a general property of such compositions that the result is a rotation about the point of intersection of the lines through an angle that is double the angle between the two lines (from first line to second line). **Note:** That is more than we expect students to get out of this Exercise. It is revisited in Extensions.

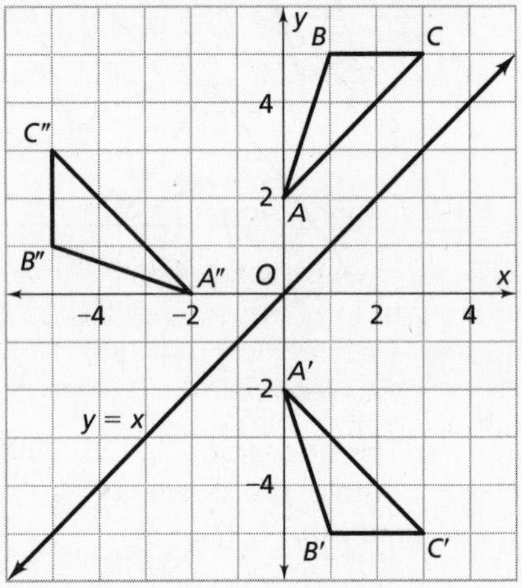

Figure 7

Point	A	B	C	D	E
Original Coordinates	(−5, 1)	(−2, 5)	(0, 2)	(−2, 3)	(−3, 0)
Coordinates After a 90° Rotation	(−1, −5)	(−5, −2)	(−2, 0)	(−3, −2)	(0, −3)
Coordinates After a 180° Rotation	(5, −1)	(2, −5)	(0, −2)	(2, −3)	(3, 0)

Figure 8

Point	A	B	C
Original Coordinates	(0, 2)	(1, 5)	(3, 5)
Coordinates After a Reflection in $y = x$	(2, 0)	(5, 1)	(5, 3)
Coordinates After a Reflection in x-axis	(2, 0)	(5, −1)	(5, −3)

9. Translation effects.

a. The image after translation (i) is the right-most figure; the image after translation (ii) is the bottom left figure.

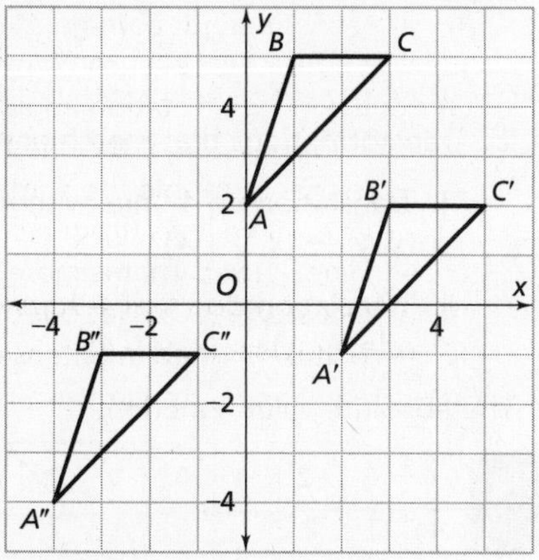

b. Comparing slopes

i. The slopes of $\overline{AB}$ and $\overline{A'B'}$ are both 3; the slopes of $\overline{AC}$ and $\overline{A'C'}$ are both 1; the slopes of $\overline{CB}$ and $\overline{C'B'}$ are both 0.

ii. The slopes of $\overline{AB}$ and $\overline{A''B''}$ are both 3; the slopes of $\overline{AC}$ and $\overline{A''C''}$ are both 1; the slopes of $\overline{CB}$ and $\overline{C''B''}$ are both 0.

c. Translations preserve slopes of lines and map lines onto parallel lines. This will be confirmed in Problem 3.4.

10. Half-turn effects.

a. The image triangle is the bottom figure.

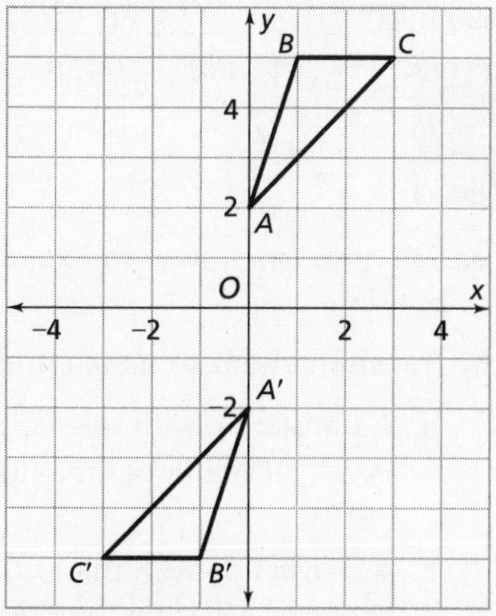

b. Comparing slopes.

i. Slopes of $\overline{AB}$ and $\overline{A'B'}$ are both 3.

ii. Slopes of $\overline{AC}$ and $\overline{A'C'}$ are both 1.

iii. Slopes of $\overline{CB}$ and $\overline{C'B'}$ are both 0.

c. The results support the discovery in work on Problem 3.4 that half-turns preserve slopes of lines and map lines onto parallel lines.

11. Angles *a*, *c*, and *e* all measure 120°. Angles *b*, *d*, *f*, and *g* all measure 60°.

12. Angle *a* measures 135°. Angle *b* measures 15°.

13. $x = 30$, $2x = 60$, and $3x = 90$.

14. Parallelogram properties

a. Assuming only that opposite sides are parallel (and $\overline{DB}$ is a transversal to both pairs of parallel sides), we can conclude that $\angle ADB \cong \angle CBD$ and $\angle ABD \cong \angle CDB$ because they are the alternate interior angles formed with parallel lines cut by a transversal.

b. The two triangles are congruent because they share a common side *DB* and thus satisfy the two angles with an included side, i.e., Angle-Side-Angle congruence criterion.

c. The opposite angles are corresponding parts of congruent triangles.

d. The opposite sides are also corresponding parts of congruent triangles.

15. Diagonals of a rectangle.

a. Any rectangle is a parallelogram, because opposite sides are perpendicular to a common side and thus parallel to each other.

So opposite sides $\overline{AD}$ and $\overline{BC}$ are congruent (from 14). Also, side $\overline{AB}$ is common to the two triangles, and $\angle DAB \cong \angle CBA$ because both are right angles. This gives criteria for triangle congruence by two sides with an included angle, i.e., the Side-Angle-Side result.

One could also make an argument using two angles with an included angle, i.e., the Angle-Side-Angle result, which mimics the work in Exercise 14.

b. Congruence of the diagonals follows from congruence of the triangles in which they are corresponding parts.

Connections

16. The sample table of values will look like this:

x	−3	−2	−1	0	1	2	3
$y = -x^2$	−9	−4	−1	0	−1	−4	−9

a. The graph (with points between data from table filled in) will look like this:

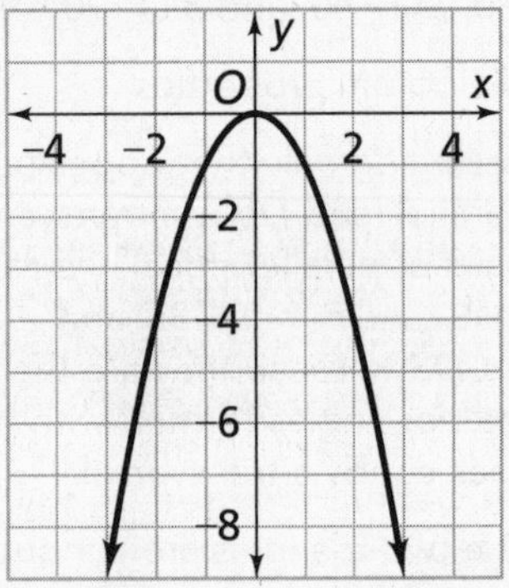

b. This graph is also symmetric about the *y*-axis.

17. The sample table of values will now look like this:

x	−3	−2	−1	0	1	2	3
$y = -x^2$	−9	−4	−1	0	−1	−4	−9
$y = -x^2 + 4$	−5	0	3	4	3	0	−5

a. The addition of the new function will yield a graph like this:

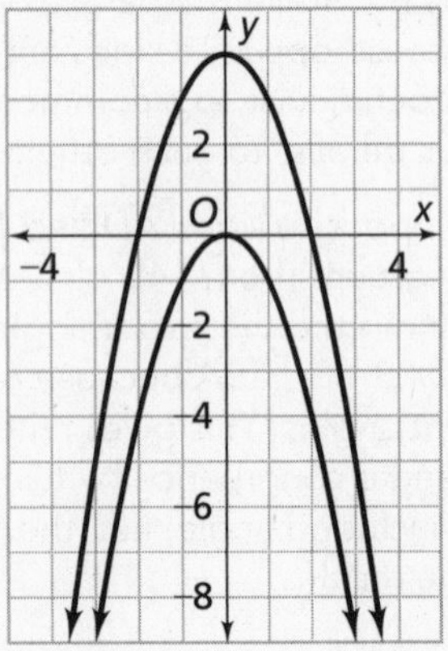

b. Transformations that match graphs.

i. Translation up 4 units with rule: $(x, y) \rightarrow (x, y + 4)$

ii. Translation down of 4 units with rule: $(x, y) \rightarrow (x, y - 4)$

18. The absolute value function.

x	−4	−3	−2	−1	0	1	2	3	4
$y = \lvert x \rvert$	4	3	2	1	0	1	2	3	4

a. Graphs of the absolute value function and the variation called for in Exercise 19 will look like this:

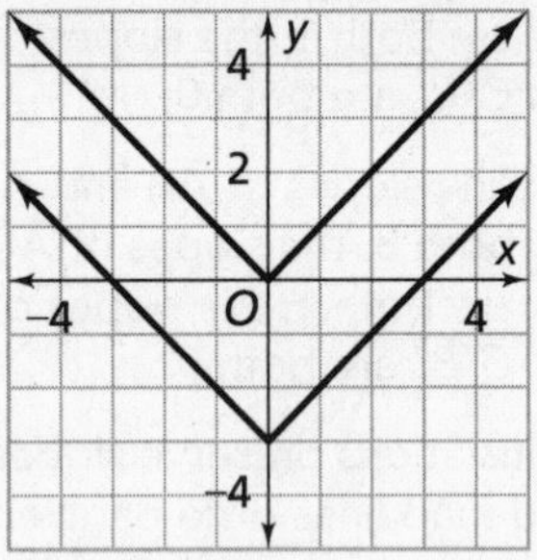

b. The graph is symmetric about the *y*-axis.

19. The table including $y = \lvert x \rvert - 3$ will look like this:

x	−4	−3	−2	−1	0	1	2	3	4
$y = \lvert x \rvert$	4	3	2	1	0	1	2	3	4
$y = \lvert x \rvert - 3$	1	0	−1	−2	−3	−2	−1	0	1

a. See graph in answer to Exercise 18, part (a).

b. Transformations to match graphs.

i. A translation with rule $(x, y) \rightarrow (x, y - 3)$ will slide the original graph down.

ii. A translation with rule $(x, y) \rightarrow (x, y + 3)$ will slide the original graph up.

20. a. $3 > -1$

b. $8 > 4$

c. $-2 > -6$

d. $-3 < 1$

e. If a and b are numbers on a number line and $a < b$, then $a + c < b + c$. (Like translating on the x-axis.)

f. If a and b are numbers on a number line and $a < b$, then $a(-1) > b(-1)$. (Like rotating the x-axis about 0.)

21. The given design appears to have reflectional symmetry across vertical and horizontal axes and half-turn symmetry.

22. The given design appears to have six lines of reflectional symmetry through vertices and midpoints of sides of the interior hexagon and rotational symmetries in multiples of 60°.

23. B; the only correct statement about all parallelograms.

24. The area of the triangle is 3 square units.

25. The side lengths are 2, $\sqrt{10}$, and $\sqrt{18}$; the perimeter is the sum of these numbers which comes to approximately 9.4.

Extensions

26. There are a number of ways that this can be done. Here's one design that was constructed by reflecting the given basic design element across the line $y = x$ and then the resulting two-part figure over the line $y = -x$.

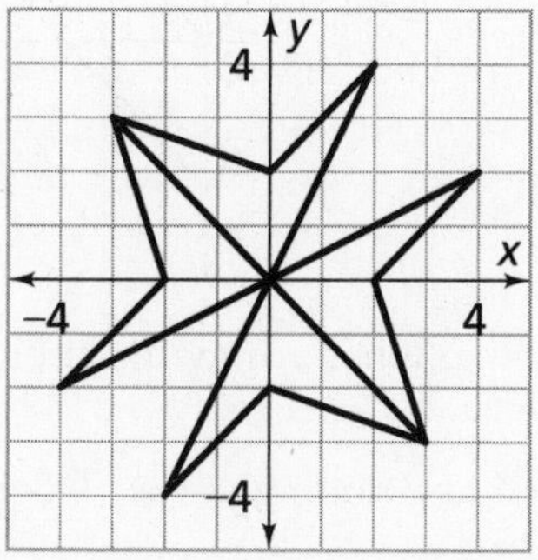

27. The simplest way to make a rotation-symmetric figure with the given basic design element is to use a half-turn of the given figure to create a two-part design. The following sketch shows what happens if 90° rotations are used (centered about the origin).

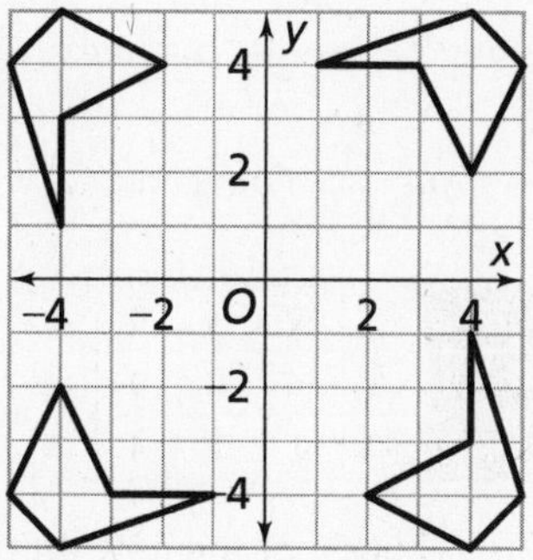

28. Again, there are probably many ways to satisfy the requirements for both reflectional and rotational symmetry. The following drawing shows the result of reflecting the given letter F across the *y*-axis and then reflecting the resulting two-part figure across the *x*-axis. The four-part final figure has two lines of reflectional symmetry and also half-turn rotational symmetry.

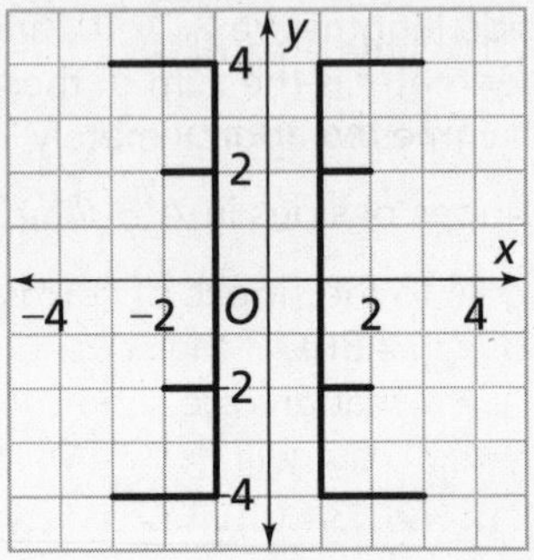

29. G; that is, this is the incorrect statement.

30. The composite of two half-turns about different centers is a translation in the direction and twice the distance of a line segment from the first center to the second center.

31. Each segment of interest can be seen to be the hypotenuse of a right triangle with legs 3 and 4, so $PQ = 5$.

a. P' has coordinates $(-2, -4)$ and Q' has coordinates $(2, -1)$, so $P'Q' = 5$.

b. P'' has coordinates $(2, -4)$ and Q'' has coordinates $(-2, -1)$, so $P''Q'' = 5$.

c. P''' has coordinates $(1, -1)$ and Q''' has coordinates $(5, -4)$, so $P'''Q''' = 5$.

ACE Answers

Investigation 4

Applications

1. The figure and its image after dilation will look like this:

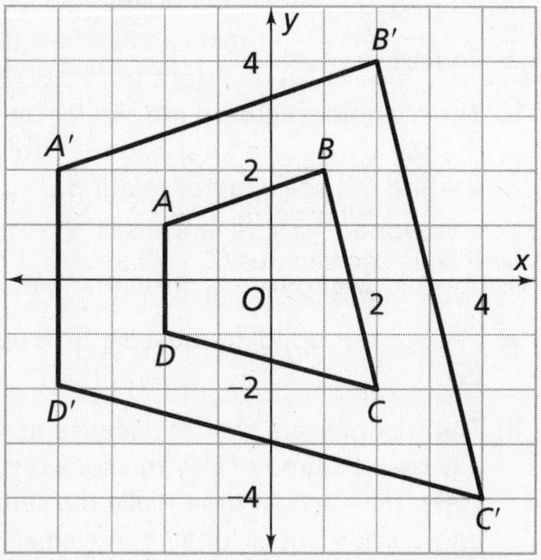

2. Side lengths of *ABCD* are: $AB = \sqrt{10}$; $BC = \sqrt{17}$; $CD = \sqrt{17}$; and $DA = 2$

   Side lengths of $A'B'C'D'$ are: $A'B' = \sqrt{40}$; $B'C' = \sqrt{68}$; $C'D' = \sqrt{68}$; and $D'A' = 4$

   Side lengths of the dilated figure are double the length of the original.

3. The perimeter of $A'B'C'D'$ is about 26.8, which is double the perimeter of *ABCD* which is about 13.4.

4. The area of *ABCD* is 10.5 square units; the area of $A'B'C'D'$ is 42 square units, 4 times that of *ABCD*.

5. The slopes of the sides of *ABCD* are: $\overline{AB}$ slope $\frac{1}{3}$; $\overline{BC}$ slope -4; $\overline{CD}$ slope $-\frac{1}{4}$; $\overline{DA}$ slope is undefined. The slopes of the corresponding sides of $A'B'C'D'$ are the same.

6. A dilation with scale factor $\frac{1}{2}$ centered at the origin will transform $A'B'C'D'$ exactly onto *ABCD*.

7. The side lengths of $A''B''C''D''$ will be:

   a. 2 times the corresponding side lengths of *ABCD*

   b. equal to the corresponding side lengths of $A'B'C'D'$

8. The perimeter of $A''B''C''D''$ will be:

   a. 2 times the perimeters of *ABCD*

   b. equal to the perimeter of $A'B'C'D'$

9. The area of $A''B''C''D''$ will be:

   a. 4 times the area of *ABCD*

   b. equal to the area of $A'B'C'D'$

10. The slopes of sides in $A''B''C''D''$ will be:

    a. equal to the slopes of corresponding sides in *ABCD* if the second transformations are slides or 180° rotation, *but will not be equal for reflections or other rotations.*

    b. equal to the slopes of corresponding sides in $A'B'C'D'$ if the second transformations are slides or 180° rotations, *but will not be equal for reflections or other rotations.*

Note: For Exercises 11–15, student responses might vary depending on the accuracy of their angle and side measurement. The point should be that they have reasons for their conclusions.

11. These triangles appear to be similar, a fact that could be shown by rotating triangle *PQR* through an angle of 90° clockwise or 270° counterclockwise about *R* and then dilating centered at *R* with scale factor about $\frac{5}{3}$.

12. These triangles appear to be similar, a fact that could be shown by reflecting triangle *PQR* across a line that is the perpendicular bisector of $\overline{RU}$ and then dilating centered at *U* with scale factor about $\frac{7}{5}$.

13. These triangles do not appear to be similar. The angles opposite the longest sides are not congruent, so the necessary correspondence of parts could not be shown.

14. These rectangles appear to be similar since the ratios of length and width are close to the same. The similarity could be shown by rotating one of the rectangles through an angle of 90°, sliding it so that one of the corners is positioned on the corresponding corner in the other rectangle, and then dilating (or shrinking) with scale factor about 2.

15. These parallelograms do not appear to be similar. The ratios of corresponding sides are not the same in the two figures.

16. True: One could imagine "moving" triangle *ABC* on top of triangle *PQR* so the 24° angles match and then dilating from *P* with scale factor 2.5 to 'move' *ABC* exactly on top of *PQR*.

17. True: $\overline{AD}$ and $\overline{BE}$ are transversals cutting the parallel lines, so $\angle A \cong \angle D$ and $\angle B \cong \angle E$. This implies that the triangles are similar. It is also true that the vertical or opposite angles at point *C* are congruent.

18. True: All angles will measure 60° so the Angle-Angle-Angle criterion for similarity will be satisfied.

19. False: For example, all rectangles have all angles measuring 90°, but not all rectangles are similar.

20. False: The two triangles could have quite different vertex angles.

21. Measuring height of a tall building.

a. 96 feet

b. The triangles pictured are similar by the same reasoning applied in Problem 4.4 and the scale factor relating corresponding side lengths is $\frac{32}{2} = 16$.

22. Using shadows to form similar triangles.

a. The shorter building must be 57.6 feet tall.

b. The triangles are similar because at any specific time of day the suns rays strike the earth at essentially the same angle when one is looking in a small geographic region. The buildings are assumed to meet the ground at right angles, so the two triangles have two congruent corresponding angles.

The taller building is 96 feet high and the scale factor from larger to smaller is 0.6. We have $0.6(96) = 57.6$.

Connections

23. Sphere of radius 5 cm.

a. Volume $= \left(\frac{4}{3}\right)\pi(5^3)$ or about 523.6 cm^3; Surface Area $= 4\pi(5^2)$ or about 314 cm^2

b. Scaling the sphere by a factor of 2:

i. Surface area becomes 4×314 or about 1,256 cm^2.

ii. Volume becomes 8×523.6 or about 4,189 cm^3.

c. Surface area always changes by the square of the scale factor; volume always changes by the cube of the scale factor.

24. Composition of dilations.

a. $(x, y) \rightarrow (6x, 6y)$

b. The rule would be the same if the composition occurs in the opposite order because multiplication is commutative.

25. Dilations and symmetry.

a. Yes, symmetry is preserved by dilation.

b. Scale factor change would not affect preservation of symmetry.

c. Using a different center of scaling would change the result. For example, if we use the point (5, 0) as the center then the entire figure will be to the left of the *y*-axis. The figure will still have reflectional symmetry, but the line of reflection will not be the *y*-axis.

26. True: All angles are 90°, and in each figure, the sides are the same length, so there is a single scale factor of dilation that would transform one square onto the other, after slides and turns to position one in a corner of the other.

27. False: The angles could be quite different in two rhombuses.

28. a. Similar triangles are *ABC*, *EDF*, *BAF*, *CDA*, and *EBC*. The scale factor from *ABD* to *EDF* is 2. The scale factor from *ABD* to *BAF*, *CDA*, and *EBC* is 1, which also makes *ABC* congruent to *BAF*, *CDA*, and *EBC*. Angles are "moved" to equal angles by the rotations named, so all these triangles have corresponding equal angles.

b. Parallelograms are *ABCD*, *ABEC*, and *AFBC*. The parallel sides are the result of half-turns.

Note: There is a theorem that states that the line segment joining the midpoints of two sides of a triangle is parallel to the third side and equal to half its length. You can see this result in the figure for Exercise 28.

Extensions

29. Side-Side-Side similarity.

a. It turns out that they are right.

b. The reasoning given is correct. Dilations preserve angle measures; the fact that the dilated triangle has side lengths congruent to those in triangle *XYZ* follows from the given information about the two original triangles. Congruence of triangle $A'B'C'$ and triangle *XYZ* follows from the Side-Side-Side criterion for congruence; the congruence of corresponding angles is due to corresponding parts of congruent triangles. Since the angles of $A'B'C'$ are congruent to those of *ABC*, we have congruence of angles that is needed to show *ABC* similar to *XYZ*.

30. The composite of two dilations, even with different centers will dilate with a scale factor that is the product of the two component scale factors. To find the center of the composite dilation, one only needs to locate two final image points and draw rays from those points through the points from which they "started" in motion. The intersection point of those two rays will be the center of the composite dilation.

31. Dilation in one direction.

a. The one-directional dilation does not produce similar image figures.

b. There is no simple rule for predicting the effect of these one-directional dilations on side lengths, perimeters, or angle measures because the position of the original figure matters. For the rule given, vertical sides will not change in length but horizontal sides will be doubled in length. Some angles will get larger [e.g. the angle determined by (1, 1), (0, 0), and (−1, 1)], some will get smaller [e.g., the angle determined by (1,1), (0, 0), and (1, −1)], and some will stay the same measure (e.g, the intersection of the *x*- and *y*-axes).

The somewhat surprising result is for any polygon (or even circle or irregular figure). The area will be multiplied by 2. If you imagine a figure covered by unit squares, the one-directional dilation stretches each into a 1 × 2 rectangle with area 2 square units.

c. The slope of any line will be cut in half by this transformation.

$$\frac{y_1 - y_2}{2x_1 - 2x_2} = \frac{1}{2}\left(\frac{y_1 - y_2}{x_1 - x_2}\right).$$

ACE ANSWERS 4

Index